The Open University

Science: a second level course

## ST240

# OUR CHEMICAL ENVIRONMENT

# BOOK 3
# NUTRITION AND HEALTH

The Open University

# ST240 Course Team

| | |
|---|---|
| **Course Team Chair** | Stuart Bennett |
| **General editors** | Michael Mortimer |
| | Malcolm Rose |
| **Authors** | Rod Barratt |
| | Alan Bassindale |
| | Stuart Bennett |
| | Michael Gagan |
| | Jim Iley |
| | Michael Mortimer |
| | David Roberts |
| | Malcolm Rose |
| | Peter Taylor |
| **Course Manager** | Charlotte Sweeney |
| **Course Secretary** | Sally Eaton |
| **BBC** | Cameron Balbirnie |
| | Sandra Budin |
| | Andrew Law |
| | Paul Manners |
| | Michael Peet |
| | Ian Thomas |
| | Nicholas Watson |
| | Darren Wycherley |
| **Editors** | Gerry Bearman |
| | Dick Sharp |
| **Graphic Design** | Sue Dobson |
| | Mark Kesby |
| | Mike Levers |
| | David Roberts |
| | Howard Taylor |
| | Rob Williams |
| **Experimental work** | Keith Cavanagh |
| | Ray Jones |
| | Pravin Patel |

The Open University, Walton Hall, Milton Keynes, MK7 6AA

First published 1995; revised edition published 2000. Reprinted 2002

Edited, designed and typeset by The Open University.

Printed in the United Kingdom by Bath Press Ltd, Glasgow.

ISBN 0 7492 5143 3

This text forms part of an Open University Second Level Course. If you would like a copy of Studying with The Open University, please write to the Central Enquiry Service, PO Box 200, The Open University, Walton Hall, Milton Keynes, MK7 6YZ. If you have not enrolled on the Course and would like to buy this or other Open University material, please write to Open University Educational Enterprises Ltd, 12 Cofferidge Close, Stony Stratford, Milton Keynes, MK11 1BY, United Kingdom.

2.2

ST240book3i2.2

A dish of polypeptides, denatured proteins, amino acids, mono-, di- and polysaccharides, cellulose, cholesterol, linoleic acid, linolenic acid, arachidonic acid, lactic acid, propionic acid, butyric acid, oleic and palmitic triglycerides, lecithin, retinol, calciferol, phytomenadione, cobalamin, ascorbic acid, *p*-isopropylbenzaldehyde, capsaicin and cinnamaldehyde.

# Introduction to Book 3

This book examines the relationship between nutrition, health and chemistry: it describes how chemistry can be used to ensure a healthy life for the majority of the population. A commonly held belief is that chemicals are bad for you – after all, they are synthetic. We believe that such a view is completely unfounded. First, not all chemicals are synthetic: there are millions of different compounds that occur naturally. Second, not all chemicals are toxic, and those that are include many naturally occurring compounds. Indeed, we could just as easily have an allergic response to a natural chemical in a particular type of food as to a synthetic food colouring.

Although we would not want to ignore the fact that all aspects of human endeavour have their failures, in this book we want to highlight the successes of chemistry – such as how chemistry helps us to understand bodily processes so we can enhance the quality of our health. The relationships between the disease scurvy and the lack of vitamin C, and between anaemia and inadequate iron are just two examples of the need for chemical understanding. This has led to the isolation, characterization and manufacture of vitamins, which can be used to enrich foods and thus ensure that such deficiency diseases become a thing of the past. As well as showing you how important chemistry is in identifying the materials the body needs, we also want to describe how we can control the chemistry that goes on in our bodies and hence combat illness and disease.

However, we must begin by defining what we mean by health. A definition from the Oxford Dictionary tells us:

> **health**  soundness of body; that condition in which its functions are duly and efficiently discharged.

This definition sounds right, but what does it really mean? What are these functions, and how do we measure whether they are being duly and efficiently discharged? Chemistry can supply one answer through the study of chemical pathways that show how material is transformed in the body. The measurement of concentrations of key compounds in these pathways gives us an indication of how smoothly these processes are running. This is often performed in hospitals, when samples are taken and analysed so that a decision can be made on the type of treatment necessary. For example, phenylketonuria is a hereditary disease in which the 'machinery' by which a particular chemical is broken down in the body is missing. Almost all untreated individuals become severely mentally retarded. Early diagnosis is essential, and there are mass screening processes that involve chemical analyses. The problems are caused by the build-up of a natural substance called phenylalanine. Although it is not possible to repair the faulty pathway, if sufferers are spotted early enough we can ensure that they develop normally by feeding them a diet low in phenylalanine.

So, chemistry can give us one answer to how healthy you are – but it is not a complete one. The reason for this is that health is very subjective and often has nothing to do with the processes of the body but rather reflects the psychological state of the individual.

■ If you were to approach a number of people and say 'Hello, how are you today?', what kinds of response do you think you would get?

■ It's likely that some people would respond by listing what was wrong with them – 'I've got a bit of a cold', 'my head aches', 'I feel very tired'.

This reflects the fact that it is easier to define what is *not* good health than what is.

Instead of focusing on bodily processes, a so-called reductionist approach, many people believe that we need to examine the whole person – the sum is more than the parts – a holistic approach. So perhaps our definition of health should refer to the output of the whole body – How far can I run? How high can I jump?

■ What problems are there in using such indicators of health?

■ Any measure of health based on the output of the whole body will depend on a number of factors, such as age, race, gender and size.

In order to progress with what is quite a difficult area, we shall simplify matters by concentrating on three topics:

● nutrition, and dietary illness;

● defences against micro-organisms;

● drugs to correct biochemical faults.

In the first half of the book we shall examine nutrition: what foods consist of, and how they are broken down to provide the body with energy and the chemicals we need to live and grow. In so doing, we shall describe some of the chemical processes in the body and how they are controlled. This provides some answers as to how we can combat dietary illness.

The second half of the book starts with a review of how we can combat micro-organisms – keeping clean through washing and antiseptics, which can prevent harmful micro-organisms getting inside our bodies. Then we examine how chemistry can be used to assist the body to defend itself against the effects of these micro-organisms, should they manage to break down our barriers and invade the body. Finally, we discuss how drugs can be developed to correct illnesses that arise from faulty chemistry in the body.

As we have seen, health is a complex area dependent on many interrelated factors and thus requires inputs from a range of disciplines, all of which are important. However, we think that chemistry often provides the cornerstone on which other specialities can build. By the end of this book, you ought to be able to make up your own mind about whether chemistry does indeed provide such a cornerstone.

# PART 1 NUTRITION

Prepared for the Course Team by Peter Taylor

# Contents

# Chapter 1
# Chemicals in our food

We start our study of nutrition by examining the chemicals we take into our bodies. Is there anything special about *these* chemicals that makes them different from the chemicals you could find on a laboratory shelf?

■   Read the advert shown in Figure 1.1. Outline in two sentences what the advert is saying to the reader.

■   The advert explains that vitamins are good for you. In addition, it implies that vitamins that come from natural sources are much better than synthetic ones.

As you will learn later in this Book, the term vitamins refers to a range of compounds that need to be taken in with food because some function of the human body relies on them, but the body is unable to make them. Each vitamin is a distinct compound, that is it is made up of only one type of molecule with its particular structure. Thus, a sample of a vitamin made in the laboratory will be identical with a sample extracted from natural sources. Both will contain only molecules of the vitamin and both samples will have the same properties.

It is perhaps not surprising that ideas like those proposed in the advert prevail. Whilst it is easy to appreciate that an inanimate rock is just a mixture of compounds, it is a little more difficult to accept that our bodies are simply a collection of chemicals. Surely there is something special about the chemicals produced by living organisms? In fact, the chemists of two hundred years ago were wrestling with just this problem. At the time, it was felt that certain chemicals, called organic chemicals, could be produced only by living organisms and that these were in some way different from other chemicals. Some chemists even felt that these organic chemicals differed because they contained some kind of 'life force'. As a result, chemistry was divided into two areas, organic and inorganic chemistry. As you saw in Book 1, this division remains today.

One of the experiments that showed that organic and inorganic compounds were not really different was performed by Wohler in 1828. He found that when he dissolved pure ammonium cyanate in water a reaction occurred and urea was obtained:

$$NH_4^+(aq) + CNO^-(aq) = \begin{matrix} H_2N \\ \diagdown \\ C=O \\ \diagup \\ H_2N \end{matrix}$$

ammonium    cyanate                urea
   ion          ion

■   Is this equation balanced?

■   Yes, there are two nitrogen atoms, four hydrogen atoms, one carbon atom and one oxygen atom on each side of the equation. Also, the charges balance – on the left-hand side the charges cancel out, and on the right-hand side urea is neutral.

# The first ever Multivitamins from entirely natural sources.

Introducing the first ever range of health supplements not only free from artificial additives and preservatives but also free from artificial vitamins.

You see, the vitamins in new Seven Seas Multivitamins from Natural Sources are not man-made. Instead each supplement contains only naturally derived vitamins, pure and simple.

Vitamins taken from natural food sources such as fish and wheatgerm oils, yeast and acerola cherries. The kind of foods rich in the very nutrients that our diet may be lacking.

Like Vitamins A and D, for example, which help to maintain healthy hair, smooth skin, and strong nails. And vitamin C which is popular throughout the cold winter months to safeguard our general good health.

One easy-to-swallow capsule taken each day provides a careful balance of the essential vitamins a healthy body needs.

What's more, because these supplements come in a natural gelatin capsule, they're not only taste-free, they're also free from chemicals.

So if you're slimming, or lead such a busy lifestyle that you don't always eat a well balanced diet, why not try a natural health supplement?

New Seven Seas Multivitamins from Natural Sources. Available both with and without iron in packs of 30s and 60s.

See below for your nearest stockist.

## SEVEN SEAS

*Good Health. Naturally.*

**Figure 1.1**
The best source of vitamins?

Ammonium cyanate was regarded as a typical inorganic salt, and urea as a typical organic compound easily isolated from urine. The fact that it was possible to make an organic compound from an inorganic one demonstrated that there was nothing special about organic chemicals or the chemicals that make up our bodies.

Table 1.1 shows the elemental composition of the human body in two ways: by mass for a person weighing 70 kg, and as a percentage based on mass. Table 1.2 lists the classes of compounds in the body.

**Table 1.1** The elemental composition of the body for a person weighing about 70 kg.

| Element | Composition by mass/kg | Percentage by mass/% |
|---|---|---|
| oxygen | 45.5 | 65 |
| carbon | 12.6 | 18 |
| hydrogen | 7.0 | 10 |
| nitrogen | 2.1 | 3.0 |
| calcium | 1.4 | 2.0 |
| phosphorus | 0.8 | 1.1 |
| potassium | 0.25 | 0.36 |
| sulphur | 0.18 | 0.26 |
| sodium | 0.11 | 0.16 |
| chlorine | 0.11 | 0.16 |
| magnesium, iron, manganese, copper, iodine, cobalt, zinc | traces | traces |

**Table 1.2** The classes of compounds in the body.

| Class | % of body weight |
|---|---|
| proteins | 15–20 |
| fats | 3–20 |
| carbohydrate | 1–15 |
| small organic molecules | 0–1 |
| inorganic compounds | 1 |
| total solid material | 20–40 |
| water | 60–80 |

▪ Hydrogen and oxygen are two of the most common elements in the body. What will be the predominant compound in the body that contains these elements?

▪ As H.G. Wells first pointed out, even the Archbishop of Canterbury is composed of 80% water, and most of the oxygen in our bodies is tied up in water molecules.

The other major element is carbon, and most of the 'solid' material in the body contains carbon in the form of organic compounds. There are very many different carbon compounds in the body. You will see later that most can be classed under the headings of proteins, fats and carbohydrates. As mentioned in Book 2, one of the interesting aspects of some of these compounds is that they are polymeric. There are also a number of inorganic compounds in the body, such as calcium phosphate, which is present in bones, and a range of metals, albeit in small amounts.

■ From your general experience, why do you think we need to eat?

■ First, we need a supply of energy; second, we need a supply of the elements in Table 1.1 to build up and renew the body.

As we saw in Book 2, to do anything we need energy. In a petrol engine, energy is released when petrol reacts with oxygen. The process of living involves work, and even when you are sleeping your heart is still pumping. These processes need energy, and this is obtained by oxidizing food – again an exothermic reaction.

The second reason for eating is to provide the body with its requisite elements. As the body develops, we clearly need more material for growth but, once we stop growing, do we still need a supply of these elements? The body can sustain life only through regeneration of its components. Our bodies engage in all sorts of activities and suffer injury and illness. To cope with these changes our bodies undergo a ceaseless process of breakdown and renewal. For example, in an average lifetime, a person sheds 18–22 kg of dead skin!

## 1.1  We are what we eat

Eating is instinctive, yet we know we have to be selective about what we consume – only certain substances such as vegetable and animal tissue will sustain us. What is so special about *these* materials? Then again, how specific does our diet have to be? Unlike some animals, we are omnivores, but, if you were dropped on a desert island, would you know what to eat to survive? In fact, the great success of *Homo sapiens* in colonizing this planet is partly due to an ability to adapt our eating habits to the food that our immediate environment provides, be it a desert, arctic waste, tropical rain forest or fast-food-infested city.

To illustrate this, let's go back into history to examine the environment in which we evolved, since it is this that has shaped our nutritional needs. From about 40 000 years ago, when our species first emerged, until about 10 000 years ago, all humans lived by hunting, fishing and gathering of plants and shellfish. In fact these hunter-gatherers practised more gathering than hunting because it was less dangerous! Nevertheless, our ancestors still had to find out what they could and could not eat. They did this by trial and error and sadly many of them sacrificed themselves (accidentally!) in finding out what was safe, whereas others used the scientific skills of observation and recording (if only to memory) to ensure it did not happen to them. Many of the plants and shellfish they ate used chemicals, that is poisons, to dissuade would-be consumers. However, *Homo sapiens* had the advantage that they could use chemistry to detoxify these foods. Cooking seems to have become well established in pre-recorded history, and these early cooks were some of the first chemists. They found that heating not only deactivated the toxic chemicals in legumes (beans, peas and lentils) and killed off any bacteria, but also aided digestion by tenderizing animal tissues and solubilizing the starch in cereals. These skills can still be observed in hunter-gatherer communities. The Aborigines of Australia knew nothing of agriculture, yet provided themselves with a healthy diet, using some potentially very toxic foods. The Inuit of Alaska and Greenland have a similar culture based on hunting and gathering, as have the bushpeople of the Kalahari desert, who are thin but not malnourished, and have few dental caries, no hypertension and low serum cholesterol levels!

For the human race, things changed about 10 000 years ago, at the end of the last Ice Age. Cereal farming began and cattle were domesticated. This meant that people became settled for the first time and civilization began. Permanent dwellings were built, and we began to accumulate possessions that the nomadic life would not allow. Our diet changed and, as well as cereal and meat, we began to consume eggs, dairy products, alcoholic beverages and salt. As agriculture developed it was no longer necessary for everyone to be involved in food production, or hunting and gathering, leading to towns and eventually cities. These were limited in size by the productivity of the farms that were close enough to provide fresh produce using the transport of the day. In Britain, the Industrial Revolution began about 200 years ago at a time when transport and storage methods were improving to support large cities.

Nowadays, transport and storage are not problems, and in the Western world we expect our shops to stock produce from all over the planet. Rather than adapting our diet to suit our environment we seem to have control over our environment to ensure that we can choose the diet we want. But, unfortunately, the availability of a wide range of food has brought its own problems. We no longer eat a diet similar to the one with which we evolved, and an 'unnatural' excess of some foods has been associated with the so-called diseases of affluence – cancer and chronic heart disease. Furthermore, we live in large urban societies, where most food is not recently harvested but processed, packaged and stored, requiring the use of a range of additives. Many people are worried about the long-term effects of these compounds.

So what are the common constituents of foods such as nuts, shellfish, broccoli, bananas and steak that enable us to use them all as foods?

### Activity 1  Nutrients in food

Stop reading for a moment and look at a range of food wrappings that give nutritional information. See if you can identify the common classifications of nutritional content in a wide variety of food. When you've done so, read the Comment on this Activity on page 136.

The information on the packaging suggests that all foods are made up of a number of common constituents. These we call **nutrients**, which are defined as one of the following:

● A substance from which the body can produce energy, to use in movement and keeping warm;

● A substance that is used in growth, repair or reproduction;

● A substance necessary to regulate the production of energy or the processes of repair and growth.

The major classes of nutrients are proteins, carbohydrates, fats, vitamins and minerals. It is interesting to note that all foods, irrespective of their source, be it animal or vegetable contain mainly these nutrients.

■ Why do you think energy is not included as a nutrient?

■ Simply because energy is not a substance. The energy listed on a packet label is the energy made available when the body chemically breaks down the food.

■ Apart from the five nutrients, can you think of two other chemicals that we need to take in to survive? (Hint: we can last for only a short time without them!)

■ To survive we must take in oxygen from the air, which is used in respiration, and water, which provides the medium in which many of the complex reactions in the body take place.

So to stay alive we need to take in five types of nutrient together with water and oxygen. One of the aims of this half of the Book is to describe each of these components in detail and to examine their role in the body. Figure 1.2 gives a simple diagram showing the relationship between the five nutrients, water and oxygen, together with their functions and foods that supply them in large amounts.

**Figure 1.2**
The nutrients, water and oxygen: their functions and representative foods in which they are found.

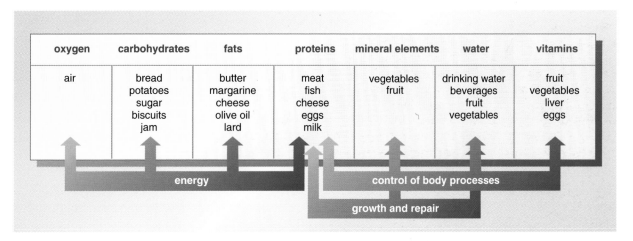

| oxygen | carbohydrates | fats | proteins | mineral elements | water | vitamins |
|--------|---------------|------|----------|------------------|-------|----------|
| air | bread potatoes sugar biscuits jam | butter margarine cheese olive oil lard | meat fish cheese eggs milk | vegetables fruit | drinking water beverages fruit vegetables | fruit vegetables liver eggs |

energy    control of body processes

growth and repair

**Question 1** From Table 1.1, how many moles of oxygen atoms, carbon atoms and hydrogen atoms are there in the average person weighing 70 kg? What do you notice about the relative proportions of these elements, based on mass and on moles?

**Question 2** From your general knowledge, can you think of any food you consume that contains only one of these nutrients?

**Question 3** Do you think, like my children, that we could live on a diet of only biscuits?

## 1.2  Our daily bread

Before we examine the chemistry of these five nutrients in detail, we shall look at some of the recommendations for healthy eating in the early 1990s. History has shown that fashions in diet change rapidly, so it is difficult to predict what recommendations may appear during the life of this Course.

### 1.2.1  The ideal diet

Tables 1.3, 1.4 and 1.5 show the food consumed over a week by a British family of five persons – two adults and three children of various ages, around 1800, 1900 and 1980. In this Book there are a number of such extensive tables of data. The information provided is only for interest or to develop ideas. *It is not necessary for you to memorize it in any way.*

**Table 1.3**  The food consumed over a week by a rural British family of five persons around 1800.

| Food | Quantity | Energy/kJ |
|------|----------|-----------|
| bread | 15.9 kg (35 lb) | 142 100 |
| bacon | 6.4 kg (14 lb) | 171 400 |
| mutton | 3.2 kg (7 lb) | 32 200 |
| beer | 47.7 litres (10.5 gallons) | 33 400 |
| Total | | 379 100 |

**Table 1.4**  The food consumed over a week by a poor urban British family of five persons around 1900.[a]

| Food | Quantity | Energy/kJ |
|------|----------|-----------|
| bread and flour | 12.7 kg (28.0 lb) | 144 200 |
| potatoes | 6.4 kg (14.1 lb) | 22 700 |
| rice, oats | 1.1 kg (2.4 lb) | 16 600 |
| sugar | 1.8 kg (3.9 lb) | 30 100 |
| meat | 2.0 kg (4.4 lb) | 26 400 |
| bacon | 0.5 kg (1.1 lb) | 13 600 |
| milk | 3.1 kg (6.8 lb) | 8 400 |
| cheese | 0.3 kg (0.7 lb) | 5 900 |
| butter | 0.5 kg (1.1 lb) | 15 500 |
| currants | 0.2 kg (0.4 lb) | 2 300 |
| fruit and vegetables | not known | not known |
| tea, coffee, cocoa | 0.3 kg (0.7 lb) | 3 800 |
| Total | | 289 500 |

[a] P. Payne, quoted in Gray, A. (ed.) (1993) *World Health and Disease*, Open University Press, Buckingham; based on Burnett, J. (1966), *Plenty and Want*, Nelson, London.

**Table 1.5** Foods consumed over a week by an average British family of five persons, 1983.[a]

| Food | Quantity | Energy/kJ |
|------|----------|-----------|
| white bread | 3.12 kg (6.9 lb) | 30 400 |
| brown bread | 1.27 kg (2.8 lb) | 11 900 |
| flour | 0.85 kg (1.9 lb) | 11 300 |
| cakes, biscuits, cereals | 2.69 kg (5.9 lb) | 39 400 |
| sugar and sweets | 1.84 kg (4.1 lb) | 30 700 |
| poultry | 0.99 kg (2.2 lb) | 6 200 |
| beef and veal | 0.99 kg (2.2 lb) | 7 000 |
| mutton and pork | 1.13 kg (2.5 lb) | 10 400 |
| bacon and ham | 0.71 kg (1.6 lb) | 9 800 |
| sausages | 0.42 kg (0.93 lb) | 5 300 |
| other meats | 1.13 kg (2.5 lb) | 4 700 |
| fish | 0.71 kg (1.6 lb) | 3 000 |
| cheese | 0.57 kg (1.3 lb) | 7 100 |
| milk | 14.2 litres (25 pints) | 38 600 |
| butter | 0.57 kg (1.3 lb) | 17 500 |
| margarine | 0.57 kg (1.3 lb) | 17 300 |
| fats and oils | 0.43 kg (0.95 lb) | 16 000 |
| eggs | 1.40 kg (3.1 lb) | 8 600 |
| vegetables: fresh | 3.97 kg (8.8 lb) | 5 000 |
| vegetables: frozen | 2.41 kg (5.3 lb) | 4 500 |
| potatoes | 5.95 kg (13.1 lb) | 18 900 |
| fruit: fresh | 2.84 kg (6.3 lb) | 5 400 |
| fruit: canned and frozen | 1.13 kg (2.5 lb) | 1 200 |
| tea and coffee | 0.43 kg (0.95 lb) | 5 000 |
| jams, pickles, sauces, spreads | 1.42 kg (3.2 lb) | 15 400 |
| Total | | 330 600 |

[a] P. Payne, quoted in Gray, A. (ed.) (1993) *World Health and Disease*, Open University Press, Buckingham; derived from the National Food Survey Committee (1983) *Household Food Consumption and Expenditure, 1981: Annual Report of the National Food Survey Committee*, HMSO, London.

From Tables 1.3–1.5, a number of trends can be identified.

● The variety of the food has increased enormously over the past 200 years (Figure 1.3).

● The energy supplied each week may have been a lot higher in the 1800s than today. The family concerned lived in a rural area, and agricultural labour demanded more energy than working in an industrial environment.

Not obvious from the tables are the changes in the level of salt and vegetable fibre. It is interesting that the price of salt has fallen by a factor of five over the past 150 years.

**Figure 1.3**
The food eaten by an
average British family in a
year.

The average proportion of fat in meat has declined significantly since the 19th century because of changes in animal husbandry. Thus, it is probable that recent generations ate more animal fat than we do today.

These Tables also show that we have a great deal more control over our diet than our forebears, who had to eat what was available. However, this wide choice often makes things more difficult. What should we eat, or avoid, to ensure a healthy diet? Unfortunately, it is not easy to answer this question, not because of incomplete scientific knowledge, but simply because each of us will have different needs. For example, the amount of food we need to convert into energy depends on age, gender, size, occupation and lifestyle. The types of food we eat will also be affected by social factors such as income, geographic location – by the sea, in the country, in an inner city – ethnic and religious background, whether you are a vegetarian or not, and finally, but nevertheless importantly, what you enjoy eating. But all is not lost, because what various organizations such as the Department of Health of the UK, the National Academy of Sciences of the USA and the World Health Organization have tried to do is to produce recommended nutrient intakes for the average person. An example is shown in Table 1.6. Sometimes the advice from these organizations is contradictory, which reflects the subjective nature of the task, but nevertheless there are a number of clear messages, which we shall look at in turn.

**Table 1.6** Recommended daily amounts of food energy and some nutrients for population groups in the UK (1979)[a]. By courtesy of HMSO.

| Age range/ years | Occupation category | Energy MJ | Energy kcal | Protein /g | Calcium /mg | Iron /mg | Vitamin A /mg | Thiamine /mg | Riboflavin /mg | Niacin /mg | Vitamin C /mg |
|---|---|---|---|---|---|---|---|---|---|---|---|
| *Men* | | | | | | | | | | | |
| 18–34 | sedentary | 10.5 | 2510 | 63 | 500 | 10 | 750 | 1.0 | 1.6 | 18 | 30 |
| | moderately active | 12.0 | 2870 | 72 | 500 | 10 | 750 | 1.2 | 1.6 | 18 | 30 |
| | very active | 14.0 | 3350 | 84 | 500 | 10 | 750 | 1.0 | 1.6 | 18 | 30 |
| 35–64 | sedentary | 10.0 | 2390 | 60 | 500 | 10 | 750 | 1.0 | 1.6 | 18 | 30 |
| | moderately active | 11.5 | 2750 | 69 | 500 | 10 | 750 | 1.1 | 1.6 | 18 | 30 |
| | very active | 14.0 | 3350 | 84 | 500 | 10 | 750 | 1.3 | 1.6 | 18 | 30 |
| 65–74 | assuming a sedentary life | 10.0 | 2390 | 60 | 500 | 10 | 750 | 1.0 | 1.6 | 18 | 30 |
| 75+ | | 9.0 | 2200 | 54 | 500 | 10 | 750 | 0.9 | 1.6 | 18 | 30 |
| *Women* | | | | | | | | | | | |
| 18–54 | most occupations | 9.0 | 2150 | 54 | 500 | 12[b] | 750 | 0.9 | 1.3 | 15 | 30 |
| | very active | 10.9 | 2610 | 62 | 500 | 12[b] | 750 | 1.0 | 1.3 | 15 | 30 |
| 55–74 | assuming a sedentary life | 8.0 | 1900 | 47 | 500 | 10 | 750 | 0.8 | 1.3 | 15 | 30 |
| 75+ | | 7.0 | 1700 | 42 | 500 | 10 | 750 | 0.7 | 1.3 | 15 | 30 |
| pregnancy | | 10.0 | 2390 | 60 | 1200 | 13 | 750 | 1.0 | 1.6 | 18 | 60 |
| lactation | | 11.5 | 2750 | 69 | 1200 | 15 | 1200 | 1.1 | 1.8 | 21 | 60 |

[a] Very recently, recommended daily amounts have been replaced by reference nutrient intakes (RNIs). Some of the values listed here have gone up slightly and others have gone down.

[b] These recommendations may not cover heavy menstrual losses.

## 1.2.2 Average daily energy requirement

Energy is required for sustaining all forms of life on Earth. In humans, this energy can be classed under three main headings: basal metabolic rate, thermogenesis, and muscular activity.

### Basal metabolism

The term metabolism covers all the chemical reactions that are going on in the body, and the **basal metabolic rate** refers to the energy requirement of keeping all these reactions going while the body is at rest. Even when you are sleeping, your body needs considerable quantities of energy to continue its essential processes. Obvious examples are the pumping action of the heart and the expansion and contraction of the lungs. However, some muscles must constantly be ready to contract in response to stimuli from the nervous system, and thus energy is continuously needed to keep the muscles in a state of tension. The basal metabolic rate is affected by size, gender, age, rate of growth and even by climate, hormonal activity and the amount of sleep a person gets. Table 1.7 lists the average values for different types of people.

**Table 1.7** Some average values of basal metabolic rate.

|        | Age     | Weight/kg | Average rate/ kJ per day |
|--------|---------|-----------|--------------------------|
| infant | 1 year  | 10        | 2 100                    |
| child  | 8 years | 25        | 4 200                    |
| woman  | adult   | 55        | 5 400                    |
| man    | adult   | 65        | 6 700                    |

The average basal metabolic rate for men and women accounts for about two-thirds of the total energy required by the body. The basal metabolic rate varies with age, falling off faster for men than for women as they get older. It also varies with climate, being reduced by 5–10% in very cold or very hot climates.

### Thermogenesis

After food has been eaten, the various processes it is subjected to before it is utilized, such as digestion and absorption, result in the release of energy. Most of this appears as heat, corresponding to about 10% of the energy content of the food.

### Muscular activity

Whenever we do any kind of activity, be it standing up, walking, running, climbing, gardening, playing sport, or going about our work, we use muscles that need energy. This energy is over and above that involved in the basal metabolic rate. Unfortunately, muscles are not very efficient machines and only 15–20% of the energy ends up doing the required work.

Table 1.8 shows some typical energy requirements for a range of activities in kilojoules per minute of activity. These include an allowance for thermogenesis and basal metabolic rate.

**Table 1.8** Average energy expenditure per minute for a range of activities.

| Activity | Average energy expenditure/kJ per min |
|---|---|
| *Everyday activities* | |
| sleep | 5 |
| sitting | 6 |
| standing | 7 |
| washing, dressing | 15 |
| walking slowly | 13 |
| walking moderately quickly | 21 |
| walking up and down stairs | 38 |
| *Light effort* | |
| most domestic work, golf, lorry driving, light industrial and assembly work, carpentry, bricklaying | 10–20 |
| *Moderate effort* | |
| gardening, tennis, dancing, jogging, cycling up to 20 km per hour, digging, shovelling, agricultural work (non-mechanized) | 21–30 |
| *Strenuous effort* | |
| coal mining, steel furnace work, squash, cross-country running, football, swimming (crawl) | over 30 |

Some of the food we take in is used for growth and repair of our bodies. Some food is oxidized to carbon dioxide and water to provide our energy needs. Any remaining food is stored as fats as adipose tissue. Clearly, if we take in more food than the body needs it will be stored and we will put on weight (strictly scientists should refer to mass gain, but here we use the common parlance). A problem arises only if an individual is obese. About 45% of males and 36% of females in the UK are obese (above the upper level of weight considered desirable by the British College of Physicians). There is good evidence that such people may suffer not only psychological trauma and social discrimination, but also from a considerably increased risk of illness and death from a number of causes, such as heart disease, strokes, breast cancer, arthritis and diabetes.

Alternatively, if not enough food is consumed, the body starts to convert its reserves of fat into water and carbon dioxide to provide energy, leading to weight loss, which again has health implications if it goes too far. So, if we use the previous data to calculate how much energy we need on average for our lifestyles, we can determine how much food we need to take in. Table 1.9 shows such a calculation for my average day, leading to an energy consumption of about 11 000 kJ per day. Thus my food should provide about 11 000 kJ per day, if I am not to get fat (or fatter). For most people, this balance is often achieved over periods of a few days. The problem, which is not just mine, is the long-term balance. Notice that playing 30 minutes squash only uses up an extra 270 J of energy compared with going out for a brisk walk for the same length of time (Table 1.8).

**Table 1.9**  Energy used in my average day!

| Activity | kJ |
| --- | --- |
| 9.5 hours sitting | 3 420 |
| 2 hours standing | 840 |
| 2 hours gentle walking | 1 560 |
| 0.5 hour going up and down stairs | 1 140 |
| 0.5 hour washing, dressing | 450 |
| 1 hour light domestic activities | 600 |
| 8 hours sleep | 2 400 |
| 0.5 hours squash | 900 |
| Total | 11 310 |

Before we leave the topic of energy, it is interesting to look at the energy supplied by a good hot meal versus that of a cold meal. The heat of food is fairly insignificant and not available to be used by us other than warming us up. The ingredients in a serving of tomato soup provide about 600 kJ of energy whereas the extra energy provided by serving it at 60 °C is only 25 kJ. Nevertheless, when we eat hot soup the warmth is immediately perceived, providing a welcome boost to morale on cold days.

> **Question 4**  A Mars bar provides about 1 200 kJ of energy. How many minutes of brisk walking would use up this energy?

## 1.2.3  Short and long term proposals for healthier eating

As well as getting the correct balance between an individual's energy needs and diet, it is also important to ensure that on average the correct quantities of other nutrients, such as vitamins and minerals, are consumed. These are needed in only small quantities, and there are often large stores of these materials in the body to cope with medium-term shortages. Although most diets in the UK are varied enough to supply these essential nutrients, this is only because many foods, such as breakfast cereals and bread, are fortified with extra vitamins.

Despite the fact that the average diet in the UK is nutritionally adequate, in the sense that it supplies the recommended daily averages of nutrients, the diseases of affluence, such as chronic heart disease and cancer, which are believed to be in some way related to diet, have become major causes of death. This has led the National Advisory Committee on Nutrition Education (NACNE) in the UK to make recommendations as to what might constitute a healthy diet. The main recommendations are given in Table 1.10.

**Table 1.10** Nutritional guidelines proposed by NACNE (1983).

| Dietary component | Current estimated intake | Proposal | |
| --- | --- | --- | --- |
| | | Long-term | Short-term |
| energy intake | – | see note *a* below | |
| fat intake | 38% of total energy | 30% of total energy | 34% of total energy |
| saturated fatty acid intake | 18% of total energy | 10% of total energy | 15% of total energy |
| polyunsaturated fatty acid intake | – | no specific recommendation *b* | |
| cholesterol intake | – | no recommendation | |
| sucrose intake | 38 kg per head per year | 20 kg per head per year | 34 kg per head per year |
| fibre intake | 10 g per head per day | 30 g per head per day | 25 g per head per day |
| salt intake | 8.1–12 g per head per day | recommend reduction by 3 g per head per day | recommend reduction by 1 g per head per day |
| alcohol intake | 4–9% of total energy | 4% of total energy | 5% of total energy |
| protein intake | 11% of total energy | no recommendation | |

*a* Recommended adjustment of the types of food eaten and an increase in exercise so that adult body weight is maintained within the advised limits of weight for height.

*b* In practice there is likely to be a greater consumption of both polyunsaturated and monounsaturated fatty acids, and a tendency for the ratio of polyunsaturated to saturated fatty acids to increase.

However, it must be remembered that the consensus of what constitutes a healthy diet does shift from time to time, depending on what is fashionable, important, reasonable or provable! We shall examine some of these recommendations in more detail, which will reveal some of the problems of identifying a link between diet and health.

### *Fat intake*

One of the recommendations is to reduce the amount of fat in our diet and move to higher proportions of unsaturated fats, because of a possible link with coronary heart disease, cancer of the breast, colon and prostate, as well as hypertension. We use the term 'possible link' not to engender total scepticism about the scientific basis for the link but to emphasize that in such matters the connection is difficult to prove – much more difficult than say the link between scurvy and vitamin C, which was nevertheless not accepted for many years. Figure 1.4 shows the relationship between deaths from heart disease and breast cancer and total fat intake as a percentage of dietary energy.

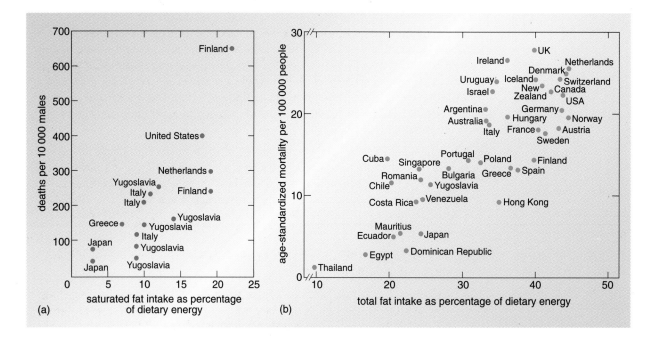

**Figure 1.4**
The relationship in various countries between total fat intake as a percentage of dietary energy and death from (a) heart disease and (b) breast cancer. Some countries occur more than once because data from different years have been used.

■ Does Figure 1.4 prove that heart disease and breast cancer are caused by excessive fat intake?

■ No: such plots merely establish an association of the two factors – countries with populations eating large quantities of fat tend to be the countries with the higher mortalities.

It is important to stress that such graphs do not establish a direct causal link. It may not be the fats themselves that are the problem but some other factor reflected by dietary fat intake, such as average annual income. If this were the case there may be other associations such as between death from heart disease and breast cancer and the number of washing machines. Nevertheless, in the case of fats, the association is backed up by other studies, which show that a falling consumption of saturated fats is matched by a reduction in the instances of heart disease, which is why it is recommended to reduce fat intake.

Such a discussion of whether fat intake needs to be reduced highlights, to some extent, the uncertainty of links between health and diet. As chemists, we can design an experiment in such a way that everything else stays constant and the effect of only one variable on one other can be examined. However, with foods there are so many variables that it is difficult to determine a causal relationship. Examination of large populations does, however, allow us to determine potential risks.

### *Cholesterol*
Cholesterol used to be regarded as the most dangerous of all the common dietary constituents. Indeed, high concentrations of cholesterol in the blood are associated with a high risk of chronic heart disease, providing a way of predicting the likelihood of chronic heart disease. However, cholesterol in the diet is now not thought to be an important cause of this disease. There seems to be little relationship between the levels of cholesterol in our food and that in our blood, which explains the lack of any recommendation in Table 1.10.

### Sugar

We shall examine the problems caused by dietary sugar, or more precisely sucrose, in detail in Section 6. Essentially, there are two: first, sucrose is used by our bodies primarily as a source of energy, thus its inclusion in our diet as a sweetener serves only to increase our energy intake, increasing the risk of obesity; second, it can cause tooth decay, the problem increasing the longer the sugar is in the mouth. Hence, on both counts, there are recommendations to reduce our intake.

### Fibre

Associations have been claimed between high fibre intake and reduced incidences of heart disease, hypertension, bowel cancer, appendicitis and piles. However, the Department of Health Standing Committee on Medical Aspects of Food Policy said in 1991 about fibre, which it calls NSP (non-starch polysaccharides):

> That it is not currently possible to identify NSP as a major factor in the aetiology of these diseases

The problem is one of multiple associations. High fibre diets are by definition high in vegetable and fruits, hence they will be associated with high levels of digestible starches and be low in animal products. Thus high fibre intake is more of a marker of a particular kind of diet.

### Salt

Sodium and chloride ions are essential and are widely distributed in body fluids. We need about 4 g of salt per day to replace that lost in sweating. On average, an adult consumes about three times that amount, the surplus being excreted in the urine. There is good evidence that there is an association between high salt intake and the development of high blood pressure. It has been shown that reducing salt intake does help to lower blood pressure in those people who already suffer from hypertension. However, other studies have shown that this association is only apparent for about 10–20% of the population who show a special susceptibility to salt.

### Alcohol

All of the drinks we imbibe are mainly water. The nutritional value of tea, coffee, carbonated drinks and squashes is minimal, but they do provide an important means of taking in water. The exception to this is alcoholic drinks, which also provide energy. Apart from water, the main constituent of alcoholic drinks is ethanol or ethyl alcohol (Figure 1.5), which is used by the body to provide energy, as shown below:

$$CH_3CH_2OH(l) + 3O_2(g) = 2CO_2(g) + 3H_2O(l) \qquad \Delta H = -1\,367 \text{ kJ}$$

The energy released per gram of ethanol is 29.7 kJ.

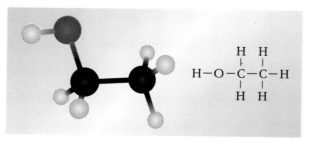

$$H-O-\underset{\underset{H}{|}}{\overset{\overset{H}{|}}{C}}-\underset{\underset{H}{|}}{\overset{\overset{H}{|}}{C}}-H$$

**Figure 1.5**
Ball-and-stick model of ethanol, and an abbreviated two-dimensional representation of the same molecule.

The average bottle of wine contains about 75 g of ethanol, which releases 2 200 kJ of energy: even if you drink only half of it, this is still equivalent to about 10% of your average daily energy requirement! Unlike most foods, ethanol can be absorbed by the body without prior digestion. This takes place mainly in the small intestines, but can also occur through the stomach walls. Absorption may take anything from 30 minutes to two hours depending on the amount of ethanol, its concentration in the drink, and the nature of any food eaten before or during its absorption. Figure 1.6 shows the fate of alcohol, together with its effects on the central nervous system. After absorption it is distributed throughout the body by the bloodstream, but in the liver it reacts with oxygen to give acetic acid:

$$CH_3CH_2OH(aq) + O_2(g) = CH_3COOH(aq) + H_2O(l)$$

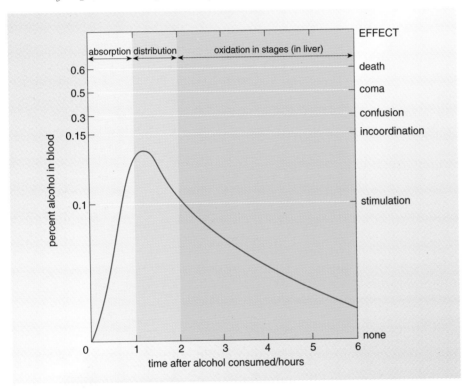

**Figure 1.6**
The fate of ethanol in the body.

The acetic acid produced is then further oxidized to carbon dioxide and water at various sites in the body. The liver can oxidize only about 7 g of ethanol an hour, so working flat out it would take five hours to remove from the bloodstream the ethanol contributed by half a bottle of wine.

As is well known, an excessive intake of ethanol has a damaging effect on health. If ethanol replaces fat as the main energy source for the liver, metabolism of fat ceases and fats accumulate, producing what is known as a 'fatty liver'. Prolonged excessive consumption of ethanol leads from this reversible damage to alcoholic hepatitis and finally to irreversible cirrhosis.

The National Advisory Committee on Nutrition Education proposes that we reduce our ethanol intake from 4–9% to about 4% of our total energy requirements.

■  What mass of ethanol could be consumed in a week by a person whose energy needs are 10 MJ per day, and yet still meet these proposals?

■  The proposal suggests that a maximum of 4% of our total energy requirement should be derived from ethanol. If we need 10 MJ per day then this means that no more than 400 kJ should come from ethanol. If each gram of ethanol provides 29.7 kJ, then we should drink no more than 400/29.7 g of ethanol, which is 13.5 g. Over a week, this amounts to 94.5 g, or about one and a quarter bottles of wine.

However, despite its general enthusiasm for giving advice about personal behaviour, the health profession is remarkably coy about the fact that there is good evidence that alcohol in *moderate* amounts exerts a protective effect against chronic heart disease.

### *Toxins*

Of course, there are many other chemicals that we would want to exclude from our diet, both synthetic and natural. Just because it's natural doesn't make it safe (Box 1.1). Foods can contain many natural harmful substances. Such compounds are produced by plants for a number of reasons, but often as a means of defence against animals (including humans) or insects that might eat them. One of the most potent liver carcinogens (aflatoxin) is produced by a mould that attacks cereals, and in particular peanuts. However, it cannot be ignored that potentially harmful substances are accidently or deliberately introduced by people, leading to residual amounts of insecticides, herbicides, fertilizers and metals such as lead. In the next Section we shall examine the level of such adulteration, and what we can do about it, by looking at how the purity of one important compound, water, is maintained. In many ways the same basic conclusions apply to all foodstuffs.

---

### Box 1.1  Cassava – food or poison?

**Figure 1.7**
A cassava plant.

Cassava (Figure 1.7) is one of the staple foods of Africa. It is used to make tapioca. Cassava contains compounds called cyanogenic glycosides, which can give rise to large amounts of poisonous hydrogen cyanide. When cassava is eaten this reaction occurs in the intestine. As you might expect, if hydrogen cyanide is formed in the body it is very dangerous.

Cyanogenic glycosides are found in many plants, including laburnum and the stones of many fruits, such as apricots. However, cassava gives rise to particularly high levels of hydrogen cyanide, 50 mg per 100 g of cassava. Consequently, the food has to be treated before it can be consumed, and this has become a well established tradition in West Africa. Decomposition of the cyanogenic glycosides can be brought about by chopping the cassava up, then fermenting it. On cooking, the volatile hydrogen cyanide is driven off, so the food is safe to eat.

Another crop that has high levels of cyanogenic glycosides is the lima bean, which is grown in many parts of the world. In this case it is more difficult to render them safe, so bean varieties have been bred that are low in cyanogenic glycosides.

## 1.3 How pure is pure?

As we saw in Book 2, the water cycle ensures a ready supply of relatively pure water. However, on its journey from the sky to our taps it picks up a range of chemicals. Atmospheric gases, such as $CO_2$, $NO_2$ and $SO_2$, dissolve in the water droplets in the air. As the water flows over rocks, ions such as calcium, sodium, magnesium, carbonate, sulfate, chloride and nitrate dissolve in the water, as does material from decaying vegetable matter. Sometimes these contaminants are beneficial – incidences of heart disease are lower in hard water areas, and whisky gains a special taste from using peaty water. However, in general, we want water to be as pure as possible. But how pure is pure?

▨    We often buy 'pure orange juice', but how pure is this orange juice, in the chemical sense?

■    Orange juice may be called pure in the colloquial sense – after all, it contains only the juice of oranges and it is not adulterated. However, it is a mixture of a wide range of different compounds in water so is not pure in the chemical sense.

So, is water pure only if it contains solely water molecules and nothing else? Based on this idea it would never be possible to describe anything as pure! For example, consider a 0.5 litre jug full of tap water. This volume comprises about seventeen million million million million ($10^{25}$) molecules. This in itself makes it very unlikely that they are all going to be molecules of water and suggests the potential difficulties in detecting any that aren't. If even a million million million ($10^{18}$) of these molecules were not those of water the 'water' would still be over 99.999 99% 'pure'! Clearly, we cannot claim absolute purity for any substance, because there are always likely to be some 'foreign' particles present. Nonetheless, so long as this level is acceptable for our purposes we can consider the substance as pure. Of course, what constitutes an acceptable level depends on our use of the substance. Take, for example, tap water. We trust that water companies supply us with 'pure' water and take it for granted that the liquid we get from the tap is just that, forgetting, perhaps, that the water contains added chlorine to protect us from infection by micro-organisms. In fact, the water that we drink from the tap is not pure enough to use in a car battery or steam-iron: in addition to small concentrations of the dissolved gas chlorine, it contains dissolved minerals that come out of solution every time we boil a kettle, causing characteristic scaling or 'furring'. Such furring can clog up a steam-iron, and the presence of ions from these dissolved minerals affects the way a battery works. In these cases distilled or deionized water is used, which is purer and does not contain these ions.

Another factor affecting our definition of purity is the limitation of the practical techniques available for detecting the presence of impurities. Our technique may be able to measure only down to a few parts per million of an impurity. If we cannot detect any of the impurity, it may not be present at all or it may be present at the level of parts per billion. In other words, purity can be guaranteed only to within the limits of detection of the instrumentation.

We are now in a position to propose a working definition of purity. This kind of definition is important not only when considering chemically pure compounds but also because it applies equally well to a discussion of the acceptable levels of a contaminant in food as well as in water. Samples can be claimed to be pure (or free from contaminants) only to the extent that, for all practical purposes and with currently available techniques, no impurity (contaminant) is detectable above a certain limit. If we suppose for a moment that compound A contains an impurity B, we can consider A to be pure only when either (i) the presence of B (the contaminant) is reduced to such a level that it becomes undetectable or (ii) the level of B is low enough that, within experimental limits, A behaves as if it were pure and therefore acceptable for our purposes.

As described in the articles associated with the video sequence 4, *Water*, the World Health Organization has defined the maximum levels of contaminants in drinking water that are acceptable such that they have no deleterious effect on health. In the words of our previous discussion, it defines the limit of impurity such that for the purpose of drinking, the water is effectively pure and is thus acceptable (see Box 1.2).

The chemist has a number of roles to play in ensuring a clean supply, not just of water but of all foods:

- In establishing procedures for determining the levels of individual contaminants, often at very low concentrations;

- In providing safer alternatives to existing herbicides and pesticides;

- In providing safe methods of removing contaminants.

*Some time between now and the end of your study of Part 1, you should view video sequence 4, Water, and read the associated articles on water purity. There may be a question in one of the TMAs relating to this material. There is also a simple home experiment (Experiment 3.1), based on the analysis of tap water, which you should plan to do during this period.*

## Summary of Chapter 1

This chapter has focused mainly on what chemicals we take in and what makes a healthy diet.

The chemicals in our bodies are no different from others. We are made of a range of chemicals, mainly water and organic compounds. Food provides energy and renews lost chemicals.

We can eat a range of different types of food. The constituents of all food can be divided into five nutrient classes: proteins, fats, carbohydrates, vitamins and minerals. We also need water and oxygen to survive.

Over the past few centuries the average diet has changed considerably, mainly through an increase in choice.

We have an average daily energy requirement that depends on our lifestyle. If the quantity of food we consume does not match these needs, we gain or lose weight.

There are a number of recommendations for healthy eating that relate to specific nutrients. Relationships between diet and health often establish an association between factors but not necessarily a causal link.

We can consider a compound to be pure if the presence of another compound is reduced to such a level that it becomes impossible to detect and/or is acceptable for a particular purpose.

**Question 5** Which of the following is pure in the chemical sense: lemonade, milk, table salt, black coffee?

## Box 1.2  Are mineral waters pure?

The phrase 'pure mineral water' seems to be a contradiction in terms. If water is pure it should contain only water molecules. 'Mineral water' implies that the water contains minerals. Many people are making the switch to mineral water because they think it is better than water from the tap, which contains chlorine, nitrates and the like. In fact, mineral water is water that originates from a groundwater body, so it also includes spring water. If the water is boiled away the dry residue can be analysed and the levels of ionic compounds measured. These data are often printed on the side of a bottle, although sometimes it just says that the water has passed analysis in line with the Mineral Water Regulations 1985. Figure 1.8 shows the analysis data for a typical mineral water and for that from a spa.

**How to read the label**

*Natural mineral water:* Must comply with natural mineral water regulations – water extracted from the ground, untreated except for basic processes such as filtration, and bottled at source. Mineral content may vary slightly.

*Spring water:* Need comply only with regulations on quality of water for human consumption. Source may be as for mineral water, can be bottled anywhere.

*Naturally carbonated natural mineral water:* Water that is sparkling at source. However, the carbon dioxide that causes the fizz can be removed before it is bottled and then re-introduced. The final product may contain less fizz than it would naturally, but not more.

*Carbonated natural mineral water:* This has added carbon dioxide.

| TYPICAL ANALYSIS mg/L: | | | |
|---|---|---|---|
| BICARBONATES | 190 | MAGNESIUM | 15 |
| SULPHATES | 7 | FLUORIDES | 0.1 |
| CHLORIDES | 15 | SODIUM | 9 |
| NITRATES | 1 | POTASSIUM | 1 |
| IRON | <0.001 | ALUMINIUM | 0.005 |
| CALCIUM | 39 | T.D.S. | 175 |
| pH | | 7.6 | |

LOW IN SALTS AND NITRATES.
BEST SERVE CHILLED; DO NOT FREEZE IN BOTTLE

## ANALYSES

By Dr. Horace Swete, Public Analyst for the Counties of Worcester and Radnor, and Mr. Raymond Ross, Society Public Analysts, of the Two Mineral Springs discovered by Mr Thomas Heighway in the Park, Llandrindod Wells, in 1893.

### ROMAN SPRING:

Temperature of Spring, 80° F.

Dissolved Gases in Cubic Inches per Gallon :—

| | | |
|---|---|---|
| Nitrogen | ... | 4·20 |
| Oxygen | ... | 1·20 |
| Carbon Dioxide | ... | ·80 |
| | | 6·20 |

Mineral Constituents in grains per gallon :—

| | | |
|---|---|---|
| Sodium Chloride | ... | 263·37 |
| Potassium Chloride | ... | 2·60 |
| Calcium Chloride | ... | 98·00 |
| Magnesium Chloride | ... | 23·80 |
| Lithium Chloride | ... | traces |
| Thallium Chloride | ... | traces |
| Oxide of Aluminium | ... | ·56 |
| Oxide of Iron | ... | 1·4 |
| Calcium Carbonate | ... | 1·05 |
| Ammonium Carbonate | .. | ·30 |
| Silica | ... | 4·28 |
| Nitrites | ... | nil |
| Nitrates | ... | traces |

### MAGNESIUM SPRING:

Temperature of Spring, 49·8° F.

Dissolved Gases in Cubic Inches per Gallon :— ,

| | | |
|---|---|---|
| Sulphuretted Hydrogen | ... | ·80 |
| Nitrogen | ... | 4·28 |
| Oxygen | ... | ·23 |
| Carbon Dioxide | ... | 1·60 |
| | | 6·91 |

Mineral Constituents in Grains per Gallon :—

| | | |
|---|---|---|
| Sodium Chloride | ... | 236·46 |
| Potassium Chloride | ... | 1·4 |
| Calcium Chloride | ... | 88·9 |
| Magnesium Chloride | ... | 49·42 |
| Lithium Chloride | ... | traces |
| Thallium Chloride | ... | traces |
| Aluminium Oxide | ... | 1·06 |
| Iron Oxide | ... | ·7 |
| Silica | ... | 4·14 |
| Ammonium Carbonate | ... | ·19 |
| Nitrites | ... | nil |
| Nitrates | ... | traces |

To Mr. Thos. Heighway,
　　Park Pump Room,
　　　　Llandrindod Wells.

The two Samples of Water from the Roman Spring and from the Magnesium Spring, received from Mr. Thomas Heighway, Park Pump Room, Llandrindod Wells, on June 4th, 1894.

They are very similar to those previously examined by Dr. Swete, but both of them while possessing the same constituents are very much stronger as regards those matters likely to produce a beneficial effect when taken as medicine.

　　　　　　HORACE SWETE, M.D., D.Ph.,
　　　　　　　　　　　　Member Society Public Analysts.
　　　　　　RAYMOND ROSS, A.S.P.A.

**Figure 1.8**
Analysis of a typical modern mineral water and water from Llandrindod Wells spa in 1893.

# Chapter 2
# What's in a meal?

*Before you read this Chapter and the rest of this Book, it's important that you are familiar with the material in AV sequences 3 and 4. You should have studied AV sequence 3 'The shape of organic chemistry' during your reading of Book 2; if not, you should study it now, and also AV sequence 4 'Making sense of organic chemistry'; lack of the knowledge in these sequences may hamper your study of the remaining chapters in this Book.*

Most of the food we eat, be it meat, cereal or dairy product, is clearly a complex mixture of compounds. For example, honey, which contains 20% by mass of water and 76% by mass of a mixture of two different types of sugar, with the balance made up from other carbohydrates, proteins, minerals, vitamins and flavourings, could never be described as pure in the chemical sense!

For the moment, rather than look at a range of foods and examine their make up, we shall study the five common nutrients in turn. Words like protein, carbohydrate and polyunsaturated fats are terms that are frequently used in newspapers, magazines and commercials. Most people have a vague idea what these terms mean but, without some chemical description, it is difficult to understand what these substances are, and why we need them for a healthy diet. However, although we examine these terms individually, it must be remembered that food is more than just a collection of chemicals. Eating is not only essential but also a pleasurable experience. Food can be analysed in terms of its ingredients, but its presentation, taste, smell, texture, colour and temperature all have an important role to play in satisfying our senses. Although such subjective responses are difficult to measure, chemistry and chemists are also at the heart of enhancing these sensuous experiences.

## 2.1 Fats and oils

Each year, the human race uses nearly 80 million tonnes of fats and oils from animal and vegetable sources. The difference between a fat and an oil is that a fat is a solid or semi-solid at room temperature whereas an oil is a liquid. However, this definition is not particularly precise because it depends on what you call room temperature. Palm oil and coconut oil are liquids in the hot countries where they are produced, but in the colder climate of the UK they are solid.

As you will see later in this Book, a range of different compounds can be classed as edible fats and oils. However, for the moment, we shall concentrate on the most important class, the **triglycerides**. These compounds are the main constituents of vegetable oils and animal fats. Triglycerides are large molecules, as shown in Figure 2.1.

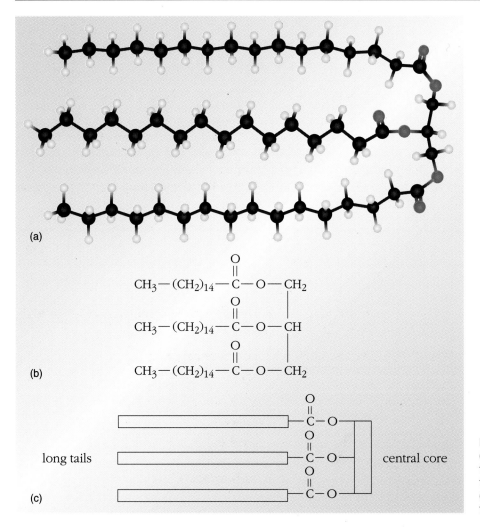

**Figure 2.1**
(a) Ball-and-stick model of a triglyceride; (b) structural formula of a triglyceride; (c) simplified model of a triglyceride.

Triglyceride molecules consist of three long tails connected to a central core. These long tails are chains of carbon atoms, usually between eight and twenty atoms long, with sufficient hydrogen atoms attached to satisfy the valency of carbon. The central core consists of three carbon atoms with their associated hydrogen atoms.

As you see, things are starting to get a little more complicated, and this is true for most of the food nutrients we shall talk about in this chapter. However, there is a method of classification that helps us to simplify things – the **functional group approach**, which you met in AV sequence 4. This simplification can be applied to most organic compounds. We can regard organic molecules as having distinct parts: the functional group or groups, which usually involve atoms such as oxygen or nitrogen, and the rest of the molecule, which usually involves just carbon and hydrogen atoms. The reason we regard them in this way is because when organic compounds react *only the functional group undergoes chemical change*. In this Book we shall generally highlight functional groups with a blue background. So, we can portray triglycerides as shown in Figure 2.2.

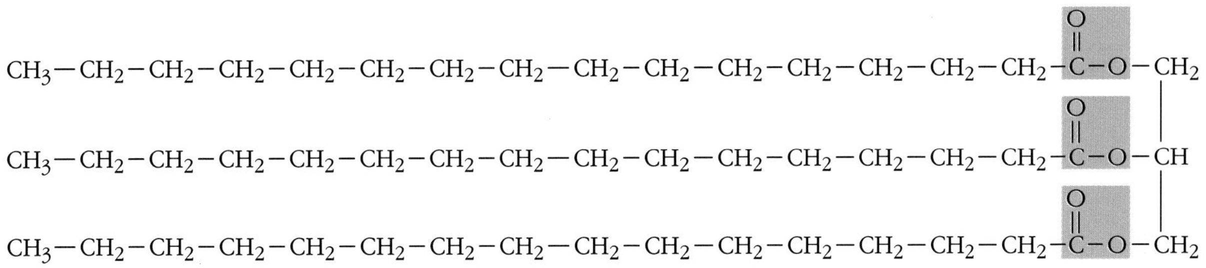

$$CH_3-CH_2-CH_2-CH_2-CH_2-CH_2-CH_2-CH_2-CH_2-CH_2-CH_2-CH_2-CH_2-CH_2-CH_2-\overset{\displaystyle O}{\overset{\|}{C}}-O-CH_2$$

$$CH_3-CH_2-CH_2-CH_2-CH_2-CH_2-CH_2-CH_2-CH_2-CH_2-CH_2-CH_2-CH_2-CH_2-CH_2-\overset{\displaystyle O}{\overset{\|}{C}}-O-CH$$

$$CH_3-CH_2-CH_2-CH_2-CH_2-CH_2-CH_2-CH_2-CH_2-CH_2-CH_2-CH_2-CH_2-CH_2-CH_2-\overset{\displaystyle O}{\overset{\|}{C}}-O-CH_2$$

**Figure 2.2**
Portraying triglycerides according to the functional group approach.

■ Using the table of functional groups in the notes for AV sequence 4 (Table 2.1 here), identify the type of functional group in the triglyceride shown in Figure 2.2.

■ The functional group corresponds to an ester functional group:

$$R^1-\overset{\displaystyle O}{\underset{\displaystyle O-R^2}{C}}$$

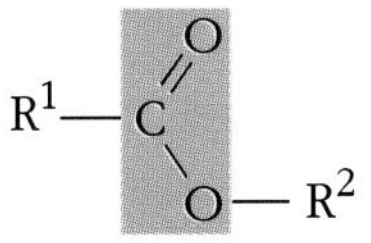

In fact there are three of these ester functional groups in a triglyceride, and they are highlighted in Figure 2.2.

**Table 2.1** The structures of the main functional groups.

| Structure | Name |
|---|---|
| $CH_3-CH_2-OH$ | alcohol |
| $CH_3-CH_2-NH_2$ | amine |
| $CH_3-CH=CH-CH_3$ | alkene |
| $CH_3-C{\overset{O}{\underset{OH}{}}}$ | carboxylic acid |
| $CH_3-C{\overset{O}{\underset{O-CH_2-CH_3}{}}}$ | ester |
| $CH_3-C{\overset{O}{\underset{NH_2}{}}}$ | amide |

These three ester functional groups provide the links by which the three tails are attached to the central core. As well as rationalizing its structure, the identification of the functional group helps us to understand how triglycerides are produced in nature and, as we shall see later, how they are broken down in the body.

**Esters** (see Box 2.1) result from the reaction of a carboxylic acid with an alcohol. The other product is water. For example, the ester ethyl butanoate, the major constituent of artificial pineapple flavouring, is made from butanoic acid and ethanol.

$$CH_3-CH_2-CH_2-C{\overset{O}{\underset{OH}{}}} \quad + \quad HO-CH_2-CH_3 \quad = \quad CH_3-CH_2-CH_2-C{\overset{O}{\underset{O-CH_2-CH_3}{}}} \quad + \quad H_2O \qquad (2.1)$$

butanoic acid              ethanol                    ethyl butanoate                    water

■  This is an example of a **condensation reaction**. Why do you think it is given this name?

■  In Book 2, Part 1, Chapter 5, you saw that condensation polymerizations are reactions in which a small molecule, such as water, is formed as a by-product. The ester formation above is also a condensation reaction because water is formed as a by-product.

This reaction is common to nearly all carboxylic acids,

$$R^1 - C{\overset{\displaystyle O}{\underset{\displaystyle OH}{\phantom{|}}}}$$

and alcohols, $R^2$—OH. So, we can write the general Equation 2.2, where the abbreviation $R^1$ represents the rest of the carboxylic acid molecule and $R^2$ represents the rest of the alcohol molecule.

$$R^1 - C{\overset{O}{\underset{OH}{\phantom{|}}}} \;+\; R^2 - OH \;=\; R^1 - C{\overset{O}{\underset{O-R^2}{\phantom{|}}}} \;+\; H_2O \qquad (2.2)$$

    carboxylic acid        alcohol              ester              water

■  Which carboxylic acid and alcohol would you use to make isopentyl acetate (**2.1**), a constituent of banana oil?

$$CH_3 - C{\overset{O}{\underset{O - CH_2 - CH_2 - CH{\overset{CH_3}{\underset{CH_3}{\phantom{|}}}}}{\phantom{|}}}}$$

**2.1**

■  Equation 2.3 shows the required carboxylic acid and alcohol.

$$CH_3 - C{\overset{O}{\underset{OH}{\phantom{|}}}} \;+\; HO - CH_2 - CH_2 - CH{\overset{CH_3}{\underset{CH_3}{\phantom{|}}}} \;=\; CH_3 - C{\overset{O}{\underset{O - CH_2 - CH_2 - CH{\overset{CH_3}{\underset{CH_3}{\phantom{|}}}}}{\phantom{|}}}} \;+\; H_2O \quad (2.3)$$

      acetic acid                      isopentanol                              isopentyl acetate                        water

We get a different compound if the hydrocarbon groups in the alcohol and the acid are swopped over – the atoms are joined in a different order:

$$CH_3{\overset{}{\underset{}{\phantom{|}}}} \atop CH_3 {\diagup}{\diagdown} CH - CH_2 - CH_2 - C{\overset{O}{\underset{O - CH_3}{\phantom{|}}}}$$

## Box 2.1 Esters

An example of an ester is ethyl acetate, which smells of pear drops and was used as nail varnish remover:

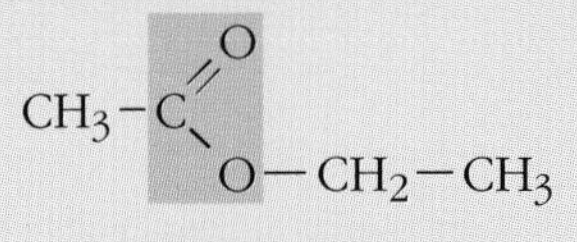

ethyl acetate

The ester group is highlighted in blue.

As we saw in Book 2, polyesters are polymers in which the monomers are joined together by ester groups. An example is

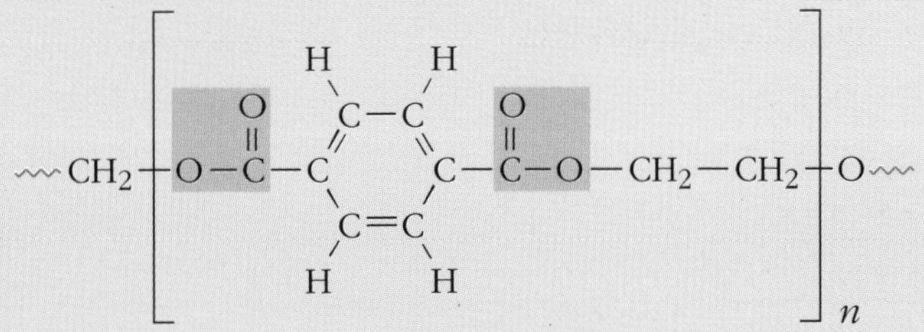

a polyester

Another ester that you may be familiar with is methyl salicylate, the active constituent in oil of wintergreen, a liniment applied to leg muscles before taking part in sports:

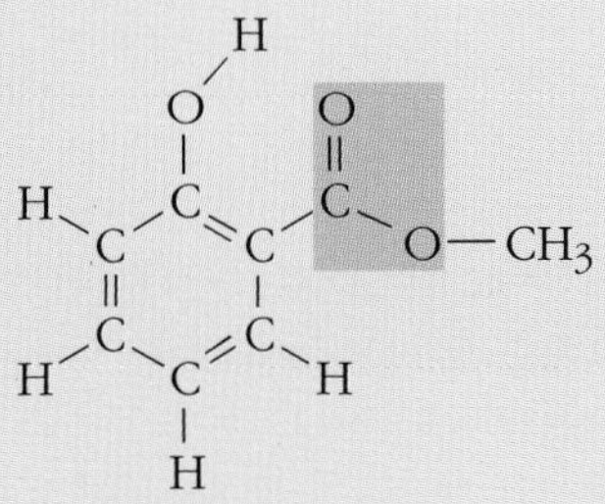

methyl salicylate

The generalized structure, where $R^1$ and $R^2$ are other parts of the molecule, is:

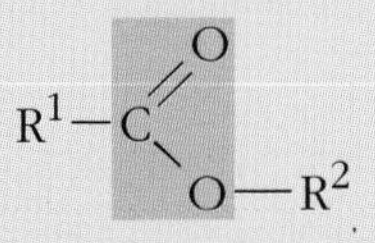

In ethyl acetate $R^1$ is $CH_3$ and $R^2$ is $CH_2CH_3$.

In esters, $R^2$ cannot be a hydrogen atom. If this were the case the functional group would be a carboxylic acid!

**Question 6** Identify the ester groups in the following compounds. From which carboxylic acids and alcohols would you make these esters?

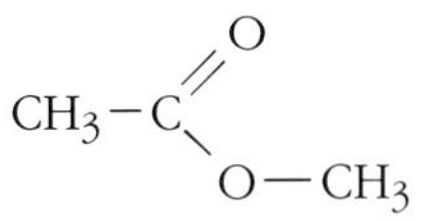

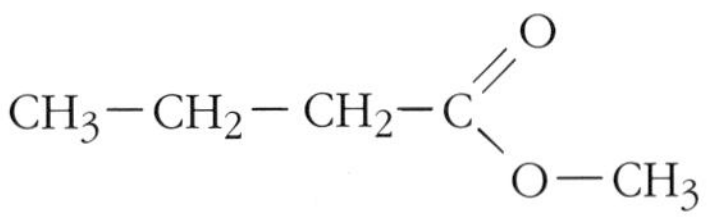

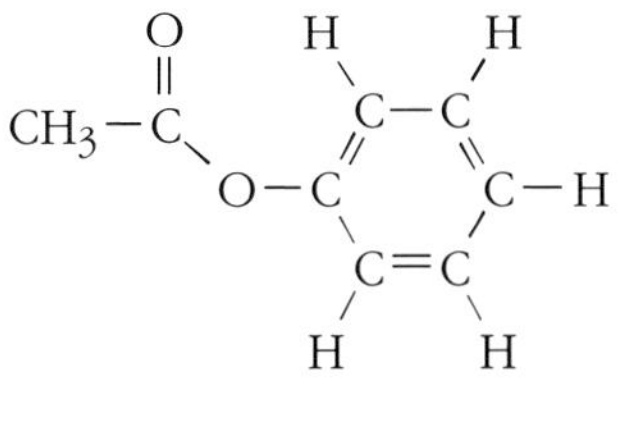

In triglycerides, the core to which the three tails are attached is derived from glycerol (**2.2**), more commonly called glycerine, the syrupy liquid sometimes used in cooking. This molecule contains three alcohol functional groups, each of which can be converted into an ester.

$$
\begin{array}{l}
CH_2-OH \\
| \\
CH-OH \\
| \\
CH_2-OH
\end{array}
$$

**2.2**  glycerol

■    What does each molecule of glycerol need to react with to create three ester groups, as in a triglyceride?

■    Each molecule of glycerol needs to react with three molecules of a carboxylic acid to give three ester groups.

Equations 2.4 to 2.6 show the successive reactions of each of the three alcohol functional groups with carboxylic acid molecules.

$$
R^1-C\underset{OH}{\overset{O}{\diagdown}} \quad + \quad
\begin{array}{l} CH_2-OH \\ | \\ CH-OH \\ | \\ CH_2-OH \end{array}
\quad = \quad
\begin{array}{l} CH_2-O-\overset{\overset{\textstyle O}{\|}}{C}-R^1 \\ | \\ CH-OH \\ | \\ CH_2-OH \end{array}
\quad + H_2O \qquad (2.4)
$$

a monoglyceride

$$
R^1-C\underset{OH}{\overset{O}{\diagdown}} \quad + \quad
\begin{array}{l} CH_2-O-\overset{\overset{\textstyle O}{\|}}{C}-R^1 \\ | \\ CH-OH \\ | \\ CH_2-OH \end{array}
\quad = \quad
\begin{array}{l} CH_2-O-\overset{\overset{\textstyle O}{\|}}{C}-R^1 \\ | \quad\;\; O \\ CH-O-\overset{\|}{C}-R^1 \\ | \\ CH_2-OH \end{array}
\quad + H_2O \;\; (2.5)
$$

a diglyceride

$$
R^1-C\underset{OH}{\overset{O}{\diagdown}} \quad + \quad
\begin{array}{l} CH_2-O-\overset{\overset{\textstyle O}{\|}}{C}-R^1 \\ | \quad\;\; O \\ CH-O-\overset{\|}{C}-R^1 \\ | \\ CH_2-OH \end{array}
\quad = \quad
\begin{array}{l} CH_2-O-\overset{\overset{\textstyle O}{\|}}{C}-R^1 \\ | \quad\;\; O \\ CH-O-\overset{\|}{C}-R^1 \\ | \quad\;\; O \\ CH_2-O-\overset{\|}{C}-R^1 \end{array}
\quad + H_2O \;\; (2.6)
$$

a triglyceride

Notice that fat molecules are called *tri*glycerides because there are three tails attached to the glycerol core. If two tails are attached the molecule is called a diglyceride, and if only one is attached it is called a monoglyceride. The basic structure of a triglyceride is the same irrespective of whether the fat comes from animals, in meat, lard or butter, or from plants, in cooking oil, olive oil or margarine.

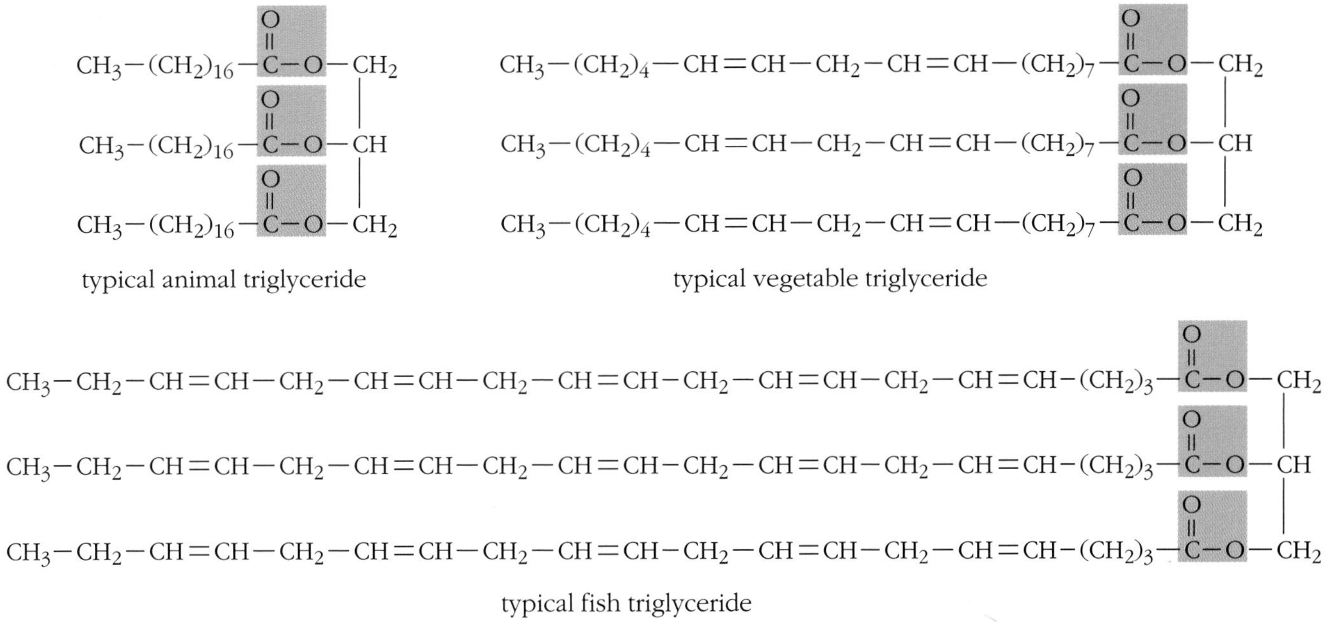

typical animal triglyceride

typical vegetable triglyceride

typical fish triglyceride

**Figure 2.3**
The molecular structures of three triglycerides, one from an animal, one from a vegetable and one from a fish.

■ Figure 2.3 shows the molecular structures of three triglycerides, one from an animal, one from a vegetable and one from a fish. What are the similarities and differences between these three structures?

■ All three consist of a central core connected to three long chains via ester groups. The only difference between the various triglycerides is in the structure of the three long hydrocarbon chains.

Because each of the triglyceride molecules is formed from glycerol and three carboxylic acids, the difference between the triglycerides of the three species results from each organism producing *different* carboxylic acids. Table 2.2 shows the structures of some of the common carboxylic acids, known as **fatty acids**, used in nature to make triglycerides, together with their names and origins.

**Table 2.2** Structures of some fatty acids together with their names and origins.

| Name | Carbon atoms | Structure | Type | Origin of name |
|------|------|------|------|------|
| butyric | 4 | $CH_3(CH_2)_2COOH$ | saturated | Latin for butter is butyrium |
| capric | 10 | $CH_3(CH_2)_8COOH$ | saturated | smell of goats (Latin for goat is caper) |
| lauric | 12 | $CH_3(CH_2)_{10}COOH$ | saturated | from laurel |
| myristic | 14 | $CH_3(CH_2)_{12}COOH$ | saturated | from nutmeg (genus *Myristica*) |
| palmitic | 16 | $CH_3(CH_2)_{14}COOH$ | saturated | from palm oil |
| stearic | 18 | $CH_3(CH_2)_{16}COOH$ | saturated | Greek for fat is stear |
| oleic | 18 | $CH_3(CH_2)_7CH=CH(CH_2)_7COOH$ | monounsaturated | from oil (Latin, oleum) |
| linoleic | 18 | $CH_3(CH_2)_4CH=CHCH_2CH=CH(CH_2)_7COOH$ | polyunsaturated | from linseed oil |
| linolenic | 18 | $CH_3CH_2CH=CHCH_2CH=CHCH_2CH=CH(CH_2)_7COOH$ | polyunsaturated | Latin for flax is linum |

■ What do you notice about the number of carbon atoms (including the carbon in the —C⟨=O, OH group) in the fatty acids?

■ The number of carbon atoms is always an even number.

The chains are even because the building block from which fatty acids are made contains two carbons. So, however many building blocks are added together the chain always contains an even number of carbons.

Notice that some of the fatty acids in Table 2.2 are called saturated fatty acids and others are called unsaturated fatty acids. If a carbon atom is attached to four other atoms by single bonds it is known as a **saturated carbon atom**. However, a carbon atom can be attached to fewer than four other atoms, but still have four bonds to it. For example, as we saw in Book 1, Section 7.5, the carbon could be part of a double bond, as shown in Figure 2.4, where it is attached to only three other atoms. In such cases the carbon is known as an **unsaturated carbon atom**.

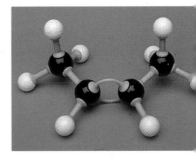

**Figure 2.4**
Model of the carbon–carbon double bond in the *cis*-but-2-ene molecule.

■ Apart from the carbon in the —C⟨=O, OH functional groups, do palmitic or stearic acids contain any unsaturated carbon atoms in their hydrocarbon chains? (The structures are given in Table 2.2.)

■ No: each of the carbon atoms in the hydrocarbon chains is attached to four other atoms by single bonds. Thus, they are all saturated chains.

Acids such as palmitic and stearic are known as **saturated fatty acids**, and the triglycerides made from them give rise to **saturated fats**. Note that, using this nomenclature, we examine only the chains. The unsaturated carbon atom in the functional group is not considered. Oleic acid has one double bond in its hydrocarbon chain. The carbon atoms of this double bond are attached to only three other atoms and are thus unsaturated. Oleic acid is therefore known as a **monounsaturated fatty acid**. Linoleic acid contains two double bonds in its hydrocarbon chain and is known as a **polyunsaturated fatty acid** or PUFA. Any fatty acid containing two or more double bonds in its hydrocarbon chain is a PUFA.

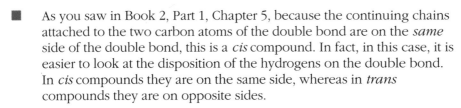

**Figure 2.5**
Stereoscopic model of the structure of oleic acid.

■ Figure 2.5 shows a stereoscopic ball-and-stick representation of oleic acid. Does oleic acid contain a *cis* or a *trans* double bond?

■ As you saw in Book 2, Part 1, Chapter 5, because the continuing chains attached to the two carbon atoms of the double bond are on the *same* side of the double bond, this is a *cis* compound. In fact, in this case, it is easier to look at the disposition of the hydrogens on the double bond. In *cis* compounds they are on the same side, whereas in *trans* compounds they are on opposite sides.

Most fatty acids in nature involve *cis* rather than *trans* double bonds.

Figure 2.6 shows the range of fatty acids that lead to the triglyceride molecules that make up a particular fat or oil. The data are presented as a series of histograms, where the relative heights of bands reflect the percentage composition of the different fatty acids that are used to make the fat. The percentages are based on the relative numbers of molecules of each of the fatty acids. Fats are an essential part of the diet, but, as we saw earlier, there have been recommendations that we should eat less fat in general, but in particular we should eat less fat derived from saturated fatty acids.

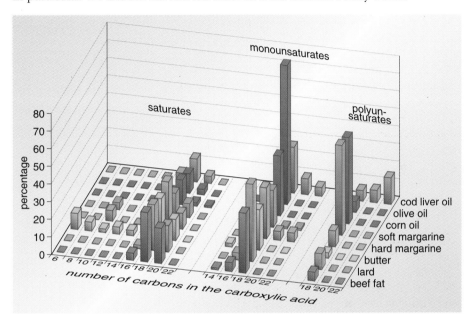

**Figure 2.6**
Histogram of the fatty acids used to make fats and oils.

▪   Which of the fats in Figure 2.6 should we avoid to fulfil this recommendation and which fats are more acceptable?

▪   Beef fat, butter, lard and hard margarine should be avoided because they contain a high level of triglycerides made from saturated fatty acids. Fats arising from polyunsaturated fatty acids, such as soft margarine or fish oils, are more acceptable.

The structure of a triglyceride molecule shows that it is made from three fatty acids, and Figure 2.6 shows that for a particular fat or oil, there is a large range of fatty acids used to make the triglycerides. Thus, rather than being a pure compound, a fat or oil is made up of a mixture of different triglyceride molecules, each derived from different combinations of three fatty acids. Although some of the triglycerides will be made from three identical fatty acids, the majority of triglyceride molecules are derived from two or three *different* fatty acids, for example compounds **2.3** and **2.4**.

$$CH_3-(CH_2)_{14}-\overset{\overset{\displaystyle O}{\|}}{C}-O-CH_2$$
$$CH_3-(CH_2)_{14}-\overset{\overset{\displaystyle O}{\|}}{C}-O-CH$$
$$CH_3-(CH_2)_{16}-\overset{\overset{\displaystyle O}{\|}}{C}-O-CH_2$$

**2.3**

$$CH_3-(CH_2)_{14}-\overset{\overset{\displaystyle O}{\|}}{C}-O-CH_2$$
$$CH_3-(CH_2)_{16}-\overset{\overset{\displaystyle O}{\|}}{C}-O-CH$$
$$CH_3-(CH_2)_{18}-\overset{\overset{\displaystyle O}{\|}}{C}-O-CH_2$$

**2.4**

Even if a fat were made from just five of the fatty acids in Table 2.2 then it would be possible to get up to 75 different triglyceride molecules, each containing a different permutation of three fatty acids from the five available. However, the way the fatty acids are combined to make the triglycerides is not random, and the proportion of each triglyceride molecule is controlled by the organism to give the fat the required properties. In lard, there is a definite tendency for unsaturated fatty acids to occupy the outer positions (Figure 2.7a); however, in cocoa butter they tend to occupy the central position (Figure 2.7b). This type of structural difference and distribution affects such properties as the melting range: lard softens 20 °C lower than cocoa butter. Notice we referred to a melting range rather than a melting temperature. As we saw in Book 1, pure compounds, such as salt and sugar, have distinct melting temperatures. If the compound contains some impurities then the melting temperature is lowered and the substance melts over a range of temperature. Substances such as lard and cocoa butter, which contain a mixture of different molecules, melt over a wide range of temperature. At the bottom of the range the compounds with a low melting temperature melt, and as the temperature is raised so more of the compounds melt.

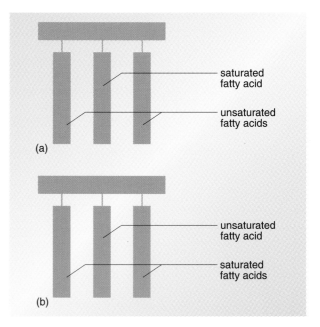

**Figure 2.7**
The distribution of saturated and unsaturated fatty acids in (a) lard and (b) cocoa butter.

Most fats are soft and can spread, but do not flow – they have properties intermediate between those of solids and liquids. This again arises because fats are a mixture of a number of different triglycerides. A large proportion of these triglycerides have a melting temperature above room temperature and will tend to solidify. Hence, the mixture consists of solid particles in a matrix of viscous liquid oils made up of triglycerides with lower melting temperatures. A solid material is thus produced that is not rigid because the crystals can slide over each other. This gives rise to the spreading properties associated with a fat.

▨     What do you think happens when a fat is heated?

▨     As the fat is heated, the temperature will rise above the melting temperatures of more and more triglycerides and these will melt. Thus, there will be fewer solid particles. This means the fat gets runnier and eventually liquefies completely.

▨     What can you say about the range of melting temperatures of the triglycerides in lard compared with those of cooking oil?

▨     Lard is fairly solid whereas cooking oil is a liquid. Thus, most of the triglycerides in lard have a melting temperature higher than room temperature. However, in cooking oil most of the triglycerides have a melting temperature below room temperature.

---

**Box 2.2 Chocolate**

Chocolate is made from cocoa, cocoa butter and sugar. Cocoa butter is made up of only a few different types of triglyceride molecule so can have a fairly sharp melting temperature. In fact it can solidify in six different forms. This means the molecules can pack together in different ways leading to different types of crystal. One of these forms melts at 33.8 °C. Thus it melts in your mouth (36.9 °C) not in your hand. This form is also smooth and glossy. To persuade it to solidify in this form the chocolate is cooled and maintained at just below 33.8 °C. It is also stirred so the fat crystallizes into very small crystals, which gives chocolate its velvety texture.

If chocolate is subjected to fluctuations in temperature, as in a shop window, a bloom develops on the chocolate. This is not mould but is the fat crystallizing out in different crystalline forms. Since cocoa butter is such a difficult fat to crystallize in the desired form, chocolate substitutes have to be used in cooking.

---

**Question 7**  Predict the products of the reaction of ethylene glycol with a mixture of the two fatty acids stearic acid and myristic acid.

$$CH_2-OH$$
$$|$$
$$CH_2-OH$$

ethylene glycol

$$CH_3-(CH_2)_{12}-C{\overset{O}{\underset{OH}{}}}$$

myristic acid

$$CH_3-(CH_2)_{16}-C{\overset{O}{\underset{OH}{}}}$$

stearic acid

## 2.2 Proteins

Most people will know what fats or sugar physically look like. Proteins, however, are more difficult to identify because they occur in so many different forms. Most people would identify protein with eggs, cheese or beef, but even in lean beef there is only 20% by mass of protein, the rest being water and fat. In eggs the figure is 12%. Low fat soya flour has one of the highest levels of protein at 45%. Some proteins turn up in nature as the structural part of tissue, as in muscle, tendons and hair. Others play an important part in cells as the molecules that carry out and control many of the body's functions.

In Book 2 you were introduced to polymers and saw how they were formed by joining together many smaller molecules, known as monomers, to give long chain-like molecules. Proteins are also long-chain molecules, and are also known as biopolymers. Proteins are made by joining together smaller compounds called amino acids. Alanine (**2.5**) is a typical amino acid.

$$H_2N-\overset{\overset{\displaystyle CH_3}{|}}{\underset{\underset{\displaystyle H}{|}}{C}}-C{\overset{O}{\underset{OH}{}}}$$

**2.5**  alanine

▨  Using the table of functional groups from AV sequence 4 (Table 2.1), identify the two functional groups in alanine.

▪  They are a carboxylic acid functional group $-C{\overset{O}{\underset{OH}{}}}$ and an amine functional group, $-NH_2$.

In fact there are 20 or so different common naturally occurring amino acids; alanine is one, and the structures of some others are shown in Figure 2.8.

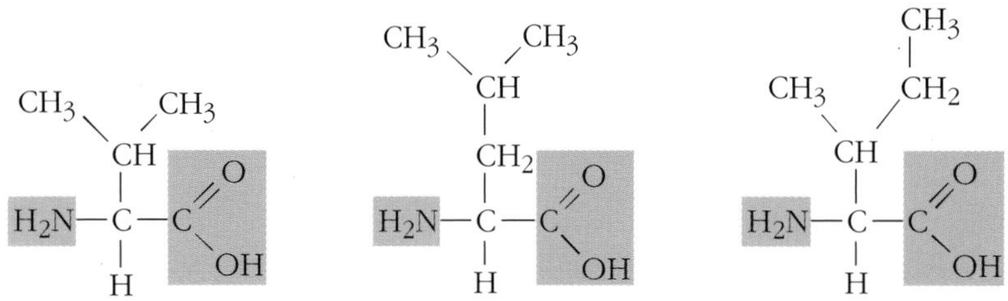

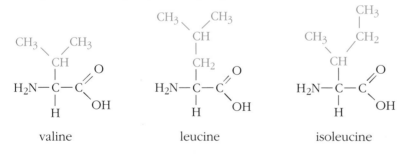

**Figure 2.8**
Molecular structures of the amino acids valine, leucine and isoleucine.

■ What are the common structural features of these amino acids?

■ They all contain an amino group and a carboxylic acid group attached to the same carbon atom:

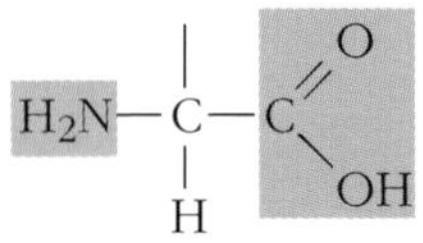

Structure **2.6** shows the general formula of all the amino acids. The group R is known as the side-chain, and represents a range of different structures.

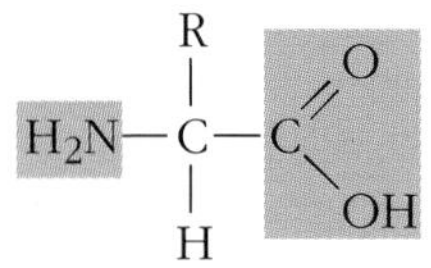

**2.6**

■ Identify the R groups in the amino acids in Figure 2.8.

■ In Figure 2.9 the R groups are highlighted in blue.

**Figure 2.9**
The R groups in valine, leucine and isoleucine.

Just as alcohols react with carboxylic acids to give esters, so amines, such as amino acids, react with carboxylic acids to give **amides** (see Box 2.3):

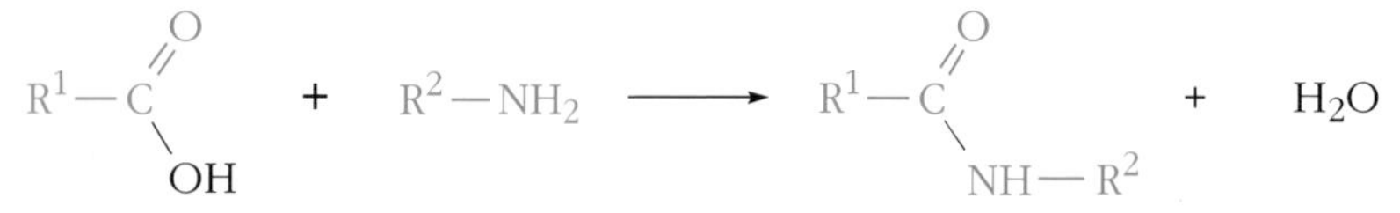

$$R^1-C\overset{O}{\underset{OH}{\Big<}} \quad + \quad R^2-NH_2 \quad \longrightarrow \quad R^1-C\overset{O}{\underset{NH-R^2}{\Big<}} \quad + \quad H_2O \quad (2.7)$$

carboxylic acid          amine                              amide                          water

Notice that in drawing this reaction we have used an arrow in place of the equals sign. The arrow still means 'goes to', but the equation is not necessarily balanced. We shall use this arrow convention increasingly frequently.

## Box 2.3 Amides

An example of an amide is acetamide, which smells of mice!:

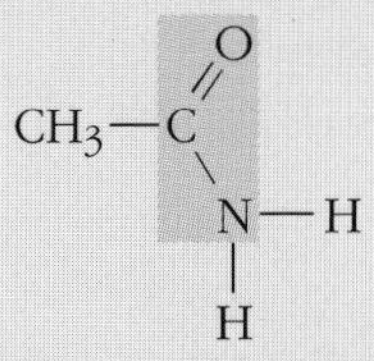

The amide group is highlighted in blue.
Nylon is a polymer in which the monomers are joined together by amide groups:

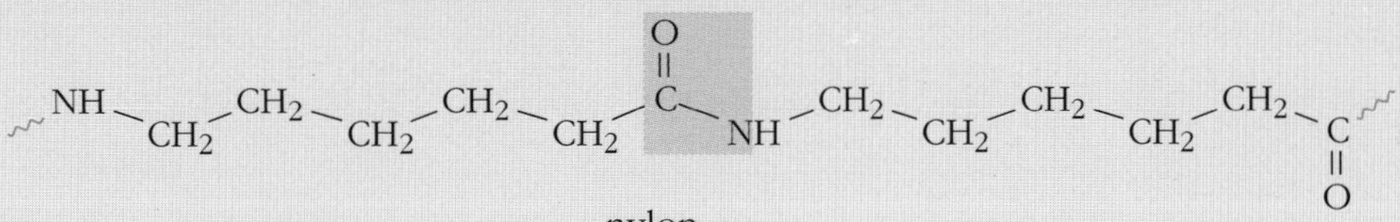

nylon

In proteins the amino acids are also joined together by amide groups:

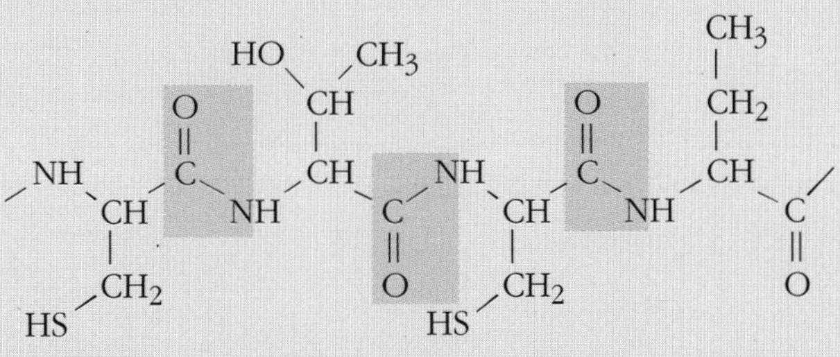

protein

The generalized structure of amides, where R[1], R[2] and R[3] are other parts of the molecule, is:

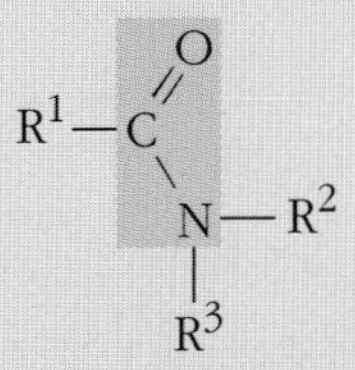

In acetamide, R[2] and R[3] are hydrogen atoms and R[1] is a methyl group.
   In amides in general, the nitrogen atom can be attached to one, two or three carbon atoms. For example, either or both of R[2] and R[3] could be a methyl group.

■ Draw the main product of the reaction between the carboxylic acid group of alanine and the amino group of valine.

■ Following the pattern of Equation 2.7 we get Equation 2.8, where the reacting functional groups of the reactants are highlighted.

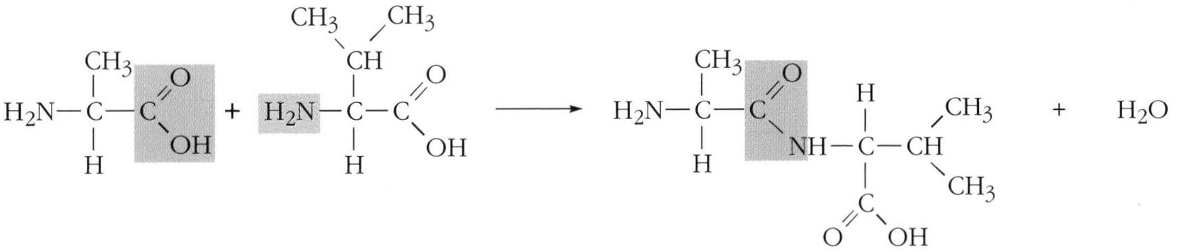

$$(2.8)$$

alanine      valine                        water

Figure 2.10 shows that the main product of this type of reaction also has a carboxylic acid group at one end and an amino group at the other, so it can react with more amino acids. Irrespective of how many amino acid groups are added, the chain will always have a carboxylic acid group at one end and an amino group at the other. Very long chains can be built up, and these are the **proteins**.

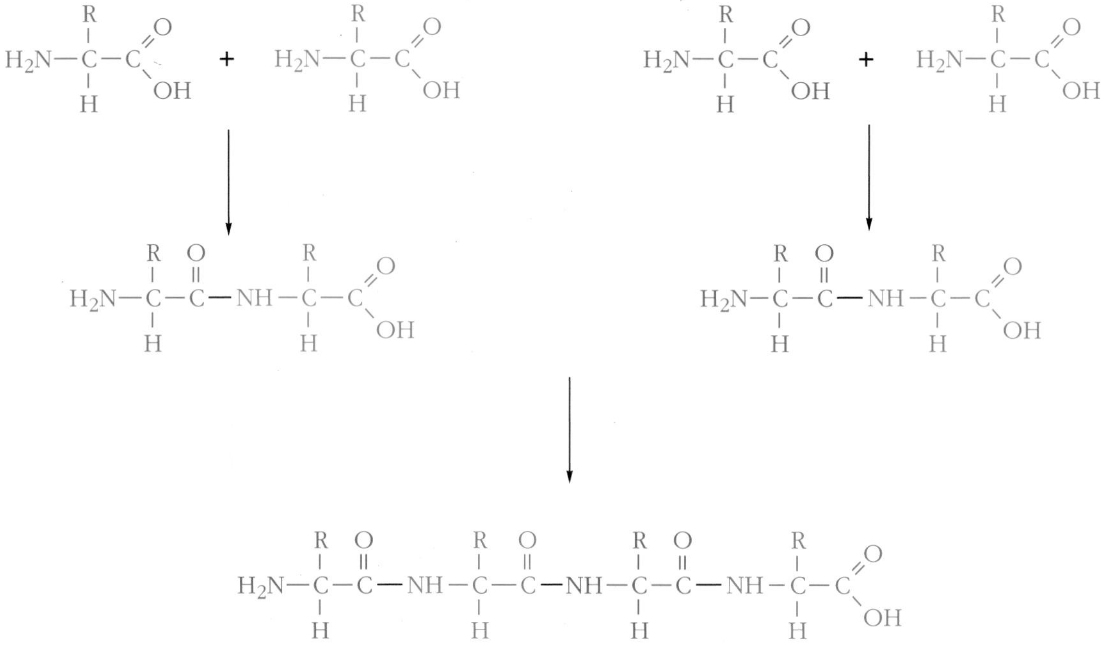

**Figure 2.10**
A generalized representation of the formation of a protein from amino acids.
In each step a molecule of water is lost.

**Question 8**   What product is obtained when four leucine amino acids are linked together?

- Is the reaction in Figure 2.10 an example of an addition or a condensation polymerization?

- Because water is produced in this reaction it must be a condensation polymerization.

Notice that, unlike synthetic polymers where only one or two monomers are involved in building up the chain, proteins are made from a variety of amino acids. Although the backbone of the protein has the same repeating unit, there will be a rich diversity in the order of side-chains and this leads to the many different properties and uses of proteins. The monomer unit that each amino acid contributes to the biopolymer is known as the **amino acid residue**, as shown in Figure 2.11a. The sequence of amino acid residues in a particular protein is known as the **primary structure** of the protein. When writing out the sequence of amino acid residues, rather than draw out the structure, a three-letter code is often used to show the order, as shown in Figure 2.11b. The convention used is that the amino end of the chain is always on the left and the carboxylic acid group always on the right.

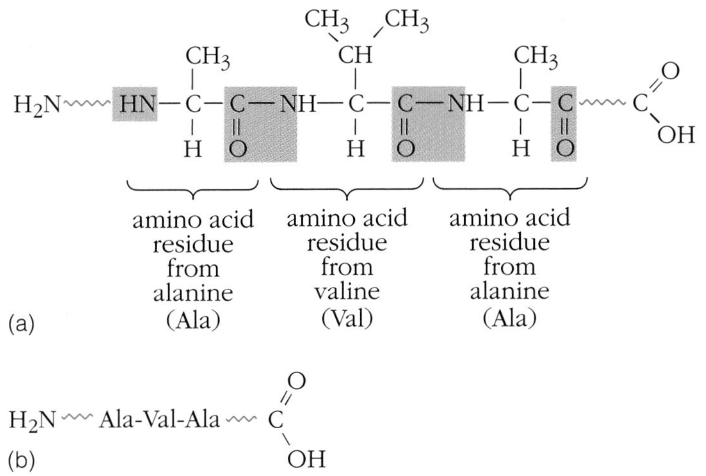

Figure 2.11 representation at top right:

$$H_2N \text{~~~} HN-\underset{\underset{H}{|}}{\overset{\overset{CH_3}{|}}{C}}-\underset{O}{\overset{\|}{C}}-NH-\underset{\underset{H}{|}}{\overset{\overset{CH}{\underset{CH_3}{\diagdown}}{\diagup}}{C}}-\underset{O}{\overset{\|}{C}}-NH-\underset{\underset{H}{|}}{\overset{\overset{CH_3}{|}}{C}}-\underset{O}{\overset{\|}{C}} \text{~~~} C\overset{O}{\underset{OH}{\diagdown}}$$

amino acid residue from alanine (Ala)    amino acid residue from valine (Val)    amino acid residue from alanine (Ala)

(a)

$$H_2N \text{~~~} Ala\text{-}Val\text{-}Ala \text{~~~} C\overset{O}{\underset{OH}{\diagdown}}$$

(b)

**Figure 2.11**
Two representations of part of a protein chain: (a) using structural formulas; (b) using the three-letter code. (The red zig-zags represent the rest of a long chain of atoms.)

With roughly 20 amino acids to choose from, and each chain containing hundreds and sometimes thousands of amino acid residues, it is clear that the number of different possible protein molecules is almost limitless. It can be calculated that for a medium-sized protein containing 288 amino acid residues using only 12 different amino acids, there are over $10^{300}$ possibilities! However, as you might imagine, in nature nothing is left to chance, especially with such long odds. When proteins are made, the organism controls the order in which amino acids are added. Almost all proteins fall into one of two classes, fibrous or globular proteins; each plays a different role in the body.

### Fibrous proteins

Fibrous proteins are generally used as structural material in the body. They are an important part of skin, hair and fingernails. At the molecular level, they tend to have repeating segments of similar amino acids, as shown in Figure 2.12.

**Collagen** is the most abundant protein in the body. It is used to form the connective tissue that surrounds the bundles of muscle fibres and connects muscles to the skeleton. Bones consist of a matrix of collagen containing calcium phosphate. The polymer chain is very long, containing about a thousand amino acid residues. The main repeating segments involve the amino acids glycine, proline, and hydroxyproline, although the exact make-up varies slightly from one molecule to the next.

With such long chains of molecules, you might think that a sample of protein would be rather like a plate of cooked spaghetti, with all the chains entwined haphazardly, but this is not the case. The polymer chains group together in threes and wrap around each other, rather like a rope, as shown in Figure 2.13a. The strands in the 'rope' are held together by hydrogen bonds, as shown in Figure 2.13b.

glycine

proline

hydroxyproline

others

**Figure 2.12**
A section of the fibrous protein collagen. Notice that every third residue is a glycine (red) and the sequence glycine, proline, hydroxyproline (Gly-Pro-Hyp; red, yellow, green) recurs frequently.

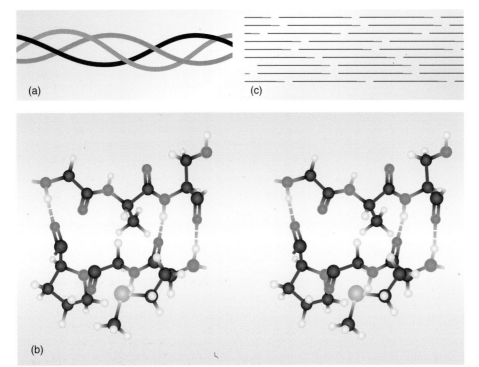

**Figure 2.13**
(a) The triple helix structure of collagen; (b) stereoscopic model showing the hydrogen bonding between polymer chains in collagen; (c) longitudinal alignment of collagen 'ropes'.

These 'ropes' then line up, as shown in Figure 2.13c, to give a strong tissue. Extra cross-linking via covalent bonds between the 'ropes' gives added strength. Such cross-links are most abundant in connective tissue where great strength is needed, as in the Achilles tendon. It is a common observation that meat from young animals is more tender than that from older ones. This is because as the animal ages, the number of cross-links between the collagen 'ropes' increases, making it tougher (see Box 2.4). When meat is cooked in water, molecules of water squeeze in between the collagen chains and replace the hydrogen bonds between the chains with hydrogen bonding to water molecules. This breakdown of the cross-linking means the meat is easier to eat. On cooking, some collagen can also dissolve into the water, forming what is known as gelatin.

---

### Box 2.4 Meat tenderizing

Meat can be tenderized in several ways before it is cooked by breaking down some of the links between collagen chains. Soaking meat in acid, such as vinegar, destroys some of the collagen on the surface of the meat. Papain from papaya, bromolain from pineapples or ficin from figs are enzymes that break the collagen up. Thus meat can be tenderized using the fruit. Alternatively a commercial extract can be used.

Physical pounding or grinding, as used to make hamburgers, also breaks up the collagen. Finally, extended cooking, as in boiling or stewing, also disrupts the collagen. Eventually the meat falls apart!

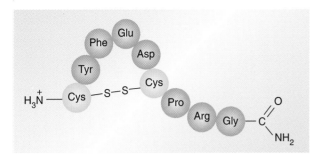

**Figure 2.14**
The primary structure of vasopressin. Note the sulfur–sulfur linkage between the two cysteine residues. This will be discussed shortly.

### Globular proteins

The other class of proteins in the body is the globular proteins. These are of a fixed chain length and have a strict order of amino acid residues. Thus, all the molecules of a particular globular protein are identical, which is not the case with a fibrous protein. Figure 2.14 shows the sequence of amino acid residues in vasopressin, a hormone that is involved with controlling water balance in the body. Each long-chain polymer molecule of a globular protein has the same specific job to do, be it breakdown of food, transferring information in the body, or fighting bacteria. Only if it has the right sequence of amino acid residues will it have the correct activity. Although the sequence of amino acid residues in any particular type of globular protein is specific to that protein, the sequence varies greatly between one type of globular protein and another.

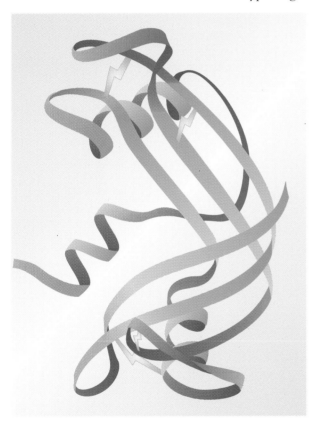

**Figure 2.15**
A 'ribbon' model of ribonuclease. This globular protein, which consists of a chain of 124 amino acid residues, is used to break down ribonucleic acid (RNA) in the stomach. Most globular proteins are very long chains, and this is one simple way of representing them. Extensive hydrogen bonding between parts of the chain occurs in the regions where the ribbon is coloured red, and sulfur–sulfur cross-links are shown in yellow (see also Figures 2.16 and 2.17).

However, a globular protein is characterized not only by its primary structure. As with fibrous proteins, globular proteins have a precise overall shape rather than just a random one. With fibrous proteins, we saw how cross-linking between chains is important to produce a strong biopolymer. With globular proteins, we no longer concentrate on cross-links between different chains of biopolymers but on cross-links *within* a particular chain, leading to the joining of one section of the chain to another. Look at Figure 2.15, which shows how a globular protein is folded into one particular shape.

The chain is anchored to itself at points along the backbone, and is thus forced to take up a specific shape. As we shall see later, this precise three-dimensional shape is necessary for the activity of the protein: only this shape will do. If the cross-links are broken, the chain unfolds and takes up a random structure, and the old structure cannot easily be reformed. This is what happens when you heat an egg (see Box 2.5). The polymer chains are cross-linked so that they have a precise shape in the egg, but when you heat the egg the cross-links are broken and the chain takes up a random shape. In the same way that you cannot unscramble an egg, the random coils of polymer chain will not reorder themselves! Loss of shape of a globular protein is called **denaturation**, and is usually accompanied by the loss of the activity of the protein.

## Box 2.5  Cooking eggs

Most materials turn from solids to liquids to gases on heating, but heating eggs leads to them solidifying! Eggs contain many globular proteins, which fold into compact balls. High temperatures denature these proteins so that the chains tangle with each other and become cross-linked by hydrogen bonds. This leads to a solid three-dimensional network of protein molecules. Heating eggs with milk also leads to a progressively more solid product. Overheating creates too many hydrogen bonds between the proteins, and some of the water is squeezed out. Hence, overcooked quiche becomes runny, custard gets lumpy and scrambled eggs rubbery!

Adding salt or lemon juice (acid) causes the proteins to denature and coagulate more easily. So boiling eggs in salt water means that if the eggshell cracks, the protein released quickly coagulates and seals the hole. Egg whites can be denatured by whipping them. This also incorporates air into the mixture. Thus air is trapped in a three-dimensional network of protein leading to a light fluffy form. Baking causes more protein to coagulate, giving a solid meringue. Fats tend to coat the denatured proteins preventing them from coagulating, so it is important not to have egg yolk, which contains fats, in the egg white.

The main type of cross-linking within the chain is hydrogen bonding, although the other types of force between molecules that you met in Book 1 are also present, such as the attraction between oppositely charged ions, dipole–dipole interactions and London forces. One other type of cross-link in proteins is known as a **cystine bridge**, where the chains are held together by covalent bonds involving two sulfur atoms (Figure 2.16).

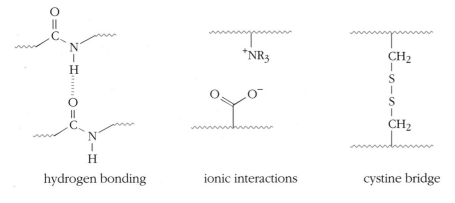

hydrogen bonding          ionic interactions          cystine bridge

**Figure 2.16**
Types of cross-link used to anchor the molecules of globular proteins.

■   Where have you seen sulfur being used to cross-link chains?

■   There were two examples in Chapter 5 of Book 2 Part 1. Sulfur is used to hold together the protein chains in wool, and to cross-link the long polymer chains in rubber to give it strength.

The amino acid cysteine has a sulfur atom as part of its side-chain. Two such cysteine amino acids in different parts of a protein backbone can be brought together to form a sulfur–sulfur bond, which links the two parts together forming a cystine bridge:

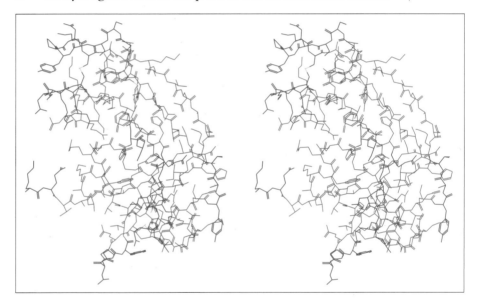

$$\text{(2.9)}$$

▢ What type of chemical reaction is this?

■ As hydrogen is lost in the process it is an oxidation reaction.

**Figure 2.17**
Stereoscopic framework
model of ribonuclease.
Here, none of the atoms are
shown. For clarity, only the
bonds between the atoms
other than hydrogen are
used, to show the intricate
shape of the backbone of
the chain.

Figure 2.17 shows a model of ribonuclease. The red regions are where parts
of the chain are cross-linked by hydrogen bonding. The four sulfur–sulfur
bonds are in yellow. Clearly, the most common type of cross-link is the
hydrogen bond.

**Question 9**  Identify the opportunities for cross-linking between the
side-chains in the following protein segments:

## 2.3 Carbohydrates

Carbohydrate in the diet is usually associated with sugar, but there are many compounds that come under the heading of carbohydrates. Ordinary sugar is sucrose, which is obtained from sugar cane or sugar beet. There are also milk sugar (lactose), malt sugar (maltose), grape sugar (glucose) and fruit sugar (fructose). On top of that there are cellulose, starch, pectin, glycogen, gums and even the alginates or carrageenans that are obtained from seaweed and used to make, among other things, synthetic cherries for the bakery trade and 'apple' and 'apricot' pieces that are sold as pie fillings. Clearly, carbohydrates are an important and widespread class of organic compounds, but even this list does not really do justice to the wide range of different carbohydrates in nature where they are used in a variety of ways, such as structural material and energy stores. Nevertheless, despite the variety, they are all based on the same unit.

The structures of carbohydrates are complex, but you needn't worry too much about them. The main factors will be highlighted. Rather than remember each complete structure, it is more important that you get a feel for how the structures can differ.

We shall start with the simplest of the carbohydrates, **glucose**, sometimes called dextrose. This is found in grapes (7% by mass) and onions (2%), but the richest source is honey (31%). It plays an essential part in the metabolism of all plants and animals and is the main product of photosynthesis, the method by which plants store energy from the Sun. Human blood has about 80–120 mg of glucose in every 100 ml, and glucose is the only sugar that plays a significant role in human metabolism.

Glucose has the molecular formula $C_6H_{12}O_6$. Its molecular structure (Figure 2.18) consists of a ring of six atoms, made up of five carbon atoms and one oxygen atom. Attached to the carbon atoms are four OH groups and one $CH_2OH$ group. This structure really needs to be viewed in three dimensions, and to help with this, you should carry out the following activity with your Molymod kit.

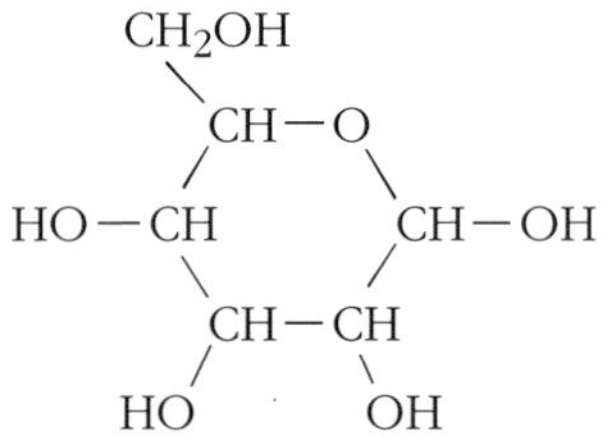

**Figure 2.18**
Ring structure of glucose.

## Activity 2  A molecular model of glucose

Start by making a ring by joining together six atoms. Use short bonds throughout this activity. You should use five black centres to represent the carbon atoms, and one red centre to represent the oxygen atom. Arrange the atoms so they take up the 'chair' shape shown in Figure 2.19.

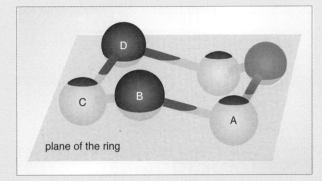

(a)

**Figure 2.19**
The chair shape of the model of glucose ring.

Make five OH groups by joining a hydrogen (white centre) to an oxygen (red centre). To each oxygen also attach one short bond, as shown in Figure 2.20. Make one CH$_2$OH group by joining two hydrogens to a carbon centre and then attaching to this carbon centre one of the OH groups you have just made, using the spare bond attached to the oxygen. To finish the CH$_2$OH group add a short bond to the remaining hole on the carbon centre, to give you the model also shown in Figure 2.20.

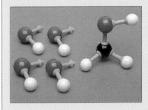

**Figure 2.20**
Models of four OH groups and one CH$_2$OH group.

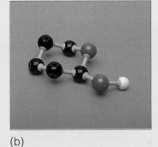

(b)

(c)

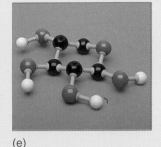

(d)

(e)

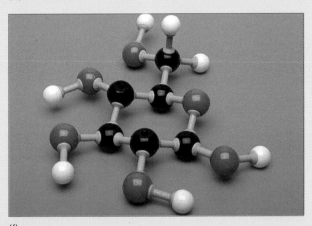

(f)

**Figure 2.21**
Attachment of groups to the ring. Notice that the groups lie roughly in the plane of the ring, as indicated in part (a) of the figure.

Position the ring as shown in Figure 2.21a and attach one of the OH groups to the carbon marked A. There are two holes on this carbon, and you should choose the hole so that the OH group is pointing towards you rather than straight down. Now put an OH on the carbon marked B, ensuring that the OH group is pointing towards you rather than straight up. Notice that the two oxygen atoms of the OH groups lie approximately in the plane of the ring, as shown in Figure 2.21c. Attach the remaining two OH groups to centres C and D, so that the oxygens of the OH group still lie in the approximate plane of the ring (Figure 2.21d and e). Now attach the CH$_2$OH group so that the carbon centre of the CH$_2$OH group lies approximately in the plane of the ring (Figure 2.21f). To finish the model attach five white hydrogen centres to five bonds and attach these to the spare holes on your model. These hydrogens should stick up and down, away from the plane of the ring. Your complete model should look like that shown in Figure 2.22. It is important to get the various atoms in the right positions, otherwise you could end up with a model of a different compound.

(continued overleaf)

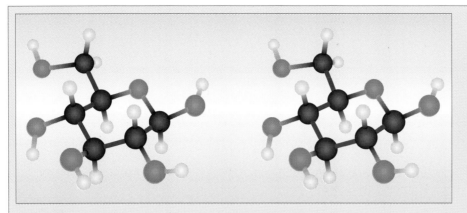

**Figure 2.22**
Stereoscopic model of the structure of glucose.

It would be tiresome if we had to draw out the ball-and-stick picture every time we wanted to represent the three-dimensional structure of glucose, so we use the abbreviated structure shown in Figure 2.23. Here we have removed some of the detail of the ring so that the structure is more clear. Most of the hydrogens on the ring carbons have been removed and the carbon centres in the ring have not been identified. Wedges have also been used to show which bonds are coming towards you in the ring. Compare your model with that in Figure 2.23 to confirm

they both represent the same structure. Although this representation gives you an idea of the shape of the molecule you must always remember that at each unmarked junction in the ring there is a carbon with one hydrogen attached. We shall further develop line drawings of molecules and wedges in Part 2.

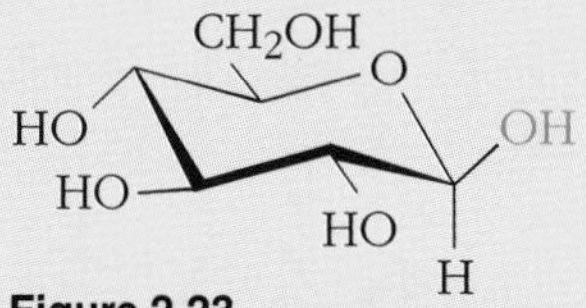

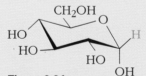

**Figure 2.23**
Abbreviated structure of glucose. The wedge-shaped bonds show that the carbons at the bottom are in front of the plane of the paper.

■ When glucose is dissolved in water, 64% of it exists in the form represented by Figure 2.23, which is known as the β (beta) form. The other 36% exists in the form represented by Figure 2.24, the α (alpha) form. Modify your model to represent this second form of glucose. What is the difference between these structures?

CH₂OH group... 

**Figure 2.24**
Abbreviated form of α glucose.

■ The two structures are almost identical. The only difference is that the OH on the carbon adjacent to the ring oxygen (coloured red in Figures 2.23 and 2.24) points into the plane of the ring in the β form but points down, away from the plane, in the α form. To interchange the models you need to pull off this 'red' OH group and the hydrogen attached to the same carbon, and swop them over. Figure 2.25 shows a model of the α form.

**Figure 2.25**
Model of α glucose.

This small difference in structure may not seem to be important, but the properties of the two forms of glucose are significantly different. As we shall see later, it explains why we can eat starch but not cellulose. You should keep your model of glucose for use later in this Book.

Let's now look at another 'simple' carbohydrate, **fructose**, which is also found in honey (about 35%). Gram for gram, fructose is about twice as sweet as table sugar, so only half as much is needed to sweeten a meal. Fructose, therefore, can be part of a calorie-controlled diet. It can also be used by people who suffer from the disease diabetes mellitus, since, unlike glucose, it does not require insulin for its use by the body. Fructose has the same molecular formula as glucose, but a slightly different structure. Like glucose, when fructose is dissolved in water it exists in different forms. About 75% of fructose has a ring structure of six atoms, just like glucose; however, the CH₂OH group is attached to a different carbon, as shown in Figure 2.26. The other 25% has a ring structure of five atoms, as shown in Figure 2.27. You don't need to worry about the exact structural details here.

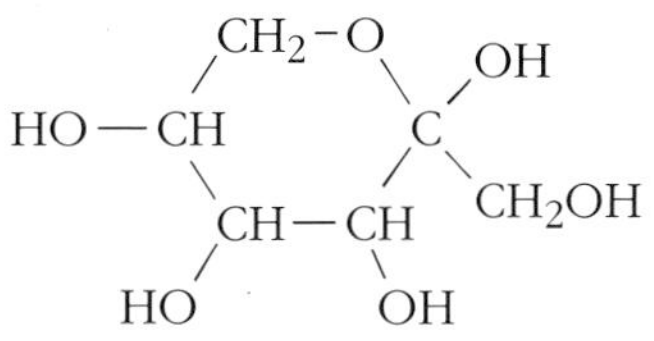

**Figure 2.26**
Simple six-membered ring
structure of fructose.

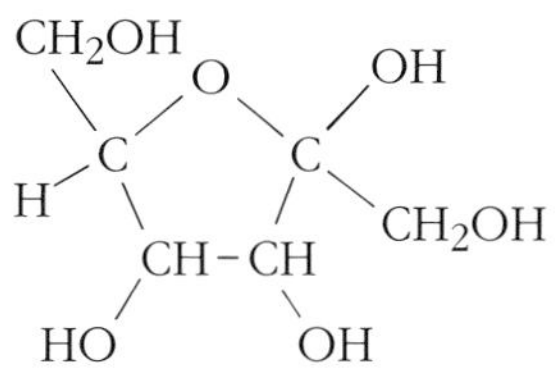

**Figure 2.27**
Simple five-membered ring
structure of fructose.

▨ What is the structural relationship between the compounds shown in Figures 2.26 and 2.27?

■ As we discussed in Book 1, compounds that have the same molecular formula but different structures are known as isomers.

The next carbohydrate, and the last structure we are going to examine in any detail, is **sucrose**. This is most familiar as the sugar used to sweeten tea or in cooking. Sucrose obtained from sugar beet is the same as sucrose obtained from sugar cane. About two million tonnes of sucrose are used annually in the UK. Sucrose has the molecular formula $C_{12}H_{22}O_{11}$ and is made by joining a glucose unit to a fructose unit as shown in Figure 2.28. Notice that the fructose unit exists in the five-membered ring form in sucrose. Sucrose can be readily broken down into glucose and fructose by a process known as inversion. The product may be familiar to you as invert-sugar, which is similar to honey! Bees collect nectar, which is essentially sucrose, from flowers and it is broken down into glucose and fructose on passing through the bees' bodies. This inversion also occurs in cooking when making jam.

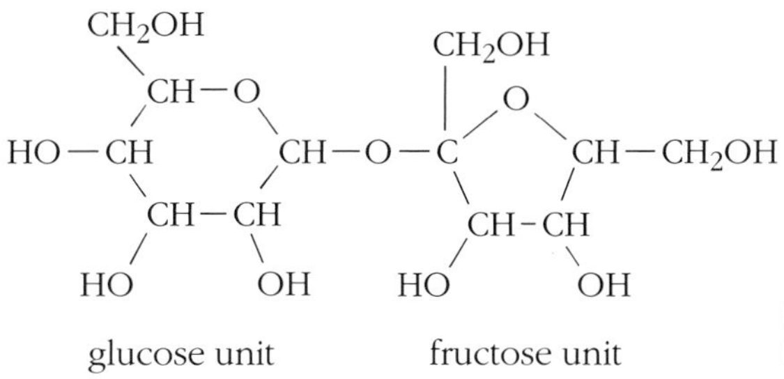

glucose unit          fructose unit

**Figure 2.28**
Ring structure of sucrose.

Carbohydrates such as fructose and glucose that involve only one sugar unit are known as **monosaccharides**, from the Latin for sugar – saccharide. Sucrose involves two sugar units, fructose and glucose, and so is known as a **disaccharide**. Other disaccharides are maltose, obtained when starchy material is broken down, and lactose, present in human milk (5%) and cows' milk (8%). Maltose involves joining two glucose units together, and lactose is made from glucose and another monosaccharide, galactose.

Trisaccharides, made from three sugar units, are also known, but only raffinose and stachyose deserve particular attention here. They occur in legume seeds, such as peas and beans. These trisaccharides cannot easily be broken down in the small intestine, so provide a feast for the bacteria in the large intestine. Their breakdown involves formation of large quantities of hydrogen and carbon dioxide, flatulence being the inevitable result!

The last important class of carbohydrates is the **polysaccharides**, which are polymers made from monosaccharide monomers. We shall look at two, cellulose and starch.

**Cellulose**, which we met in Book 2, is the main structural carbohydrate of plants, and as such is widely distributed from the toughest tree trunk to the softest cotton wool. Cellulose is the most abundant organic compound on Earth, comprising more than half of the organic carbon: $10^{15}$ kg of cellulose are synthesized and degraded on Earth each year! This polymer is made by joining together glucose units, as shown in Figure 2.29, and as many as 12 000 units may be linked together.

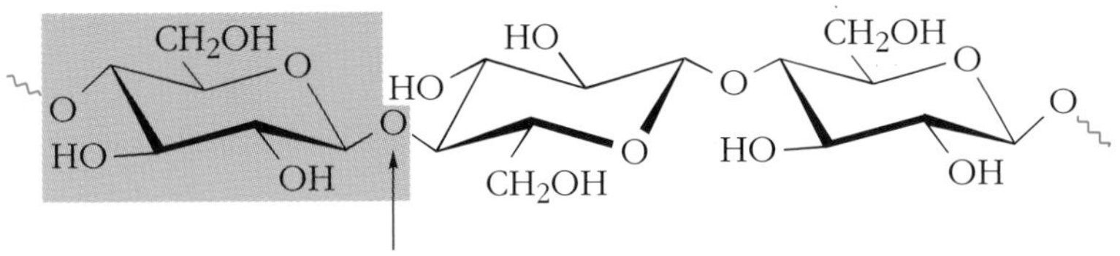

oxygen linking glucose units together

**Figure 2.29**
Glucose units in cellulose.

▪ Using the model you made earlier, determine whether or not the oxygen that links the glucose units together is in the plane of the ring of the glucose monomer unit shaded red.

▪ It is in the plane of the ring. Comparison of this structure with the two alternatives, Figures 2.23 and 2.24, confirms that cellulose is like the β form of glucose.

By analogy with glucose, this way of joining the glucose units is known as a β linkage. This method of linking allows the cellulose to form very long straight chains, which is maintained by hydrogen bonding between the oxygen atom in one ring and an OH group on an adjacent glucose unit, as shown in Figure 2.30.

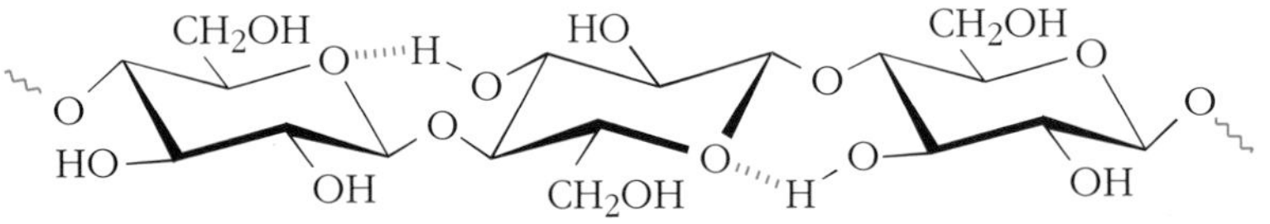

**Figure 2.30**
Hydrogen bonding in cellulose.

The linear biopolymers in cellulose lie side by side and are cross-linked by hydrogen bonds between the OH groups on the rings in a very ordered way. In plant material this forms small fibres several micrometres long and about 10 to 20 nm in diameter. This kind of molecular architecture gives rise to very strong fibres. Despite being the most abundant natural product, cellulose is indigestible to humans and most other carnivorous animals. It can, however, be used by ruminants, such as horses, cows and rabbits, which harbour bacteria in their digestive tracts that can breakdown the cellulose. The digestion of wood by termites also requires the use of bacteria in their guts!

Cellulose does play an important role in our food as dietary fibre, even though it is not digested and passes straight through us. Why this is the case is a matter for conjecture.

**Starch** is another important polysaccharide that you met in Book 2. It is the chief food reserve of all plants, stored in stems, as in the sago palm, or in tubers, as in potatoes and cassava. Under a microscope, starch granules can be seen in the cells of such foodstuffs.  These starch granules are made of two components, amylopectin and amylose, in a ratio of about three or four to one by mass. Amylose is a polymer that contains between 70 and 350 glucose units, joined as shown in Figure 2.31.

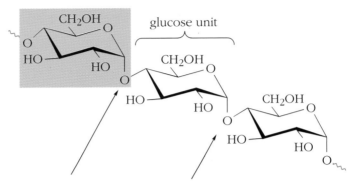

oxygen linking glucose units together

**Figure 2.31**
The structure of amylose.

▨ Using the model you made earlier, determine whether or not the oxygen that links the glucose units together in amylose is in the plane of the monomer unit shaded red.

■ It is out of the plane of the ring. Comparison of this structure with the two alternatives, Figures 2.23 and 2.24, confirms that amylose is like the α form of glucose.

By analogy with glucose, this way of joining the glucose units in amylose is known as an α linkage. This small difference between the α and β linkages means that amylose can be digested by mammals whereas cellulose cannot. The glucose monomers in starch cannot form linear ribbons because the α linkage causes the chain to bend, and a hollow helix is produced. These hollow helices do not pack together, or hydrogen bond, as tightly as the straight chains in cellulose, so starch is not useful as structural material. However, the more open structure means that it can be broken down more easily by enzymes and thus is more suited to forming an accessible store of glucose.

Amylopectin is a much larger polymer, containing up to several million glucose units. A portion of amylopectin is shown in Figure 2.32a, where each hexagon represents a glucose unit. AB and DE are short chains of about 24 glucose units connected at C. Another connection is shown at F. Branching is so extensive that a bush-like structure is formed as shown in Figure 2.32b. Just like proteins, the carbohydrate polymers can cross-link by hydrogen bonding either between straight-chain portions of the amylopectin or between straight-chain portions of amylopectin and amylose. Such cross-linking makes starch granules hard.

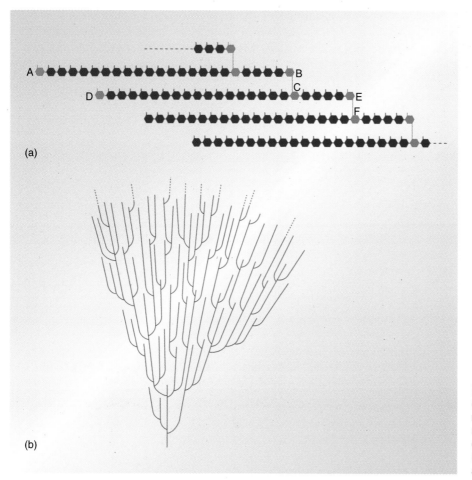

(a)

(b)

**Figure 2.32**
(a) Part of an amylopectin molecule: each hexagon represents a glucose unit. (b) One possible pattern of branching of the chains in amylopectin.

**Question 10**  Maltose contains two glucose units. By comparison with Figures 2.23 and 2.24, can you say whether they are joined by an $\alpha$ or a $\beta$ linkage?

**Question 11**  The exoskeletons of insects and crustacea (Figure 2.33a) are made from chitin, a biopolymer very similar to cellulose (Figure 2.33b). What are the similarities and the differences between chitin and cellulose?

**Figure 2.33**
(a) A Sally-lightfoot crab;
(b) the structure of chitin.

## 2.4 Minerals

Other than carbon, hydrogen, oxygen and nitrogen, at least another 25 elements occur in foods, about 16 of which are known to be essential to life and must be present in the diet. These elements are known collectively as the **mineral elements**: the major ones are listed in Table 2.3. The other essential trace elements are listed in Table 2.4. Remember that in these very detailed tables, the information is given for interest rather than for memorizing. Some of these elements are taken in as ions. For example, iodine is needed to prevent goitre, the overdevelopment of the thyroid gland in the neck. The incidence of goitre is related to the levels of iodide ion in local soils and water supplies. Where this level is low, people are recommended to use iodized salt, which contains sodium iodide. Not all the elements in the diet will be absorbed: only 20–30% of the calcium in the diet is taken into the body and the proportion may be lower if vitamin D is not available. This lack of vitamin D leads to the calcium deficiency disease rickets, even though there is sufficient calcium in the diet. Other chemicals present in food may prevent the element being absorbed. For example, oxalates, which are present in small amounts in rhubarb and spinach, may react with calcium to form insoluble calcium oxalate, rendering the calcium unavailable for absorption.

**Table 2.3** Major mineral elements needed by the body.

| Element | Approx. adult daily intake | Approx. adult body content | Functions in body | Main food sources |
|---|---|---|---|---|
| calcium (Ca) | 1 g | 1 000 g | present in bones and teeth; necessary for blood clotting, muscle contraction and nerve activity | milk, cheese, bread and flour (if fortified), cereals, green vegetables |
| phosphorus (P) | 1.5 g | 800 g | present in bones and teeth; essential for energy storage and transfer, cell structure, cell division and reproduction | milk, cheese, bread and cereals, meat and meat products |
| sulfur (S) | 0.9 g | 150 g | present in body in proteins; important for cross-linking proteins | protein-rich foods, such as meat, fish, eggs, milk, bread and cereals |
| sodium (Na) | 4.5 g | 100 g | present in body fluids as $Na^+$; essential for maintenance of fluid balance in body and for nerve activity and muscle contraction | main source is salt (sodium chloride, NaCl) used in food processing, cooking and at the table; bread and cereal products are main sources in processed food |
| chlorine (Cl) | 6.0 g | 100 g | present in gastric juice and body fluids as $Cl^-$ ions | |
| potassium (K) | 3.3 g | 140 g | present in cell fluids as $K^+$ ions; similar role to sodium, but they are not interchangeable | widely distributed in vegetables, meat, milk, fruit and fruit juices |
| iron (Fe) | 15 mg | 4.9 g | essential component of haemoglobin of blood cells | meat and offal, bread and flour, potatoes and vegetables |
| magnesium (Mg) | 0.3 g | 20 g | present in bone and cell fluids; needed for activity of some enzymes | milk, bread and other cereal products, potatoes and vegetables |
| zinc (Zn) | 15 mg | 2.5 g | essential for the activity of several enzymes involved in energy changes and protein formation | meat and meat products, milk and cheese, bread, flour and cereal products |

**Table 2.4** Some essential trace elements needed by the body.[a]

| Element | Approx. average daily intake | Approx. adult body content | Functions in body | Main food sources |
|---|---|---|---|---|
| cobalt (Co) | 0.3 mg | 1.5 mg | required for formation of red blood cells | liver and other meat |
| copper (Cu) | 3.5 mg | 75 mg | component of many enzymes; necessary for haemoglobin formation | green vegetables, fish and liver |
| chromium (Cr) | 0.15 mg | 1 mg | contained in all tissues; may be involved in glucose metabolism | liver, cereals, beer, yeast |
| fluorine (F) | 1.8 mg | 2.5 g | required for bone and tooth formation | tea, sea food, water |
| iodine (I) | 0.2 mg | 25 mg | component of thyroid hormones | milk, sea food, iodized salt |
| manganese (Mn) | 3.5 mg | 15 mg | forms part of some enzyme systems | tea, cereals, pulses, nuts |
| molybdenum (Mo) | 0.15 mg | ? | enzyme activation | kidney, cereals, vegetables |
| selenium (Se) | 0.2 mg | 25 mg | present in some enzymes; associated with vitamin E activity | cereals, meat, fish |

[a] Nickel, silicon, tin and vanadium may also have some part to play in human metabolism.

## 2.5 Vitamins

The last of the nutrients that we shall consider are the **vitamins**, which constitute a rather untidy collection of compounds with no structural relationship. What they have in common is that the body cannot make these essential compounds and thus they have to be provided in the diet. However, generally only small amounts are required. If a diet lacks sufficient of these compounds then illness occurs. The name vitamins comes from *vit*al *amine*s, a term from earlier times when it was thought that they were all amines. However, this has subsequently been shown to be wrong. Most were identified before their chemical structures could be elucidated, so they were given letters A, B, C, etc. This designation ran into trouble when it was discovered that the original vitamin B was in fact a collection of quite distinct vitamins, and so each was assigned $B_1$, $B_2$, etc. This system was finally thrown into chaos and abandoned when it was discovered that a number of vitamins were identical. Thus we no longer have vitamins F to J or $B_3$ to $B_5$. The reason we need to get these compounds from external sources is that at some time in our evolution we lost the ability to synthesize them in adequate amounts. They were available in our diets and the risk of deficiency disease was a small price to pay for the discarding of the synthetic machinery for making such a diverse range of compounds in our bodies.

Table 2.5 lists the various vitamins, together with typical sources and roles in the body. The vitamins can be divided into two types, water-soluble and fat-soluble. This classification arose from the manner in which the vitamins were isolated, and it has important nutritional consequences.

**Table 2.5** Vitamins needed in the human body.

| Name | Main sources | Functions in the body and effect of shortage |
| --- | --- | --- |
| *Fat-soluble vitamins* | | |
| vitamin A or retinol | milk, dairy products, margarine, fish-liver oil; also made in the body from carotenes found in green vegetables and carrots | necessary for healthy skin and also for normal growth and development; deficiency will slow down growth and may lead to disorders of the skin, lowered resistance to infection, and disturbances of vision, such as night blindness |
| vitamin D or cholecalciferol | margarine, butter-milk, fish-liver oils, fat fish | necessary for the formation of strong bones and teeth; shortage may cause bone diseases or dental decay |
| vitamin E or tocopherols | plant-seed oils | antioxidant |
| vitamin K or naphthoquinones | green vegetables | assists blood clotting |
| *Water-soluble vitamins* | | |
| the B vitamins: thiamine, $B_1$ riboflavin, $B_2$ niacin pyridoxine, $B_6$ pantothenic acid biotin | bread and flour, meat, milk, potatoes, yeast extract, fortified cornflakes | involved in many of the reactions that make use of food; shortage causes loss of appetite, slows growth and development and impairs general health; severe deficiency disease such as pellagra or beriberi |
| cobalamin, $B_{12}$ | offal, meat, milk, fortified cornflakes. | necessary for formation of nucleic acids and red blood cells; shortage may lead to megaloblastic anaemia and (for cobalamin) to pernicious anaemia |
| folic acid | potatoes, offal, green vegetables, bread, Marmite, fortified cornflakes. | |
| vitamin C or ascorbic acid | green vegetables, fruits, potatoes, blackcurrant syrup, rosehip syrup. | necessary for the proper formation of teeth, bones and blood vessels; shortage retards the growth of children and if prolonged may lead to scurvy |

Table 2.6 shows the vitamin content of ordinary milk and skimmed milk. In the process of producing skimmed milk the fat is separated from the rest of the milk. The fat-soluble vitamins are dissolved in the fat globules and so are removed from the milk in the skimming process.

**Table 2.6** Composition of fresh summer cows' milk and of skimmed milk.

| Nutrient | Quantity in 100 g fresh milk | Quantity in 100 g skimmed milk |
|---|---|---|
| energy | 272 kJ | 135 kJ |
| protein | 3.3 g | 3.4 g |
| carbohydrate | 4.7 g | 4.7 g |
| fat | 3.8 g | 0.1 g |
| water | 88 g | 91 g |
| calcium | 103 mg | 108 mg |
| iron | 0.1 mg | 0.1 mg |
| vitamin A | 56 µg | 2 µg |
| thiamine | 50 µg | 48 µg |
| niacin | 90 µg | 88 µg |
| riboflavin | 170 µg | 179 µg |
| ascorbic acid | 1.5 mg | 1.5 mg |
| vitamin D | 0.1 µg | 0.0 µg |

■ Table 2.7 shows the vitamin content of some vegetables after they have been cooked in boiling water for various times. Can you suggest one reason why the amount of vitamin C in the vegetable decreases the longer it is boiled in water?

■ Table 2.5 shows that vitamin C is a water-soluble vitamin. Boiling will lead to the loss of water-soluble vitamins, which dissolve in the boiling water. (A good reason for making gravy from water that has been used to cook vegetables is that it contains dissolved vitamins.)

**Table 2.7** Relation between cooking time and retention of vitamin C.

| Cooking time /min | Percent retention of vitamin C during boiling | | | |
|---|---|---|---|---|
| | Brussels sprouts | Cabbage | Carrots | Potatoes |
| 20 | 49 | – | 35 | – |
| 30 | 36 | 70–78 | 22 | 53–56 |
| 60 | – | 53–58 | – | 40–50 |
| 90 | – | 13 | – | 17 |

Some vitamins are lost from food because they decompose on heating. In the previous question, some of the vitamin C in the cooked vegetables could have been lost in this way. This is usually a problem only if the food is maintained at a high temperature for a long time, as in canteens. Indeed, reheating the food from cold in a microwave oven leads to a higher vitamin content than keeping it hot.

Although we need to be aware of such vitamin loss from our food, most people in the UK will not suffer vitamin deficiency. First, only small amounts of vitamins are needed. Second, whereas some foods are rich in one vitamin and low in another, providing we eat a range of foods our overall vitamin intake will be above our needs. Third, vitamins are usually stored within the body, so although the intake may vary from day to day, it is the long term intake that should be the major concern (see Box 2.6).

---

### Box 2.6  Vitamin C

Jacques Cartier described the effects of scurvy in 1536, when it affected all but 10 of his 110 men when they were exploring the Saint Lawrence River.

*Some did lose all their strength, and could not stand on their feet... Others also had all their skins spotted with spots of blood of a purple colour: then did it ascend up to their ankles, knees, thighs, shoulders, arms, and necks. Their mouths became stinking, their gums so rotten that all the flesh did fall off, even to the roots of the teeth, which did also almost fall out.*

The captain of one of the ships learnt from an Indian how to cure the disease using the leaves of a certain evergreen tree. Scurvy is a dietary deficiency disease arising from lack of vitamin C. Most animals can make vitamin C, but primates, guinea-pigs and some fruit-eating bats have lost the chemical machinery for making it, and thus need it in their diets. Figure 2.12 shows that collagen contains many hydroxyproline residues, which are needed for cross-linking the chains by hydrogen bonds, giving strength. Vitamin C is necessary to make the hydroxyproline from proline:

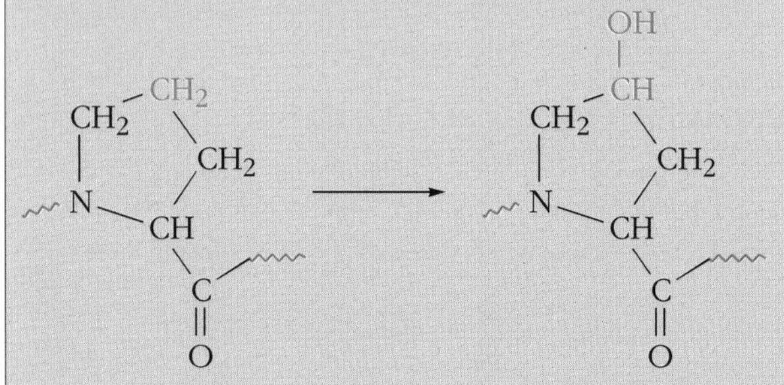

In the absence of vitamin C, collagen is formed from proline rather than hydroxyproline so the collagen chains do not hydrogen bond together so well. The fibres are thus weak and lead to the skin lesions and blood vessel fragility described in the quote.

A cure was found by James Lind, a Scottish naval physician, in 1753. He was the first person to conduct a controlled clinical trial. He found that out of a group of 12 sailors with scurvy the two seamen provided with two oranges and a lemon each day made a speedy recovery, whereas those given dilute sulphuric acid, vinegar or seawater did not. Lind recommended that all sailors include citrus fruit in their diet, but it was forty years before this policy was adopted. Later guinea-pigs were used for trials, since they too suffer from scurvy, and this is how 'guinea-pig' came to mean a test subject.

Vitamin C or ascorbic acid (**2.7**) was first isolated from Hungarian sweet peppers by Albert Szeat-Györgyi, who won the Nobel Prize for Chemistry in 1937. Its structure was worked out in Birmingham, where it was subsequently synthesized by Edward Hirst and Walter Howarth.

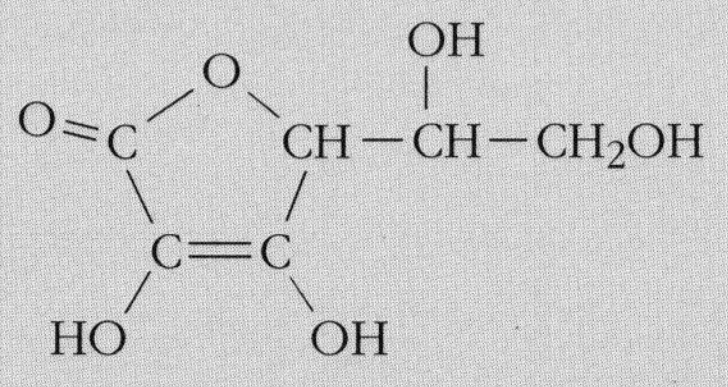

**2.7**

Currently vitamin C is being touted as a panacea for a variety of human ills, from the common cold to cancer.

---

**Question 12**  What happens to the vitamin content of meat in the following processes?

(i) When frozen meat is defrosted there is usually a pool of water. This does not come only from the outside of the meat. Water from inside the meat is also lost.

(ii) When meat is roasted fat drips off it.

## 2.6 Fats, proteins, carbohydrates, minerals and vitamins in food

In this Section we shall take a typical meal and identify how the classes of nutrients that we have just discussed turn up on our plate. Figure 2.34 (overleaf) shows the meal in question – a full English breakfast of bacon, egg and tomato, with toast and marmalade, fruit juice and black coffee.

## Summary of Chapter 2

In this chapter we have looked at the chemical nature of five classes of nutrients.

Fats and oils are mixtures of triglyceride molecules. Triglycerides are esters formed when three fatty acids react with glycerol, which contains three OH groups. Ester formation is a common reaction of all carboxylic acids and alcohols.

Fats and oils are usually derived from a range of fatty acids. Some contain carbon–carbon double bonds (unsaturated) and some do not (saturated). Polyunsaturated fatty acids contain more than one carbon–carbon double bond.

Because fats and oils are derived from a range of fatty acids, a mixture of triglyceride molecules is present, which give each substance its characteristic properties.

Proteins are biopolymers made from amino acids. There are twenty or so naturally occurring amino acids, of the general form

$$H_2N - \underset{\underset{H}{|}}{\overset{\overset{R}{|}}{C}} - C \overset{\displaystyle O}{\underset{\displaystyle OH}{\Big\langle}}$$

Amides are formed when an amine reacts with a carboxylic acid. Proteins are made by joining amino acids together using amide linkages. Each amino acid gives rise to a monomer unit called an amino acid residue. The order of these residues is known as the primary structure of the protein.

Fibrous proteins tend to have repeating segments of amino acid residues. Often the chains coil up, cross-linked with hydrogen bonds.

Each type of globular protein has a set primary structure. The chains fold up and are held in position by cross-links. Denaturation involves the loss of this folded structure.

Carbohydrates are based on sugar units. Glucose exists in a ring structure, and there are two forms, the $\alpha$ and $\beta$ forms, which differ in the relative direction of the bond to just one OH group.

Polysaccharides are chains of glucose units. The properties depend on whether they are linked by $\alpha$ or $\beta$ linkages.

There are 25 or so mineral elements other than oxygen, hydrogen and carbon that are needed by the body.

Vitamins are a collection of unrelated compounds that the body needs in its diet because it cannot make them.

**Figure 2.34**
A full English breakfast!

Figure 2.35 shows the structure of an egg. It is an interesting food because it is designed to contain all the nutrients that a developing chick embryo will need. The outer shell is made of calcium carbonate, but is porous enough to allow sufficient oxygen to reach the chick.

The egg white accounts for about 60% of the mass of the egg and is one-eighth protein and seven-eighths water. The main protein, ovalbumin, is of the fibrous type. It provides a store of amino acids for the growing chick. Globular proteins are also present, in smaller amounts. Dissolved in the water are small amounts of salts and the vitamin riboflavin. In the centre of the egg is the yolk, which is an oil-in-water emulsion stabilized by the fat-related compound lecithin. It is one-third fat, half water and one-sixth protein, again with salts and vitamins. Associated with the protein are relatively large amounts of phosphorus. When the egg is fried the protein is denatured, which results in the egg becoming more solid. However, the nutritional value of the egg is not altered greatly. There is virtually no carbohydrate in eggs because the chick gets all its energy from fats, which, as we shall see, take up a lot less space.

The bacon on the plate contains mainly fat and protein. The fat is quite obvious as a layer between the skin and the muscle. The muscle contains about three-quarters water and one-quarter protein together with small amounts of fat, minerals and vitamins. Both fibrous and globular proteins are present, with the former predominating. The main minerals are sodium, potassium, calcium and iron, although meat is also a good source of zinc. The key vitamins in bacon are niacin, thiamine and riboflavin.

Tomatoes contain mainly water, 95% by mass, with about 3% carbohydrate, 1% protein and no fat. The main minerals are calcium, sodium and iron. The main vitamins are vitamin C and niacin, together with small amounts of riboflavin and thiamine; however, tomatoes are a reasonable source of vitamin A.

The orange juice is again mainly water (88%) with about 0.5% protein and 10% carbohydrate. It is a particularly rich source of vitamin C and contains small amounts of minerals and other vitamins.

There is little nutritional value to black coffee, unless it has sugar added. The average cup of fairly strong coffee contains about 100 mg of potassium, 100 mg of caffeine and 1 mg of niacin. Caffeine is not a nutrient in that it is not used by the body for growth or energy. However, it is a stimulant and can have unwanted side-effects if consumed in large amounts. We shall return to caffeine in Part 2 of this Book.

Bread comes from flour, which in turn comes from wheat. The constituents of wheat are shown in Figure 2.36. The outer layer, the bran, is rich in vitamins and contains about half the minerals in the grain of wheat. It is mainly cellulose, which is indigestible by humans and so provides fibre. The germ is rich in fats – especially those containing the essential fatty acids, protein, vitamins – in particular vitamin E and thiamine, and iron. Most of the grain is taken up by the endosperm, which contains starch granules embedded in a matrix of protein. About 7–15% of the endosperm is protein, mainly fibrous. Milling involves grinding the flour into small particles. At this point various parts of the grain, such as the bran and the germ, can be removed, along with their nutrients. To counteract this, iron, thiamine and niacin are often added to the flour.

To make the bread, water is mixed with flour and yeast to give a dough, which is then baked in the oven.

The butter or margarine we spread on the toast contains mainly fat, and the marmalade is made from oranges and sugar – about 67%. The pectin that makes the marmalade so viscous is a polysaccharide.

This brief description of a meal shows that, by eating a variety of foods, a range of nutrients is consumed. Some foods are rich in one vitamin or amino acid and others are rich in another. In this case variety really is the spice of life, ensuring a balanced intake of nutrients.

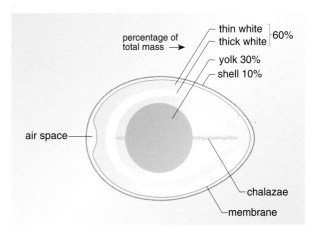

**Figure 2.35**
Structure of an egg.

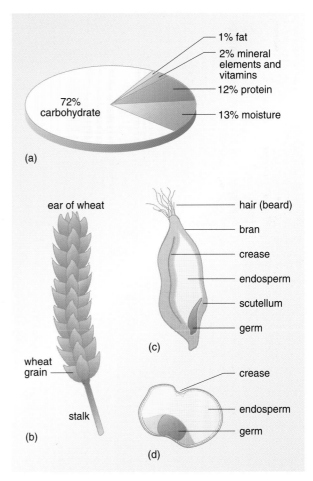

**Figure 2.36**
(a) Composition of wheat; (b) an ear of wheat; (c) longitudinal section of a wheat grain; (d) transverse section of a wheat grain.

# Chapter 3
# Where do we put it all?

Having identified the chemical nature of the food we take in, we now move on to examine why we need to eat. To some extent this was discussed earlier when we were trying to identify what a food is.

■    What are the bodily processes that food sustains?

■    In Chapter 1 we saw that the body needs food to produce movement, to release energy, and to bring about growth, repair or reproduction.

All these processes involve chemical change. In passing through the body, food is chemically modified to provide energy, or is chemically broken down by digestive processes to provide the basic building blocks for repair, growth or reproduction. In the first case, the energy is obtained by the food being transformed into other chemicals, which are then discarded from the body. In the second case, the products of digestion are retained to become part of the chemical make-up of the body.

In this Chapter we shall examine the starting point of these important chemical changes, the processes of digestion.

## 3.1  Digestion

> *It's a very odd thing–*
> *As odd as can be*
> *That whatever Miss T eats*
> *Turns into Miss T*
>
> *(Walter De la Mare)*

It may seem strange but, no matter what we eat, be it corn flakes, fillet steak, jelly, cheese, Brussels sprouts or bananas, within a few hours it is transformed into the same thing – our flesh and blood. This remarkable transformation is achieved by breaking all food down into a few basic constituents. Proteins are broken down into amino acids, fats and oils into smaller chemicals such as fatty acids, and carbohydrates into glucose. These useful materials are absorbed into the bloodstream, together with essential vitamins and minerals, and then transported to other areas of the body for further processing. The unwanted residues from the food continue their journey through the digestive system and are expelled as waste. Thus the essence of digestion is that large molecules are broken down into their constituent building blocks, which are either recycled to build up the body or 'burned' to provide energy.

This process of breaking down, or digestion, is both physical and chemical. The physical process involves the conversion of large food particles into smaller ones, and the chemical process involves the same thing, but at a different level, breaking larger molecules into smaller ones. The breakdown process generally involves reaction with water, known as hydrolysis (Box 3.1).

## Box 3.1  Hydrolysis

**Hydrolysis** is a general term used for the reaction that involves breaking a compound into smaller parts using water as a reactant. The word comes from the Greek hydro, meaning water, and lysis, meaning split. For example, an ester can be broken up using water to give an alcohol and a carboxylic acid:

$$CH_3-C\overset{O}{\underset{O-CH_2-CH_3}{}} \quad + \; H_2O \; \longrightarrow \; CH_3-C\overset{O}{\underset{OH}{}} \quad + \; HO-CH_2-CH_3$$

ethyl acetate                                   acetic acid                    ethanol

All esters are broken up in this way, irrespective of the structure of the rest of the molecule, so a generalized equation can be written:

$$R^1-C\overset{O}{\underset{O-R^2}{}} \quad + \; H_2O \; \longrightarrow \; R^1-C\overset{O}{\underset{OH}{}} \quad + \; HO-R^2$$

■ Triglycerides, such as compound 3.1, contain three ester functional groups. What will be the result when one mole of triglyceride molecules reacts completely with three moles of water molecules?

$$\begin{array}{l} R-\overset{O}{\overset{\|}{C}}-O-CH_2 \\ R-\overset{O}{\overset{\|}{C}}-O-CH \\ R-\overset{O}{\overset{\|}{C}}-O-CH_2 \end{array}$$

**3.1**

■ Each of the three ester groups will be broken up by a water molecule to give an alcohol functional group and a carboxylic acid. Thus three moles of fatty acid molecules are produced, together with a mole of glycerol molecules.

$$\begin{array}{l} R-\overset{O}{\overset{\|}{C}}-O-CH_2 \\ R-\overset{O}{\overset{\|}{C}}-O-CH \\ R-\overset{O}{\overset{\|}{C}}-O-CH_2 \end{array} \; + \; 3\,H_2O \; \longrightarrow \; \begin{array}{l} HO-CH_2 \\ HO-CH \\ HO-CH_2 \end{array} \; + \; 3\,R-C\overset{O}{\underset{OH}{}}$$

Notice that hydrolysis is the reverse of formation of an ester from a carboxylic acid and an alcohol by condensation.

Amides also undergo hydrolysis. In this case, the amide is broken down by the water to give a carboxylic acid and an amine:

$$R^1-C\overset{O}{\underset{NH-R^2}{}} \quad + \; H_2O \; \longrightarrow \; R^1-C\overset{O}{\underset{OH}{}} \quad + \; R^2-NH_2$$

*(continued overleaf)*

■ What will be the result when one mole of the polyamide 3.2 reacts with three moles of water molecules?

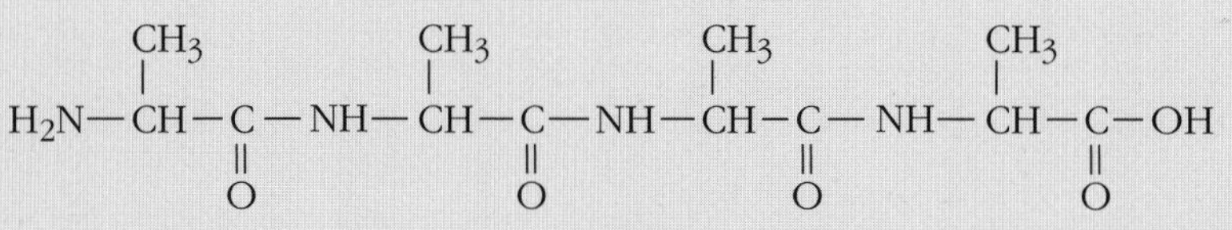

**3.2**

■ Each of the amide bonds in the polyamide will be cleaved by a water molecule to give a carboxylic acid functional group and an amine. Thus the product will be four moles of an amino acid, as shown in Figure 3.1. This is how proteins are broken down.

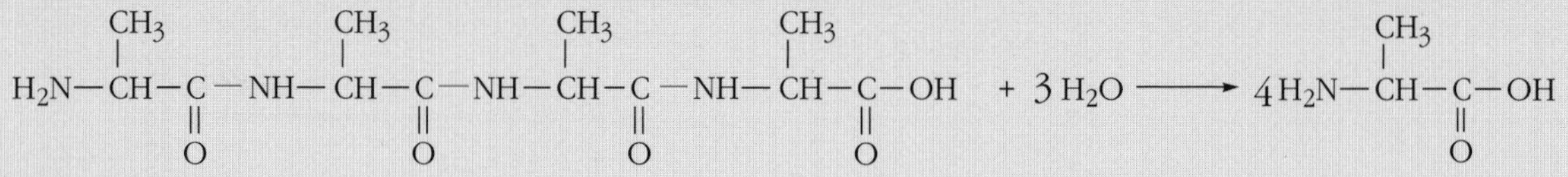

**Figure 3.1**
The hydrolysis of proteins. The bonds that break are shown in red.

Polysaccharides are also broken down by water to give monosaccharides. In this case, the linking carbon–oxygen bonds between the monomers are cleaved, as shown in Figure 3.2.

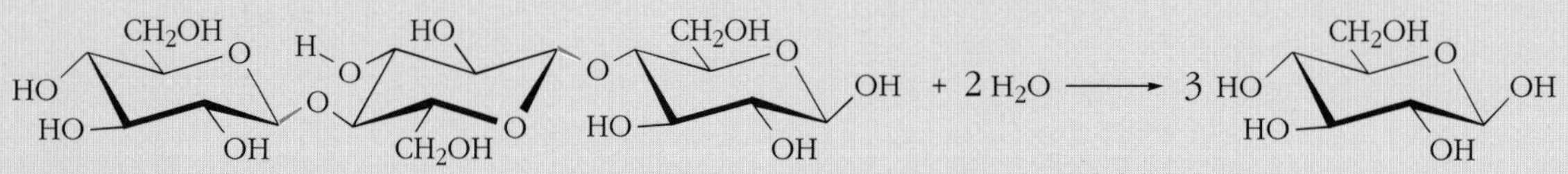

**Figure 3.2**
The hydrolysis of polysaccharides. The bonds that break are shown in red.

In digestion, the chemical processes are facilitated by **enzymes**, which we shall examine later in this chapter. For now, it is sufficient for you to think of them as large molecules that help particular reactions to occur efficiently. In the absence of the enzyme a particular reaction may proceed very slowly, but the enzyme can speed the reaction up. They are so good at doing their job that in the space of three or four hours the nature of the food you eat will have changed completely. For example, large carbohydrate polymers containing 6 000 glucose monomer units will be broken down completely into separate glucose molecules. The digestive process involves various different classes of enzymes, as shown in Table 3.1, which reflect the type of chemical reaction that each class helps to speed up.

**Table 3.1** Classes of enzymes involved in digestion.

| Enzyme class | Reactant | Product |
| --- | --- | --- |
| lipases | fats | fatty acids and glycerol |
| peptidases and proteases | proteins | amino acids |
| amylases | carbohydrate (starch) | maltose |
| maltases | carbohydrate (maltose) | glucose |

The digestive system can be thought of as a long tube, with a few valves, that stretches from the mouth at one end to the anus at the other, as shown in

Figure 3.3a. Food enters the system at the mouth where it is chewed into smaller pieces. The food is mixed with saliva, which is excreted by the salivary glands in response to external stimuli, such as the sight, smell, or even the thought of a good meal. Saliva is 99% by mass water, and 1% of it is other chemicals, such as mucin, which lubricates the food for further passage, and an enzyme called salivary amylase, as shown in Figure 3.3b.

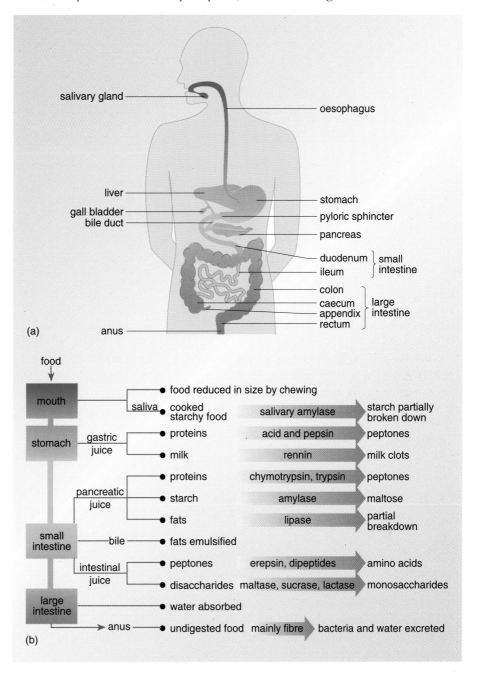

**Figure 3.3**
(a) The digestive system; (b) a summary of digestive processes. (Peptones are short chains of amino acid residues.)

What classes of nutrients will be broken down by salivary amylase?

Table 3.1 shows that amylases catalyse the hydrolysis of starch.

The food is carried down the oesophagus by gentle muscle action and gravity till it reaches the stomach. This is essentially a reservoir where food is prepared for the main stage of digestion in the small intestine. In the stomach the food is mixed with gastric juices, which are produced in the lining of the stomach, stimulated both chemically – the taste of food – and psychologically – just thinking about food. However, their production may be inhibited by factors such as excitement, depression, anxiety and fear. This mixing takes place via vigorous muscular activity in the lower region of the stomach about 20 minutes after eating a meal. The gastric juice contains hydrochloric acid so is acidic, with a pH of about 1.5. This dilute acid aids the breakdown of the chemicals in the food and also kills off any bacteria. The gastric juice also contains two enzymes: pepsin, which starts breaking down the protein component of the food into individual amino acids, and rennin, which aids the coagulation of any milk in the food. The stomach has an outlet valve, which opens at intervals so allowing the food and gastric juices to pass into the first part of the intestines, the duodenum.

The main stage of digestion occurs on passage through the small intestine using a new set of compounds provided by:

- bile: a range of chemicals produced in the liver and stored in the gall bladder
- pancreatic juice: a group of chemicals secreted by the pancreas
- intestinal juice: chemicals secreted by the lining of the intestine.

These three juices are basic and so neutralize the acidity of the gastric juice. They also provide new enzymes, such as peptidases, amylases and maltases, and lipases.

▨    What type of compound does each of these enzymes break down?

▤    Peptidases break down proteins into amino acids, amylases and maltases together break down carbohydrates into glucose, and lipases break down fats into smaller components, such as fatty acids.

The bile does not contain any enzymes, only bile salts. These are emulsifying agents that stabilize the formation of emulsions from the fats and fatty acids. In this more dispersed state, the enzymes known as lipases can get at the fat molecules more easily and break them down. The digestive process is almost complete after the food has been in the small intestine for four hours. All the protein has been broken down into amino acids, all carbohydrates, except dietary fibre, will have been broken down into simple soluble sugars, and fatty acids will have been produced from the fats. During this stage these basic building blocks are absorbed into the body. The walls of the long small intestine are folded into finger-like projections, which contain both blood capillaries and lymph vessels. Water-soluble materials, such as amino acids, sugars, minerals and some vitamins, dissolve into the blood in the capillaries and are then transported away through the bloodstream to other areas of the body. Fatty acids, which do not dissolve in the blood, are absorbed into the lymph vessels, where they are converted back into triglycerides. These new triglycerides contain combinations of fatty acids that are more suitable for use in the body. They are then emulsified so they can be carried round in the bloodstream. This gives blood its 'milky' appearance after a meal rich in fat has been eaten. Other water-insoluble materials, such as cholesterol and some vitamins, are also emulsified with the fats, for transportation.

Approximately seven to nine hours after the food was eaten, any that has not been digested and absorbed in the small intestine passes through another valve into the wider, but shorter, large intestine. No new enzymes are produced, but the large intestine is rich in bacteria, which break down some of the remains of the food. In this way, small but important amounts of vitamins, such as vitamin K, are produced and absorbed by the body. However, the main function of the large intestine is to recover water from the fluid mass, so that after about twenty hours, by the time it reaches the anus, it is in a semi-solid form. Each day between 100 g and 200 g of moist faeces may be produced, consisting of undigested food material such as fibre, residues from digestive juices, living and dead bacteria from the large intestine, and water.

## 3.2  How enzymes work

As we have seen, nearly all of the chemical transformations that go on in the body are helped along by enzymes. In digestion they speed up the hydrolysis of fats, carbohydrates and proteins into their constituent parts. Enzymes are very effective at their job. They enable reactions to be carried out in the body that would require quite stringent and extreme conditions in the laboratory. In the laboratory it is easy to 'cook' some substances for 30 minutes at 100 °C to make them react more quickly, but the body does not have this facility. If it needs that same product, it has to find a different way of making it at a rather lower temperature. Enzymes are a subset of the globular proteins that we met earlier. Figure 3.4 shows a representation of the enzyme carboxypeptidase A, which breaks down protein in the gut. Like all globular proteins, enzymes consist of a large number of amino acid residues, arranged in a specific order from one end of the chain to the other: carboxypeptidase A has 307 of them. All molecules of the same enzyme have exactly the same primary structure. One of the essential features of an enzyme is that it has a precise shape, dictated by this primary structure, which causes the chain to fold up in an exact and reproducible way. This means that every single molecule of the enzyme will have the same convoluted pattern of folding. The enzyme is held in this shape by hydrogen bonding and a number of other interactions. If proteins, and particularly enzymes, are abused in some way, such as heating them up or putting them in acidic solutions, the carefully folded chain unravels; this is denaturation. Once this has happened the intricate structure is lost and the enzyme loses its activity. There are very many ways in which it could fold up again, and the likelihood of this corresponding to the original structure is very low.

The active site in Figure 3.4a is expanded in Figure 3.4b. It is in here that the reactant molecule is converted into the product. Effectively the active site fits like a glove around the reactant molecule and provides the ideal environment for reaction.  The active site is a cavity that has particular atoms or functional groups placed in just the right position for reaction. This precise three-dimensional ordering can be achieved only by using complex molecular architecture, which is one of the reasons why enzymes are such large molecules.

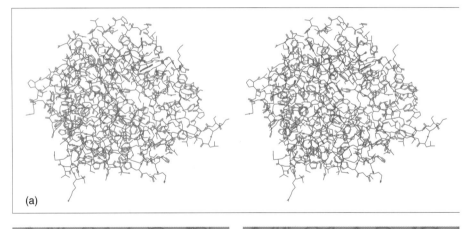

(a)

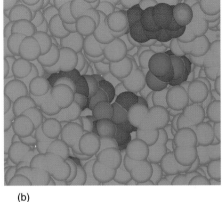
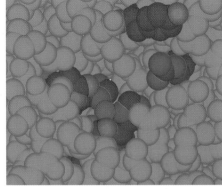

(b)

**Figure 3.4**
(a) Stereoscopic framework model of the structure of carboxypeptidase A; the active site is the cavity just to the right of centre.
(b) Stereoscopic space-filling model of the active site of carboxypeptidase A. This representation highlights the cavity. The important amino acid side-chains are shown in colour. Notice the zinc atom, coloured olive green, which is essential for the activity of the enzyme.

Because the enzyme fits the reactant like a glove, the active site will accommodate only a very small range of different molecules. This specificity is the key to enzyme action. The relationship between reactant and enzyme has been likened to a lock and key (Figure 3.5): the enzyme is like a lock where only one type of key, the correct reactant, will fit the active site. Thus one type of enzyme will speed only one type of reaction for only one particular molecule or type of molecule – we say that enzymes are highly selective. For example, hydrolysis of the amide bond is the key reaction in breaking down proteins to amino acids:

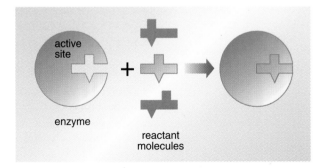

**Figure 3.5**
'Lock and key' representation of the active site in an enzyme.

$$\sim\!\!\sim\text{NH}-\text{CH}-\overset{\overset{\displaystyle O}{\|}}{\text{C}}-\text{NH}-\text{CH}-\overset{\overset{\displaystyle O}{\|}}{\text{C}}-\text{NH}\!\!\sim\!\!\sim \; + \; \text{H}_2\text{O} \; \longrightarrow \; \sim\!\!\sim\text{NH}-\text{CH}-\overset{\overset{\displaystyle O}{\diagup\!\!\diagup}}{\underset{\text{OH}}{\text{C}}} \; + \; \text{H}_2\text{N}-\text{CH}-\overset{\overset{\displaystyle O}{\|}}{\text{C}}-\text{NH}\!\!\sim\!\!\sim$$
$$\qquad\qquad\quad \underset{\text{R}^1}{\big|} \qquad\qquad \underset{\text{R}^2}{\big|} \qquad\qquad\qquad\qquad\qquad\qquad\quad \underset{\text{R}^1}{\big|} \qquad\qquad\qquad \underset{\text{R}^2}{\big|}$$

In the digestive system this hydrolysis is catalysed by proteases. Different proteases differ in their selectivity. Subtilisin, which comes from certain bacteria, is quite undiscriminating, and $R^1$ and $R^2$ could be any amino acid side-chain. Trypsin, a digestive enzyme, is quite specific for cleaving only amides in which $R^1$ is the side-chain of lysine or arginine amino acids, although $R^2$ can be any amino acid side-chain. Thrombin, an enzyme that participates in blood clotting, is even more specific: it hydrolyses only the amide bond between arginine ($R^1$) and glycine ($R^2$).

There are a great many enzymes in the human body, each speeding up a different reaction. Their efficiency, coupled to their ability to speed up only one reaction, has extremely important consequences. An individual compound could possibly undergo a great number of different reactions. The products of these reactions in their turn could react in many different ways, as could their products, as shown in Figure 3.6. Enzymes, by virtue of their selectivity, will speed up only one process, such that a series of enzymes working in sequence will enhance one particular pathway, through the maze of possible reactions. One way in which the body can control the reactions going on within it is to control the concentration and activity of the various enzymes involved. To turn on a particular pathway the requisite enzymes are produced, and to turn the pathway off the enzymes are removed.

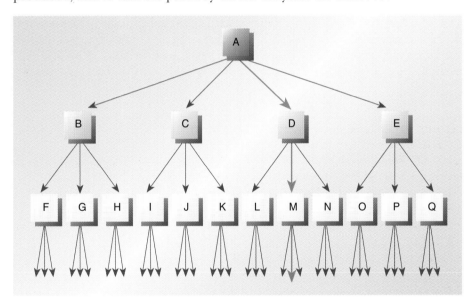

**Figure 3.6**
Selectivity in a maze of reactions.

## Box 3.2  Phenylketonuria

As we saw earlier, this genetic disease leads to severe mental retardation if not recognized early. Sufferers do not make the enzyme that converts one amino acid, phenylalanine, into another, tyrosine. This is one step of an important biosynthetic pathway. Thus the phenylalanine accumulates in all body fluids because the body has no way of getting rid of it. However, tyrosine can be obtained in other ways, for example from the diet. The high level of phenylalanine reduces the formation of the skin pigment melanin so sufferers tend to have light skin and hair colour.

Phenylketonuria sufferers appear normal at birth but, if they remain untreated, irreversible brain damage occurs by the age of one year.

Nowadays, early screening identifies sufferers. If these babies are fed a diet low in phenylalanine, there is no build-up in the body and the brain develops properly. Sufferers can thus lead quite normal lives.

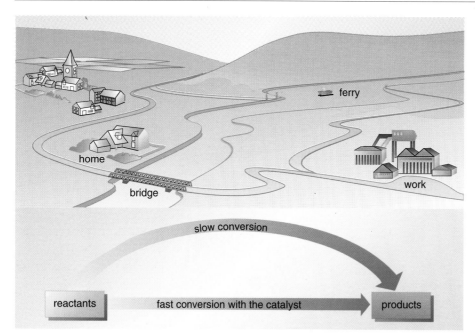

**Figure 3.7**
If the bridge wasn't there it would take longer to get to work by ferry; if the catalyst wasn't there the conversion of reactants into products would take longer.

Enzymes belong to a group of compounds known as catalysts. A **catalyst** is a substance that increases the speed of a reaction without itself being consumed or chemically altered. As we saw in Book 2, when we write a balanced chemical equation it tells us nothing about how the transformation occurs at the molecular level, the reaction mechanism. A catalyst works by providing the reaction with an alternative reaction mechanism – a faster pathway, as illustrated schematically in Figure 3.7. In the absence of the catalyst this pathway is not open to the reactants.

Take, for example, the hydrolysis of triglycerides to glycerol and fatty acids. If we put triglycerides in contact with water nothing much happens: hydrolysis to the fatty acids is slow. In digestion, the enzymes called lipases cause hydrolysis to occur more readily. They provide an alternative, faster, reaction mechanism for the hydrolysis reaction.

Generally, enzyme catalysis occurs by the enzyme being intimately involved in the mechanism. In first steps of the mechanism the enzyme actually reacts with the reactant to give intermediates:

$$\text{reactant} + \text{enzyme} = \text{intermediates} \tag{3.1}$$

However, the enzyme is regenerated in a later step from other intermediates:

$$\text{intermediates} = \text{enzyme} + \text{products} \tag{3.2}$$

Thus, the catalyst, an enzyme in this case, is not consumed, it is continually recycled. Because the catalyst is not consumed, it does not end up as part of the product. This means that the catalyst is not part of the overall balanced equation, which is the same irrespective of whether the reaction is catalysed or not.

■    Can a catalyst be used to help a non-spontaneous reaction occur?

■    No. Whereas a catalyst has a large effect on the rate of reaction, it cannot turn a reaction that is not spontaneous into one that is (Book 2, Part 2).

The way that enzymes work is an area of great interest to chemists, because if we know how the body controls the conversion of reactants into products then it should be possible to help when things go wrong. Such an approach will be examined in more detail later in this Book. For the moment, we are interested in how enzymes aid digestion of food.

Effectively, enzyme action can be divided into three stages, as shown schematically in Figure 3.8. First the reactant molecule or molecules, in this case molecules in our food, find their way into the active site; we say they *bind* to the active site.

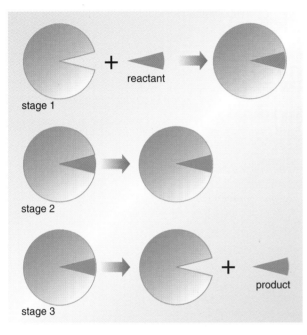

Then, while bound to the active site, the reactants are converted into products. The last stage involves the products leaving the active site, making the site available to aid the conversion of more reactant molecules into product. This recycling of the enzyme is what makes it a catalyst: one molecule of enzyme will cause the conversion of many molecules of reactant into product, so only a small amount of the catalyst is required.

Our brief foray into the world of enzymes has enabled us to appreciate how the body controls digestion. As the food we eat is moved from one compartment to the next on its journey through the body, it is exposed to different enzymes, each with a particular task. Amylases are built so they bind starch and convert it into the disaccharide maltose, and maltases are built so they bind maltose: there is a particular type of enzyme for each different sugar. These enzymes provide each type of reactant with an alternative faster reaction mechanism for the formation of product. After reaction the product leaves so the enzyme is available to aid the breakdown of more carbohydrate. Peptidases do a similar job for proteins, and lipases for fats. The products are building blocks for other processes in the body. Therefore they are transported across the wall of the gut into the bloodstream, then by the bloodstream to cells where other enzymes are responsible for building new proteins from amino acids, and glycogen from glucose. Enzymes are also responsible for ensuring that fat and carbohydrate are oxidized in a controlled way, so that the energy released can be employed to do work.

**Figure 3.8**
Schematic representation of the three stages of enzyme activity.

## Summary of Chapter 3

This Chapter has been concerned with digestion, the breakdown of food in the body, and with the mechanism of enzyme action.

As food passes through the body the food is broken down into its building blocks and absorbed into the bloodstream. The remaining food is excreted.

The breakdown often involves hydrolysis, which is reaction with water. Proteins are broken down into amino acids, fats into fatty acids and polysaccharides into monosaccharides.

These reactions are catalysed by a range of enzymes, as the food passes through the body. Each type of reaction requires a different type of enzyme.

Enzymes are catalysts, compounds that speed up reactions but are not consumed. They provide the reactants with an alternative, faster reaction mechanism.

Enzymes are large globular proteins with a cavity known as the active site. The active site provides the ideal environment for reaction to occur.

Enzymes are recycled. First the reactant binds to the active site. Then it undergoes transformation to the products. Finally the product leaves the active site.

**Question 13** Milk is rich in a disaccharide called lactose. Nearly all infants and children are able to digest lactose because they have an enzyme called lactase in the stomach which breaks it down. Most adults also have this enzyme but certain population groups have a high incidence of lactase deficiency. For example, 97% of all adult Thais do not have this enzyme. In the intestine, bacteria break the lactose into lactic acid, which causes discomfort. What do you think is the effect of drinking milk on people with this deficiency?

**Question 14** Antifreeze contains ethylene glycol, and a number of deaths occur each year from ingestion of antifreeze. Although ethylene glycol is not toxic, its oxidation product, oxalic acid, is. It severely damages the liver. Oxalic acid is also found in rhubarb leaves! In the body, the oxidation of a range of alcohols, including ethanol and ethylene glycol, is catalysed by an enzyme called alcohol dehydrogenase (Equations 3.3 and 3.4). There is only a certain amount of this enzyme in the body.

$$
\begin{array}{ccc}
\underset{\text{ethylene glycol}}{\overset{\displaystyle CH_2-OH}{\underset{\displaystyle CH_2-OH}{|}}} & \xrightarrow[\text{dehydrogenase}]{\text{alcohol}} & \underset{\text{oxalic acid}}{\overset{\displaystyle O{=}C{-}OH}{\underset{\displaystyle O{=}C{-}OH}{|}}}
\end{array} \tag{3.3}
$$

$$
\underset{\text{ethanol}}{CH_3-CH_2-OH} \quad \xrightarrow[\text{dehydrogenase}]{\text{alcohol}} \quad \underset{\text{acetic acid}}{CH_3-C\overset{\displaystyle O}{\underset{\displaystyle OH}{\diagup}}} \tag{3.4}
$$

The antidote to ethylene glycol poisoning involves administering a nearly intoxicating dose of ethanol! Why do you think this is?

# Chapter 4
# Water

**Figure 4.1**
Water is best – from the
pump room at Bath.

We now take a short rest from looking at complicated structures of organic molecules and examine some properties of a very simple molecule – water. Of all the chemicals needed to sustain life, we need water in the largest quantity (Table 4.1).

**Table 4.1** Water balance in the body in a temperate climate.

| Intake source | Water intake /cm³ per day | Excretion source | Water loss /cm³ per day |
|---|---|---|---|
| food | 1 120 | urine | 1 300 |
| drink | 1 180 | lungs | 300 |
| oxidation of nutrients | 280 | skin | 920 |
|  |  | faeces | 60 |
| total intake | 2 580 | total loss | 2 580 |

As the table shows, we take in about two and a half litres a day, not just from drinking but also in our food and from oxidation of nutrients, such as glucose:

$$C_6H_{12}O_6(s) + 6O_2(g) = 6CO_2(g) + 6H_2O(g) \qquad (4.1)$$

▪ How much water is produced from a teaspoonful of glucose, which has a mass of 7.00 g?

▪ The balanced equation tells us that one mole of glucose molecules produces six moles of water molecules.

The relative molecular mass of glucose, $C_6H_{12}O_6$, is $(6 \times 12.0) +$ $(12 \times 1.01) + (6 \times 16.0) = 180.1$.

The relative molecular mass of water, $H_2O$, is $(2 \times 1.01) + 16.0 = 18.0$.

So 180.1 g of glucose produce $(6 \times 18.0)$ g of water.

So 1.00 g of glucose produces $(6 \times 18.0/180.1)$ g of water.

So 7.00 g of glucose produce $(6 \times 18.0 \times 7.00/180.1)$ g $= 4.20$ g of water.

Table 4.1 also shows how water is lost from the body, mostly as urine or by evaporation from the skin – perspiration. However, quite a lot is lost as water vapour when we breathe out; and, as mentioned earlier, water is also contained in faeces.

Notice that, unlike fats, proteins and carbohydrates, which are broken down by digestion, the majority of the water we take in is chemically unchanged as it passes through the system. In fact, as Equation 4.1 shows, water is actually formed in the body (Figure 4.2)! Nevertheless, we can last only for a very short time without water; otherwise we die. The importance of water is also shown in Table 1.1, which shows that our bodies are about 80% water.

In fact, water is so important that no other liquid can be used in the body as a substitute. To understand why, we must look at some of its properties. First, we shall examine how materials dissolve in water, and this will enable us to understand how apparently insoluble compounds, such as fats, are transported in the blood. Second, we shall discuss the key role played by water in acidity, basicity and neutralization – some important features of digestion, body chemistry in general, and even cooking!

**Figure 4.2**
Oxidation of a fatty acid produces a great deal of water. Camels use the fat stored in their humps as a reserve to provide both energy and water.

## 4.1  Solubility of materials in water

The solubility of a whole range of compounds in water is important, enabling material in the body to be absorbed, transported and disposed of. In this Section we shall develop our ideas of solubility further by looking at the range of compounds that are dissolved in water to give fruit juices, milk, beer, gravy and vinegar. Such a study will also enable us to understand how nutrients dissolve in the bloodstream.

If a drink is transparent, although it may be coloured, and contains no suspended solid or liquid particles, then it can truly be regarded as a solution. If it is cloudy or opaque in any way, such as milk or fruit juices, then it is a suspension or an emulsion.

■  Why is an emulsion, such as milk, or a suspension, such as milk of magnesia, white?

■  In Book 2 we saw that although glass is transparent and colourless, powdered glass is white. This is because light hitting the glass fragments will undergo multiple reflections. White light is thus reflected back to the observer. Milk contains many small particles that reflect the light. Again, multiple reflections from the particles result in white light being reflected back to the observer. Milk of magnesia also contains many particles that reflect light.

### 4.1.1 Ionic compounds in our drinks

One group of compounds that we have already met that are dissolved in drinks are ionic solids. For example, there is about 0.5 g of potassium or sodium ions dissolved in 100 g of tomato juice.

■ Describe the structure of ionic solids.

■ Ionic solids are assemblies of positive and negative ions, as shown in Figure 4.3a, held together in a rigid three-dimensional network by electrostatic attraction between the oppositely charged ions. Because of the arrangement of the ions, this attraction is greater than the repulsion between ions with like charge.

■ Describe what happens when an ionic compound dissolves in water.

■ The electrostatic attraction between the ions is replaced by the electrostatic attraction between the ions and the partial charges on the water molecules, as shown in Figure 4.3b.

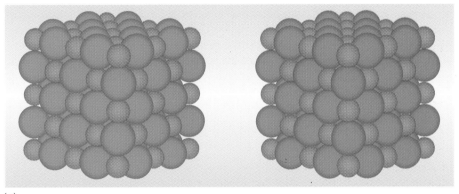

(a)

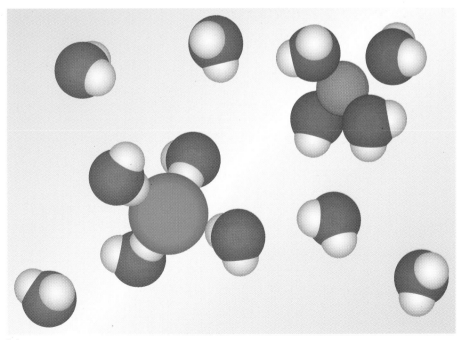

**Figure 4.3**
Structure of (a) solid and (b) dissolved ionic compounds.

(b)

This interaction of the ion with the solvent is known as solvation. When the ions are in the solid state they are in fixed positions, whereas in solution the ions can move freely, independently of each other.

Essential ions such as sodium, calcium, iron and chloride are taken into the body either dissolved in our drinks or dissolved in the water contained in food. If you suffer from diarrhoea and/or vomiting, your body loses water and ions, so a number of treatments are available that provide suitable levels of potassium chloride and sodium chloride, as well as glucose for energy.

However, not all ionic compounds are soluble. My father suffered with an ulcer for many years and was prescribed about 2 g per day of magnesium trisilicate. The quantity that he had to take was such that it did not dissolve in an average tumbler and thus he had to drink it as a suspension.

■   What is the definition of solubility, given in Book 2?

■   Solubility is the mass of the solute that will dissolve in a specified mass of solvent at a particular temperature to give a saturated solution.

The solubility of magnesium trisilicate in water at 20 °C is about $6 \times 10^{-4}$ g in 100 g of water. At this point no more magnesium trisilicate will dissolve, and the solution is said to be saturated. Thus, my father would have had to drink over 300 litres of water to take the magnesium trisilicate in as a solution.

---

### Box 4.1 Solubility

Solutions of ionic solids in water are important in the body, in the sea and in the kitchen, so, as we have discussed in Book 1, chemistry has its own language for describing solutions. However, it should be stressed that rather than being jargon for the sake of it, such language is important because it enables us to communicate precisely. Some of the terms that you have already met, together with some new ones, are listed below:

**Solvent**  This is the substance that does the dissolving. In blood or tomato juice, water is the solvent that dissolves table salt or sugar. Turpentine, or turps, is a solvent that dissolves oil, such as that in oil-based gloss paints.

**Solute**  This is the substance that is dissolved. Table salt is a solute in water, and oil is a solute in turpentine.

**Solution**  This comes about when a solute is dissolved in solvent. A sugar solution is formed when sugar dissolves in water. Oil dissolved in turpentine is a solution.

**Saturated solution**  A solution is saturated when no more solute will dissolve at that particular temperature.

**Suspension**  This consists of very small solid particles distributed within a liquid medium. Medicines and lotions, such as calamine lotion or milk of magnesia, are examples of suspensions. If sufficient time is allowed, and the suspension mixture is left undisturbed, the solid settles to the bottom.

**Emulsion**  This consists of very small liquid droplets distributed within a liquid medium. Milk is an example of an emulsion. If sufficient time is allowed, and the emulsion is left undisturbed, the droplets may separate into a distinct layer.

**Colloid**  This is a general term for an emulsion or a suspension in which the particles are between 1 and 100 mm in diameter.

**Crystallization**  This may occur when a solution is cooled. A higher temperature usually means that more solute can dissolve in a specified mass of solvent. If the solution is cooled, the solvent can hold less solute and may cool down to the point at which it is saturated. The solute starts to come out of solution and may be precipitated in the form of crystals. This process is called crystallization. Crystallization also occurs when a solvent slowly evaporates from a saturated solution, and the solute is left behind as crystals.

At the molecular level, the difference between a solution and a suspension, emulsion or colloid is that, in solution, individual solute atoms, ions or molecules are surrounded by solvent molecules and move around independently of other solute particles. In an emulsion, suspension or colloid, groups of solute atoms, ions or molecules aggregate together to form small domains of the solute within the solvent.

## 4.1.2 The importance of hydrogen bonding

Soft drinks provide water and usually sucrose in the form of a plea
flavoured drink.

▨ Why does sucrose (**4.1**) dissolve in water?

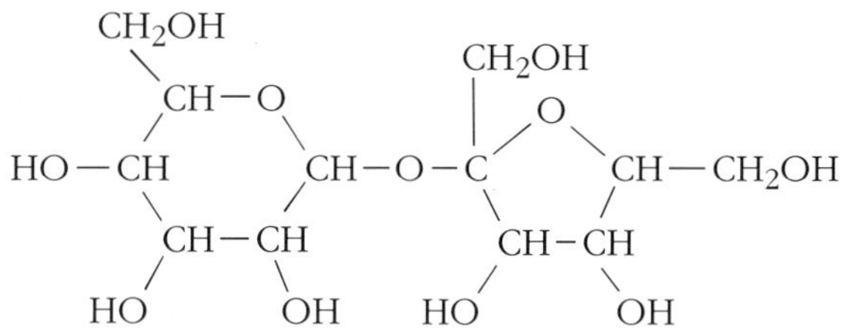

**4.1**

◼ The diagram shows that sucrose contains eight OH groups, each of
which can form a hydrogen bond with a molecule of water.

When sucrose dissolves in water, the formation of hydrogen bonds between
the sucrose and the water compensates for the loss of hydrogen bonds
between the sucrose molecules in the solid and the loss of some hydrogen
bonds between the water molecules in the solvent. Sucrose is very soluble in
water, with a solubility of 115 g in 100 g of water at 25 °C, and this increases
with increasing temperature.

Most mono- and disaccharides are soluble in water to a large extent, mainly
because they contain many OH groups that can form hydrogen bonds with
water. For example, Lucozade contains about 20 g of glucose per 100 ml of
drink, and 6–8% by mass of human milk is lactose (solubility 22 g in 100 g of
water at 25 °C).

You may expect polysaccharides, such as starch and cellulose, to be soluble in
water. After all, like sucrose, they contain many OH groups. Experience,
however, tells us that polysaccharides are not very soluble; starch does not
dissolve in cold water, and the cellulose that makes up much of trees and
plants does not dissolve. If it rains, trees and plants do not dissolve. Cellulose
does not dissolve in water because, as we saw in Chapter 2, the linear ribbon-
like chains pack together very tightly with extensive hydrogen bonding. So,
the water cannot penetrate the structure to break it up and it will not dissolve.
Even hot water will not break up cellulose, but it can penetrate the looser
structure of starch. This occurs when we thicken sauces with cornflour, which
is maize starch.

▨ Which two polymers does starch contain?

◼ Chapter 2 stated that starch contains amylopectin, which is a large
branched biopolymer, and amylose, which is a shorter straight-chain
biopolymer.

As with cellulose, the polysaccharide molecules of starch are held together so
tightly by hydrogen bonds that cold water cannot penetrate the structure. This
means we can stir the starch evenly into the sauce at low temperature (Figure
4.4a). However, when it is heated to about 50 to 70 °C, molecules of water get
in amongst the amylopectin and amylose chains and the granules swell.

(a)                              (b)

**Figure 4.4**
The formation of a starch gel at (a) low and (b) higher temperature.

At this point, the hydrogen bonds between the chains are progressively replaced by hydrogen bonds with the water, so the starch softens as the cross-linking between the chains decreases. Some types of starch can absorb and immobilize up to 25 times their own mass of water, corresponding to 400 water molecules per molecule of starch! As swelling continues the granules merge. The shorter amylose polymers are then leached out of the swollen granules to give a paste (Figure 4.4b). Effectively, the amylose chains get tangled up with each other and with the amylopectin chains, giving a three-dimensional network of polymers bonded to each other and to the water by hydrogen bonds. On continued stirring the gravy becomes thinner as the integrity of the granules is lost. However, on cooling it thickens up again as the hydrogen bonding between the amylose and the amylopectin is re-established. This is also what happens when custard or a blancmange is made.

If the starch concentration is high enough it sets to a jelly or paste, which can be used for hanging wallpaper. If starch solutions are left for a few hours, the amylose chains begin to aggregate, so they no longer hold the extended structure of amylopectin molecules together. This causes dilute solutions of starch to thin and concentrated solutions to exude water and become rubbery.

Instant desserts are required to thicken without heating. To achieve this the starch is first heated with water so the starch breaks down and the mixture thickens as before. The water is then quickly removed, before the amylose molecules have a chance to aggregate. Thus, in the powder the starch is already broken down and when water is added to this powder it returns to its thickened state.

### 4.1.3  Fats won't dissolve, or will they?

To make vinaigrette, wine vinegar is mixed with olive oil with some seasoning. Wine vinegar is mainly water and, when the mixture is shaken, small droplets of water can be seen in the oil. On standing, the oil and the water separate. Olive oil is made of triglyceride molecules that involve long chains of carbon atoms. The only polar bonds in the triglyceride are the carbon–oxygen double and single bonds and even these are not strongly polar. Thus, the oil molecules are held together by London forces. The water is held together by hydrogen bonds.

■   So why don't oil and water mix?

■   As we saw in Book 1, on mixing, many hydrogen bonds between the water molecules would have to be broken to accommodate the oil molecules. In addition, the London forces between the oil molecules would be lost. This is not compensated for by the new London forces between the oil molecules and the water, so the oil and water do not mix. Such liquids are said to be **immiscible**.

Table 4.2 lists the solubilities of five carboxylic acids in water at 25 °C. All of the compounds contain the COOH group, which is capable of forming hydrogen bonds with water, as shown in Figure 4.5. Acetic acid, which is the main constituent of vinegar, is soluble in water in all proportions. However, the fatty acid stearic acid is very insoluble in water.

Stop reading for a moment, and consider why this is.

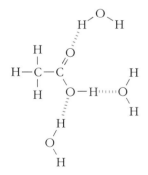

**Figure 4.5**
Hydrogen bonding of the COOH group in acetic acid with water.

**Table 4.2**  Solubility of five carboxylic acids in water at 25 °C.

| Carboxylic acid | Name | Solubility in water in grams per 100 g |
|---|---|---|
| $CH_3COOH$ | acetic acid | completely miscible |
| $CH_3(CH_2)_4COOH$ | caproic acid | 1.1 |
| $CH_3(CH_2)_8COOH$ | capric acid | $1.8 \times 10^{-3}$ |
| $CH_3(CH_2)_{12}COOH$ | myristic acid | $5.7 \times 10^{-4}$ |
| $CH_3(CH_2)_{16}COOH$ | stearic acid | too low to measure |

In acetic acid, the COOH groups can form hydrogen bonds with water but the $CH_3$ groups can not, because the C—H bonds are not polarized. Nevertheless, acetic acid dissolves in water because the changes in the hydrogen bonding caused by the $CH_3$ group are minor compared with the favourable hydrogen bonding of the COOH group.

Stearic acid contains a chain of eighteen carbon atoms. The disruption of the hydrogen bonds between water molecules caused by this long tail is large and will not be compensated for by the new hydrogen bonds to the COOH groups. Thus stearic acid does not dissolve in water.

The other carboxylic acids have intermediate chain lengths and thus the disruption to the hydrogen bonding among the water molecules increases as we go from acetic acid to stearic acid. This is mirrored by the decrease in solubility.

In Book 1 we used the idea of *like dissolving like* to explain why a compound could be dissolved by some solvents and not others. In acetic acid the hydrogen bonding of the COOH group to the water dominates, so we refer to it as a polar molecule. It thus dissolves in water, which is a polar solvent. In stearic acid the long non-polar hydrocarbon chain dominates, so we refer to stearic acid as a non-polar molecule. Thus it will not dissolve in water.

■    What do you think the relative solubilities of the carboxylic acids in Table 4.2 will be in a non-polar solvent, such as hexane?

■    Stearic acid will be the most soluble, because it is the most non-polar and thus will dissolve in the non-polar solvent. When stearic acid dissolves, the London forces between the hexane molecules will be replaced by London forces between the hexane molecules and the stearic acid hydrocarbon chain. Acetic acid will be the least soluble because it is the most polar. There is extensive hydrogen bonding in pure liquid acetic acid. If it were to dissolve in the non-polar hexane, this hydrogen bonding would be lost, to be replaced by only weak London forces between the hexane and acetic acid molecules. Thus, acetic acid does not dissolve to any large extent. As we go down the Table from acetic acid to stearic acid, the polarity of the carboxylic acids decreases so they become progressively more soluble in hexane.

Our discussion so far implies that, whenever we mix a fat with water, they will separate. Nevertheless, we know that milk contains 4% fat and we know it is important that fats and oils do disperse in some way in water so that they can be transported in the bloodstream. To see how this occurs we must consider what happens when we shake a mixture of oil and water vigorously. The result is droplets of one liquid in the other (Book 1, Figure 8.26). These droplets are spherical because a sphere can contain the maximum possible volume, while presenting the smallest possible surface to the other liquid. Over time, the mixture settles out and returns to two layers. The process of separation can be prevented by the addition of a substance, called an emulsifying agent, or **emulsifier**, that stabilizes the dispersed droplets. The result is an emulsion. You often see added emulsifiers listed on the sides of food packets. An emulsifier contains molecules that can be divided conceptually into two parts. One end is charged, or has OH groups that readily interact with water molecules, and the other end is usually a long-chain hydrocarbon, which is thus non-polar. The polar end interacts favourably with the water, and the non-polar end with the oil. These molecules sit on the surface of the oil drop as shown in Figure 4.6. In this situation the hydrogen bonding between the water molecules is replaced by interactions between the water and the polar end of the emulsifier. Spherical globules are formed again because their surface area requires the minimum quantity of emulsifier. This principle is used widely to form emulsion paints and in detergents to 'dissolve' away grease. We shall examine the chemical nature of detergents in more detail later in this Book.

**Figure 4.6**
Stabilization of an oil droplet using an emulsifier.

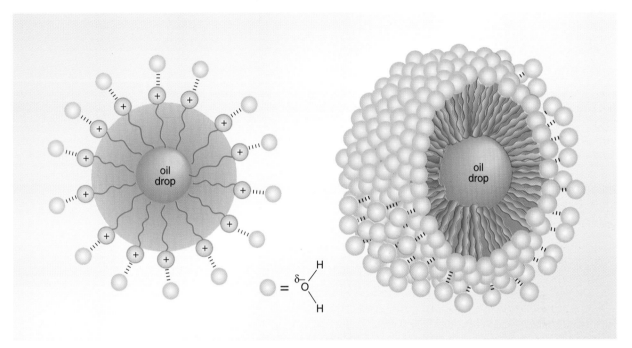

Emulsions occur widely in foods (Box 4.3). Milk, for example, is an oil-in-water emulsion containing about 3.5–4% fat. Also dissolved inside the fat droplets are fat-soluble vitamins, cholesterol and other important nutrients. These are all removed when the fat is taken out to form skimmed milk. Emulsions can also be formed the other way round, for example, water droplets in oil or fat, and these too can be stabilized by emulsifiers. Mayonnaise is an emulsion of water in a fat. Butter and margarine are also important examples of water-in-fat emulsions. We shall examine these in more detail in Chapter 6.

### 4.1.4  What makes a drink fizz?

- What type of material is dissolved in water to give fizzy drinks?

- Clearly, a gas is dissolved in drinks such as lemonade and cola. As soon as the top is taken off the bottle, the pressure is released and the gas starts to come out of solution. From Book 1 you may remember that the gas is carbon dioxide.

## Box 4.3 Lecithin and glyceryl monosteorate

$$CH_3-(CH_2)_{14}-\overset{\overset{\textstyle O}{\|}}{C}-O-CH_2$$

$$CH_3-(CH_2)_{14}-\overset{\overset{\textstyle O}{\|}}{C}-O-CH$$

$$CH_2-O-\overset{\overset{\textstyle O}{\|}}{\underset{\underset{\textstyle OH}{|}}{P}}-O-CH_2-CH_2-\overset{+}{N}(CH_3)_3$$

**4.2** lecithin

Lecithin (**4.2**) is often used to stabilize an emulsion. It can sometimes be seen listed on the side of packets as E322. Lecithin is related to the triglycerides. It contains two long hydrocarbon groups (the non-polar part of the molecule), but attached to one of the oxygen atoms of the glycerol is a

$$-\overset{\overset{\textstyle O}{\|}}{\underset{\underset{\textstyle OH}{|}}{P}}-O-CH_2-CH_2-\overset{+}{N}(CH_3)_3$$

group (the polar part of the molecule). So the surface of the oil droplet is covered with the emulsifier with the tails interacting favourably with the oil and the polar group interacting favourably with the water molecules. Lecithin is abundant in egg yolks, so egg yolk is used to stabilize emulsions in mayonnaise. Egg lecithin plays a similar role in cake-making in stabilizing the mixture of fat and water. Lecithin from soya bean oil is used as a common emulsifying agent in chocolate and other confectionery.

Another emusifier that you might see listed on packets is glyceryl monostearate (**4.3**). This is sometimes referred to as E471, and is often found in margarine. This is a monoglyceride (or monoacylglyceride) and, as you can see from its structural formula, it has two OH groups that can form hydrogen bonds with water to form the polar part. The long hydrocarbon chain provides the non-polar part.

$$CH_2OH$$
$$|$$
$$CHOH$$
$$|$$
$$CH_2-O-\overset{\overset{\textstyle O}{\|}}{C}-(CH_2)_{16}-CH_3$$

**4.3** glycerol monostearate

Many gases dissolve in water, even at atmospheric pressure, although generally this is to only a small extent. Oxygen molecules are not polar and they therefore cannot form hydrogen bonds with water molecules. Thus oxygen is only sparingly soluble in water. Nevertheless, the little that does dissolve is very important for life on this planet. For example at 20 °C, 100 g of water will dissolve only 0.000 9 g of oxygen from the air. This is still enough to allow fish to 'breathe'. Just like us, fish need to take in oxygen to react with food to get energy. Unlike most solid materials, the solubility of gases in water decreases with increasing temperature.

■ The solubility of oxygen from the air in 100 g of water is 0.000 56 g at 60 °C. What will happen as you heat water from the tap to this temperature? Assume that the water from the tap is at 20 °C and saturated with oxygen.

■ If the water from the tap is saturated with oxygen, it will contain about 0.000 9 g per 100 g of water. While the temperature of the water is rising to 60 °C there is potentially more oxygen than the water can accommodate thus oxygen will appear as small bubbles. This is exactly what happens when you heat water in a pan: bubbles appear well before the water starts to boil.

In fizzy drinks the gas that escapes is carbon dioxide. At 25 °C and 1 atm, carbon dioxide has a solubility of 0.145 g per 100 g of water. When you buy a bottle of lemonade it contains more carbon dioxide than 0.145 g per 100 g of water, yet it is clear – the carbon dioxide is dissolved in the water. As you will have guessed, this is because it is under pressure – about 2–3 atm. Just like many physical and chemical situations it is in a state of balance. The carbon dioxide that is dissolved in the water is in dynamic equilibrium with that in the gaseous form. Look at Figure 4.7, which shows a bottle of lemonade at different stages of preparation. Figure 4.7a shows the bottle open to the air at atmospheric pressure, so there is only a little carbon dioxide dissolved in the water. Figure 4.7b shows the bottle closed, but we have added some carbon dioxide to the space above the liquid. This leads to an increase in pressure of the gas.

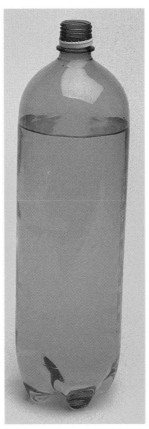  

(a)        (b)        (c)

**Figure 4.7**
Three stages in the formation of lemonade.

The extra carbon dioxide now distributes itself between the gaseous and dissolved forms, thereby increasing the concentration of the gas dissolved in the water and relieving the pressure in the gas phase. If we add more carbon dioxide to the bottle the pressure increases in the gas above the liquid and more carbon dioxide dissolves in the water, Figure 4.7c. At each stage a new balancing point, or **equilibrium**, is achieved, between the quantity of carbon dioxide in the gas and that dissolved.

When the top is removed from a bottle of lemonade, the gas that was under pressure above the liquid is released into the atmosphere – you can often hear the rush of gas. Thus the pressure of the carbon dioxide above the liquid is reduced and so the equilibrium between carbon dioxide gas and dissolved carbon dioxide is upset – the concentration dissolved is too high. Thus the carbon dioxide bubbles out of solution.

Depending on the conditions this release of carbon dioxide to the atmosphere can be a slow process, so it is possible to put the top back on the bottle before it has all escaped and a new equilibrium position is set up. However, if the top is left off the bottle for too long, all of the excess carbon dioxide escapes and the lemonade goes flat.

Whenever we state a solubility, we need to define the conditions such as temperature and pressure. As we have seen, both of these are important for gases. For solids and liquids we should also state both variables, but in practice we need state only the temperature because the solubility of liquids and solids is not greatly changed with pressure.

### 4.1.5  Water in waste disposal

Much of the discussion on solubility in this Section has focused on getting material into the body. To conclude, we shall briefly look at how materials are removed from the body. As we saw in Table 4.1, most of the water we take in is lost as urine, and this provides a means of removing water-soluble waste products from the body. The rest of the water that we take in is lost as sweat or water vapour in exhaled breath.

There are a number of chemical processes in the body that do nothing but convert water-insoluble substances into water-soluble compounds. This is often achieved by converting them into compounds containing OH groups or by attaching a small polar group to the insoluble molecules, thereby making them more ready to dissolve in water.

Some of the fat-soluble vitamins are not excreted in the urine because they will not dissolve in water. Thus they build up in the liver. This is not usually a problem with most diets because the amounts involved are so small; however, there can be a problem with small babies whose levels of vitamin A and D can get dangerously high if given excessive amounts of fish liver oil. Polar bear liver is very rich in vitamin A. In fact, one modest portion of polar bear liver contains enough vitamin A for two years' supply. Polar explorers who eat too much polar bear liver develop hypervitaminosis – they are effectively poisoned by too much vitamin A.

**Question 15** Tea is made by pouring hot water onto the dried leaves of the tea shrub – tea leaves. Tea leaves contain the following compounds:

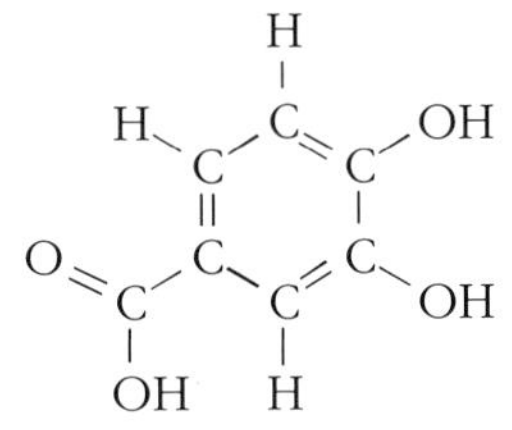

**4.4**

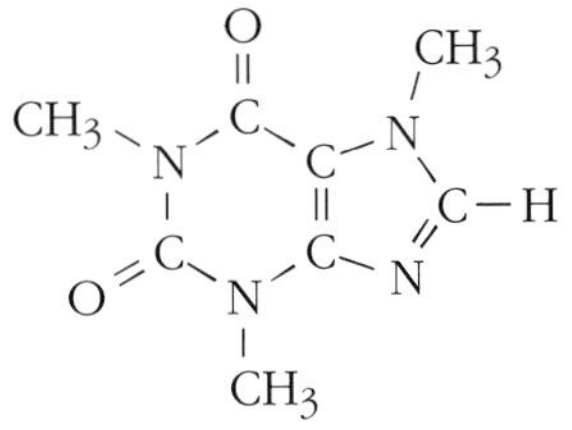

caffeine

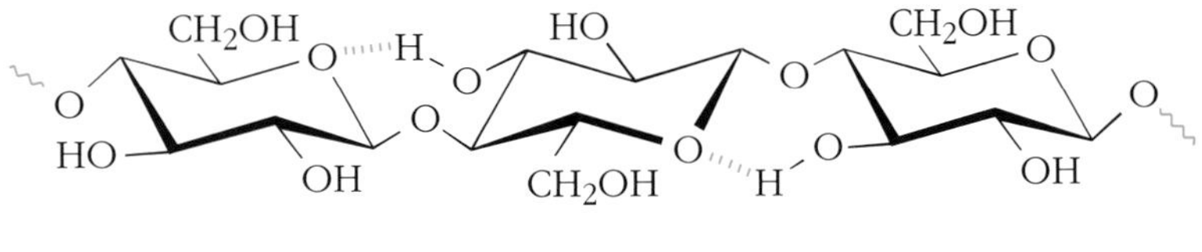

cellulose

Which of them will dissolve in water and end up in the tea we drink?

**Question 16** As we saw earlier, gelatin is a biopolymer. Every third amino acid residue is a hydroxyproline, so we can represent it schematically as in **4.5**. It can be used to thicken mousse. What happens when water is added to gelatin and the mixture is heated?

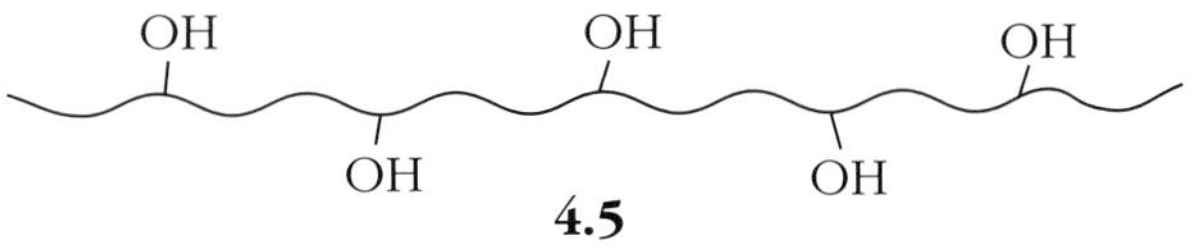

**4.5**

**Question 17** Lecithin is used to stabilize margarine, which is a water-in-oil emulsion. By analogy with Figure 4.6, show how a drop of water may be stabilized in an oil.

## 4.2  Neutral water?

One important ion whose concentration needs to be carefully controlled by the body is the hydrogen ion, $H^+$. If the concentration of hydrogen ions in the stomach is too high we suffer from acid indigestion and heartburn.

---

### Activity 3  Curing acid stomach

You came across the ideas of acids and bases in Book 2. Describe in chemical terms what happens when you take milk of magnesia, $Mg(OH)_2$, to cure acid stomach. Assume that the acid in the stomach is hydrochloric acid, HCl, and that the milk of magnesia dissolves to give $Mg^{2+}$ and $OH^-$ ions. To ensure you understand all the concepts involved we have gone through the arguments in more detail in the comments (p.137) than we would expect of you.

▨   The antacid preparation Tums uses calcium carbonate, $CaCO_3$, which is a base, to neutralize the excess acid. Can you see any problem in explaining how this works?

▨   $CaCO_3$ may well neutralize excess acid in the stomach but it does not contain hydroxide ions. So, our definition of a base must be broadened.

The problem lies with our definition of a base. The neutralization reaction that occurs when we take calcium carbonate for indigestion is as follows:

$$CaCO_3(s) + 2H^+(aq) = Ca^{2+}(aq) + H_2O(l) + CO_2(g) \qquad (4.2)$$

This is a neutralization reaction in that the excess acid is consumed by the calcium carbonate.

In 1923, some 36 years after Arrhenius introduced his ideas on acids and bases, Johannes Brønsted (1879–1947) and Thomas Lowry (1874–1936) proposed that an acid should be defined as a hydrogen ion donor and a base as a hydrogen ion acceptor. Equation 4.2 shows that calcium carbonate (or more precisely the $CO_3^{2-}$ ions in the structure) can accept hydrogen ions, so is a base according to the Brønsted definition.

$$2H^+(aq) + CO_3^{2-}(aq) = H_2O(l) + CO_2(g)$$

This definition gives a much better understanding of what goes on in many acid–base reactions, for example it explains how baking powder works. Baking powder contains sodium bicarbonate, $NaHCO_3$, and an acidic compound. This is usually tartaric acid or sodium tartrate (cream of tartar), and for simplicity we shall call it HA. $NaHCO_3$ is a base because it accepts hydrogen ions, in this case from the acid HA. In baking powder, both the acid and the base are solids. The reactants are tied up in the crystal lattice, so the majority of the acid does not come into contact with the base and neutralization is very limited. On addition of cold water the sodium bicarbonate dissolves:

$$NaHCO_3(s) = Na^+(aq) + HCO_3^-(aq)$$

However, the cream of tartar is fairly insoluble in cold water, so little neutralization occurs and no carbon dioxide is evolved. Cream of tartar does dissolve in hot water, so when the mixture is heated up, as when a cake mixture is put in the oven, the cream of tartar dissolves giving rise to $H^+(aq)$. The $H^+(aq)$ and the $HCO_3^-(aq)$ ions are now able to get together. The $HCO_3^-$ ion is basic because it can accept a hydrogen ion:

$$H^+(aq) + HCO_3^-(aq) = H_2O(l) + CO_2(g)$$

Thus neutralization occurs with the evolution of carbon dioxide. This gas causes the cake to rise – it is light and fluffy because of the pockets of carbon dioxide that become trapped. So by careful design the mixture releases carbon dioxide only when it is needed – in the oven. Notice also the key role played by water in this system in dissolving the reactants. This same mixture of a solid acid and base is also used in self-raising flour.

Armed with this new definition of acids and bases, we can also begin to understand how acidity and basicity can be measured on the same scale, namely the pH scale, which you were introduced to in Book 2. If acids donate hydrogen ions and bases remove hydrogen ions, then an acidic solution will be characterized by high concentrations of hydrogen ions and basic solutions by low concentrations of hydrogen ions. So we can create a scale of acidity and

**Figure 4.8**
A scale of acidity based on
hydrogen ion concentration.

basicity using the concentration of hydrogen ions as the measure, as shown in Figure 4.8. However, the concentration range for the hydrogen ion is very large, of the order of $10^{14}\,mol\,l^{-1}$.

■ How does the pH scale cope with such a large change in concentration?

■ The pH scale is based on the exponent of the concentration. When the concentration of hydrogen ions is written as $1 \times 10^{-n}\,mol\,l^{-1}$, the pH value is equal to $n$.

**Table 4.3** The pH scale. Values of concentration of $H^+(aq)$ and $OH^-(aq)$, with corresponding values of the index and pH (at 25°C).

| Concentration of $H^+(aq)/mol\,l^{-1}$ | Index or power of ten | pH | | Concentration of $OH^-(aq)/mol\,l^{-1}$ |
|---|---|---|---|---|
| $10^1$ or 10 | 1 | −1 | ↑ | $10^{-15}$ |
| $10^0$ or 1 | 0 | 0 | | $10^{-14}$ |
| $10^{-1}$ or 0.1 | −1 | +1 | increasingly | $10^{-13}$ |
| $10^{-2}$ or 0.01 | −2 | +2 | acidic | $10^{-12}$ |
| $10^{-4}$ or 0.000 1 | −4 | +4 | | $10^{-10}$ |
| $10^{-6}$ or 0.000 001 | −6 | +6 | | $10^{-8}$ |
| $10^{-8}$ or 0.000 000 01 | −8 | +8 | increasingly | $10^{-6}$ |
| $10^{-10}$ or 0.000 000 000 1 | −10 | +10 | basic | $10^{-4}$ |
| $10^{-12}$ or 0.000 000 000 001 | −12 | +12 | | $10^{-2}$ |
| $10^{-14}$ or 0.000 000 000 000 01 | −14 | +14 | ↓ | $10^0$ |

Table 4.3 shows the pH scale in detail. Thus a hydrogen ion concentration of $1 \times 10^{-2}\,mol\,l^{-1}$ has an exponent of −2, which corresponds to a pH of 2; a hydrogen ion concentration of $1 \times 10^{-7}\,mol\,l^{-1}$ has an exponent of −7, which corresponds to a pH of 7. So in the neutralization process, as the food passes from the stomach to the duodenum, the pH rises from 2 to 7, corresponding to a decrease in concentration by a factor of $10^5$. Lower values of the pH refer to more acidic solutions, in which the hydrogen ion concentration is relatively large, whereas the higher values of the pH refer to more basic solutions, in which the hydrogen ion concentration is relatively small. A pH of 7 refers to a neutral solution.

■ Table 4.4 gives the pH values for a range of body fluids. Fill in the right-hand column to show those that are acidic, basic or neutral.

**Table 4.4** pH values of some body fluids.

| Fluid | pH | Acid or base? |
|---|---|---|
| blood | 7.4 | |
| fluid in muscles | 6.1 | |
| fluid in liver | 7.0 | |
| gastric juice | 1.2–3.0 | |
| pancreatic juice | 7.8–8.0 | |
| saliva | 6.35–6.85 | |

Fluid in muscles, saliva, and gastric juice are acidic, although the first two are only slightly so. Fluid in the liver is neutral, and blood and pancreatic juice are basic, again only slightly.

Table 4.4 shows that we can get pH values that are not whole numbers. For example, the pH of blood is 7.4. In this case the index is −7.4 and refers to a hydrogen ion concentration of $10^{-7.4}$ mol l$^{-1}$, somewhere between $10^{-7}$ and $10^{-8}$ mol l$^{-1}$. In fact the actual value is about $4 \times 10^{-8}$ mol l$^{-1}$. If you have met logarithms before you may be interested to know that the pH of a solution is defined as the negative logarithm of the hydrogen ion concentration, that is:

$$\mathrm{pH} = -\log \left\{ \frac{\text{concentration of } H^+(aq)}{\text{mol l}^{-1}} \right\} \qquad (4.3)$$

However, if you are not sure about logarithms don't worry, in this Course you won't need to know such detail – the important thing to appreciate is that the pH value reflects the power of ten in the hydrogen ion concentration.

---

### Box 4.4 Effects of pH on food

Acids cause casein, a protein in milk, to coagulate, leading to curds. Casein protein has a number of negatively charged groups on its surface such that individual molecules repel each other (Figure 4.9). The addition of acid neutralizes these negative charges and the molecules coagulate. You never add vinegar to milk!

When many fruit are cut they quickly turn brown. This is caused by enzymes in the fruit. Addition of lemon juice, which is acidic, denatures the enzyme, so the browning process does not occur.

Jam will not set unless the pH of the solution is below 3.5, as you will see in Experiment 3.2.

**Figure 4.9**
The coagulation of casein.

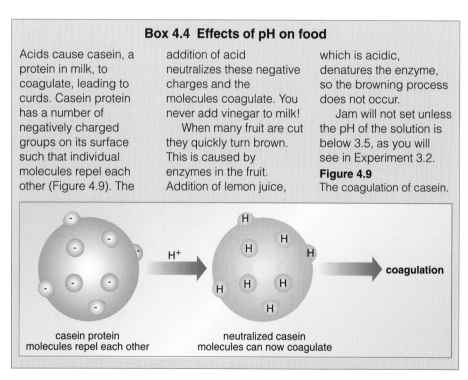

casein protein molecules repel each other

neutralized casein molecules can now coagulate

coagulation

---

If you dissolve 0.001 mol of HCl gas in a litre of water, what will be the pH? (Assume that the change in volume is negligible.)

HCl gas dissolves in water as follows:

HCl(g) = H$^+$(aq) + Cl$^-$(aq)

Thus dissolving 0.001 mol of HCl in a litre of water will lead to a concentration of 0.001 mol l$^{-1}$ of Cl$^-$(aq) and 0.001 mol l$^{-1}$ of H$^+$(aq). The hydrogen ion concentration is thus $1 \times 10^{-3}$ mol l$^{-1}$. This corresponds to a pH of 3.

Acetic acid is an acid because it generates hydrogen ions in aqueous solution:

$$CH_3COOH(aq) = CH_3COO^-(aq) + H^+(aq) \qquad (4.4)$$

■ A litre of vinegar contains about 150 g of acetic acid. How many moles does this correspond to? If all the acetic acid in vinegar ionized as shown in Equation 4.4, what would be the concentration of hydrogen ions in vinegar?

■ The relative molecular mass of acetic acid is $\{(2 \times 12.0) + (2 \times 16.0) + (4 \times 1.01)\} = 60.0$

Thus 150 g of acetic acid corresponds to $150/60.0 = 2.50$ mol

Thus 2.50 mol of acetic acid dissolved in water to a total volume of a litre could lead to a concentration of $2.50 \, \text{mol} \, l^{-1}$ of $H^+(aq)$.

This pH is so low it goes off the scale! I certainly would not want to put this strength of acid on my chips. Ignoring what it would do to the chips, it would cause severe burns to my hands and my mouth if I ate them. If we measure the pH of vinegar, which you may have done in the experiment in Book 2, we get a value of about 2.6, which is a little more friendly.

What has gone wrong with our calculation? The concentration of hydrogen ion seems to be in error by a factor of about a thousand.

Acetic acid is known as a **weak acid**, this means that only a small amount of it ionizes to give $H^+(aq)$ and $CH_3COO^-(aq)$. Most of it remains as neutral, un-ionized, $CH_3COOH(aq)$:

$$CH_3COOH(aq) \rightleftharpoons CH_3COO^-(aq) + H^+(aq)$$

This is an example of an equilibrium reaction, which is designated by the $\rightleftharpoons$ sign. Rather than not reacting at all, or reacting completely to give only the products, partial reaction occurs until a point of balance or equilibrium is reached. At this point, the rate of the forward reaction is the same as the rate of the reverse reaction, hence the double arrow sign. In this case the reaction only goes a little way before equilibrium is achieved, so only a relatively small quantity of hydrogen ions is formed. This is a characteristic of all carboxylic acids, so it also applies to fatty acids. Table 4.5 gives the concentrations of various carboxylic acids in fruit. Again they are only partially ionized. If an acid is completely ionized, such as hydrochloric acid, it is known as a **strong acid**.

**Table 4.5** Typical carboxylic acid content of fruit juices.

| Fruit | Concentration of carboxylic acid/mmol $l^{-1}$ | | |
|---|---|---|---|
| | Malic acid | Citric acid | Tartaric acid |
| orange | 13 | 51 | – |
| grapefruit | 42 | 100 | – |
| lemon | 17 | 220 | – |
| grape | 7 | 16 | 80 |

This type of partial reaction also explains why neutral water has a pH of 7. Water can ionize as follows:

$$H_2O(l) = H^+(aq) + OH^-(aq)$$

Just as with acetic acid this reaction only goes a little way, and hardly any $H^+(aq)$ and $OH^-(aq)$ are formed. For pure water, the point of equilibrium is achieved when the hydrogen ion concentration is $1 \times 10^{-7}$ mol l$^{-1}$.

■     What will be the concentration of hydroxide ions in pure water?

■     For every $H^+$ ion formed a $OH^-$ ion will also be formed, thus both their concentrations will be equal at $1 \times 10^{-7}$ mol l$^{-1}$.

Thus a neutral solution that contains equal quantities of hydrogen ions and hydroxide ions will always have a hydrogen ion concentration of $1 \times 10^{-7}$ mol l$^{-1}$, corresponding to a pH of 7, because the same point of equilibrium will always be reached.

Table 4.3 shows that the concentrations of hydrogen ions and hydroxide ions are linked. If the concentration of hydrogen ions increases by a factor of ten then the concentration of hydroxide ion decreases by a factor of ten. This is again a consequence of the reaction maintaining the same point of equilibrium. We can describe this type of behaviour using a simple mathematical equation, using square brackets to represent 'concentration of' as discussed in Book 2 Part 1:

$$[H^+] \times [OH^-] = constant$$

For water, the constant is $1.0 \times 10^{-14}$ mol$^2$ l$^{-2}$:

$$[H^+] \times [OH^-] = 1.0 \times 10^{-14}\,mol^2\,l^{-2} \tag{4.5}$$

Notice that the hydrogen ion concentration in one aqueous solution may be many orders of magnitude greater than that in another, but it always has a finite value, even in strongly basic solutions. Similarly, the hydroxide ion concentration always has a finite value, even in strongly acidic solutions.

■     If $[H^+]$ is $1.0 \times 10^{-10}$ mol l$^{-1}$, use Equation 4.5 to calculate the concentration of hydroxide ions.

■     From Equation 4.5

$$1.0 \times 10^{-10}\,mol\,l^{-1} \times [OH^-] = 1.0 \times 10^{-14}\,mol^2\,l^{-2}$$

Thus

$$[OH^-] = \frac{1.0 \times 10^{-14}\,mol^2\,l^{-2}}{1.0 \times 10^{-10}\,mol\,l^{-1}} = 1.0 \times 10^{-4}\,mol\,l^{-1}$$

In this solution, although the concentration of hydroxide ions is relatively large, there are still some hydrogen ions present, although the two concentrations differ by a factor of a million, $10^6$! This is because the reaction is still in equilibrium.

## Box 4.5  Carboxylic acids

An example of a carboxylic acid is acetic acid, which is probably familiar to you as its aqueous solution, vinegar:

$$CH_3-\overset{\displaystyle O}{\underset{\displaystyle OH}{C}}$$

The carboxylic acid functional group is highlighted in blue.

Examples of other carboxylic acids are:

$$H-\overset{\displaystyle O}{\underset{\displaystyle OH}{C}}$$

formic acid

benzoic acid

Formic acid is the active ingredient in ant and nettle stings. It was probably the first organic compound produced in pure form when, in mediaeval days, alchemists distilled crushed red ants. Benzoic acid is one of the most widely used bacteriostatic or germicidal agents in foods. Many berries contain appreciable amounts, about 0.05% by mass, of benzoic acid.

The generalized structure of a carboxylic acid, where R is used to indicate the rest of the molecule, is:

$$R-\overset{\displaystyle O}{\underset{\displaystyle OH}{C}}$$

For example for acetic acid, R is $CH_3$.

These compounds are called a carboxylic *acids* because they generate hydrogen ions in solution. However, they are weak acids because only a small proportion of the molecules are ionized:

$$RCOOH(aq) \rightleftharpoons RCOO^-(aq) + H^+(aq)$$

## Experiment 3.2  Jam-making

Another type of cooking in which thickening occurs is jam-making. A simple experiment, Home Experiment 3.2, helps to demonstrate this. You should do this experiment now, or as soon as you can.

## Summary of Chapter 4

This chapter has explored some of the properties of water, namely how materials are dissolved in water and the role of water in acidity and basicity.

We take in a large amount of water in drinks and in food. It is also formed in the body when food is oxidized.

Ionic compounds may dissolve in water. Compounds that have many OH groups also dissolve. However, some polysaccharides are cross-linked so well in the solid state that they do not dissolve. Hot water can break down the cross-linking in starch, leading to a thickening action.

Whether a molecule is polar or not depends on the proportion of polar bonds in the molecule.

The molecules of emulsifying agents contain a non-polar region that interacts favourably with oil, and a polar region that interacts favourably with water.

Gases also dissolve in water. The quantity that dissolves depends on the pressure of the particular gas.

Water provides the medium by which many waste products are removed from the body.

An alternative definition of an acid and a base is: an acid is a hydrogen ion donor and a base is a hydrogen ion acceptor. The pH is a measure of acidity: if the concentration of hydrogen ions is written as $1 \times 10^{-n}\,\mathrm{mol\,l^{-1}}$, the pH value is equal to $n$.

A strong acid is completely ionized to give hydrogen ions, whereas a weak acid is only partially ionized to give hydrogen ions.

**Question 18** Sodium bicarbonate, $NaHCO_3$, on its own is known as baking soda, and is often used in baking to make bread or cakes rise. How do you think baking soda achieves this?

**Question 19** The pH of cola is about 3. What are the concentrations of hydrogen ions and hydroxide ions in this drink?

**Question 20** When carbon dioxide dissolves in water, some of it reacts as follows:

$$CO_2(aq) + H_2O(l) = HCO_3^-(aq) + H^+(aq)$$

This is an equilibrium reaction and only a little $H^+$ is formed. What are the implications of this reaction for the pH of fizzy drinks?

# Chapter 5
# Body building

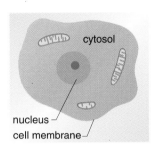

**Figure 5.1**
The main components of a body cell.

## 5.1 The human jigsaw

The human body is made up of about one hundred thousand million cells (Figure 5.1), each of which is so small that it can be seen only with a microscope. From a biological point of view, cells are the building blocks of all organisms. These cells are grouped together in the body to form tissues with specialized functions.

Some cells make up muscle or nerve tissue, some form connective tissue that binds the various organs of the body together, and some constitute the skeletal framework of bone. The complex chemistry that sustains life takes place within these cells, aided by a range of enzymes. Although each cell is built according to the same basic pattern, its function depends on what kind of tissue it is part of. This will determine what kind of chemistry it needs to perform, and this is controlled by using only a certain set of enzymes from the many available. Essentially, cells can be regarded as chemical factories – they process chemicals. Raw materials, in the form of amino acids, sugars and fats, are brought to the cell from the digestive system via the bloodstream.

Figure 5.2 shows how the heart pumps blood through the arteries. These divide into successively smaller tubes. The smallest of these are the capillaries, which allow the nutrients to diffuse into the surrounding cells ready for processing. The cell then gets to work on these raw materials, either building up new chemicals that are needed for growth or repair, or breaking them down to release energy. These processes obviously produce waste material and this is returned to the bloodstream for transportation and eventual disposal. In this Course our interest is not so much the details of the various cell activities, but the fate of the major nutrients in the blood.

As we mentioned earlier, proteins are polymers formed from amino acid monomers. Proteins are used as structural material and to control the chemistry that goes on in the cell. Thus one of the actions of our chemical factory, the cell, is to build up proteins from amino acids. These are not just any proteins, but the specific proteins, with the correct sequences of amino acids, that are required for a particular function in the human body.

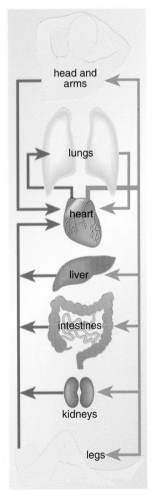

**Figure 5.2**
Circulation of the blood in the human body.

■ Why do you think the body first breaks down proteins in food then builds them up again in cells?

■ In food the proteins will have a wide range of structures, depending on the needs of the various organisms that the food consists of. The proteins in humans have a different primary structure – sequence of amino acids – from those even in other animals. So the body needs to break all the various forms of protein down into their monomers and then build up different forms according to its own blueprint.

Fats and sugars provide the main source of energy in the body, although protein can also be used for this purpose. When they are eaten, sugars such as glucose dissolve in the bloodstream for transport to muscles where the energy is required. However, not all of the energy is required straight away, and thus these materials need to be stored for subsequent use before the next meal or as a long-term store in case of food shortage. The glucose monomers are converted into polymers known as glycogen, shown in Figure 5.3a. These are very large molecules with a structure similar to amylopectin, where chain branching occurs every 18–20 glucose units, as shown in Figure 5.3b. Glycogen is present in humans in the muscles and the liver.

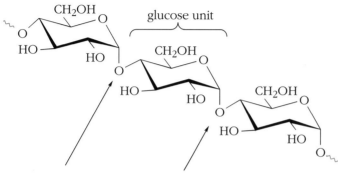

oxygen linking glucose units together

(a)

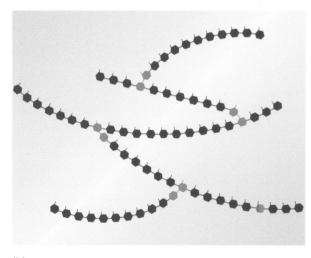

**Figure 5.3**
The structure of glycogen: (a) detailed molecular structure; (b) how the chains of glucose units (hexagons) are linked and branched.

(b)

A well-nourished male may contain several hundred grams of glycogen, about a quarter of which is stored in the liver. When the muscles and liver can accommodate no more glycogen, the surplus glucose is converted by the liver into fatty acids, which are stored in the fat deposits in the body, predominantly the adipose tissue. Excess fats are also stored in the adipose tissue, which lies under the skin in muscle, around deep blood vessels, and in mammary glands. It accounts for about 15 kg of the total body weight of a normal adult. As well as providing energy, fats are used as structural material, to form the membrane around each cell.

During a chemical reaction matter is neither created nor destroyed. This means that the material we eat must be disposed of in some way otherwise we would continually get bigger and bigger. We have seen that the undigestible, unwanted components of food that are not absorbed by the body end up in faeces. But what happens to the chemicals that are absorbed? As we shall see in the next Section, much of the carbon is released from the body as carbon dioxide, and the hydrogen and oxygen get converted into water and excreted as urine.

Unlike glucose and fats, amino acids cannot be stored in the body. Once absorbed, the amino acids are used to make proteins, and any excess is 'burnt off'. About 10% of the body's energy demands are met by amino acids. In diets low in protein, less is used in this way and the body's structural requirement for amino acids is met by recycling existing material.

▨     From what you have learnt so far, can you predict the products of 'burning off' amino acids, such as glycine, $NH_2-CH_2-COOH$?

▰     You have learnt that the carbon will be converted into carbon dioxide and the hydrogen and oxygen into water, but what happens to the nitrogen?

In most land mammals the nitrogen finally ends up in urea (**5.1**), which is a water-soluble compound that is excreted in the urine. In many aquatic animals the nitrogen is excreted as compounds containing the ammonium ion, $NH_4^+$.

$$H_2N \diagdown \atop H_2N \diagup C=O$$

**5.1**

Whatever the nutrient, we can write a balanced chemical equation for its oxidation, for example:

$$C_6H_{12}O_6 + 6O_2 = 6CO_2 + 6H_2O \tag{5.1}$$

$$C_{13}H_{27}COOH + 20O_2 = 14CO_2 + 14H_2O \tag{5.2}$$

Such equations could represent the combustion of sugars and fats in oxygen or the *overall* oxidation that goes on in the body.

▨     What do these balanced chemical equations tell us about the reaction mechanism, the individual steps that lead to the overall chemical change?

▰     As we saw in Book 2, the balanced equation is concerned only with the starting materials and the final products. In all cases, the balanced equation says nothing of the complexity of the reaction mechanism.

As you might expect, the combustion of fats and sugars in oxygen, and the oxidation that goes on in the body, follow very different mechanisms. In the body the oxidation is carried out in a very controlled manner, so that the energy released can be used most effectively. The mechanisms for such reactions in the body, known as biochemical pathways, are very complex indeed. A great deal of effort goes into their study and we are beginning to understand some of their chemistry. So, whenever we write equations such as 5.1 or 5.2 to describe the materials that we take into the body and how they are excreted, we must always be aware that there are many complex series of reactions that go on in the body to bring about this transformation.

When we use arrows to represent chemical transformations, for example

$$C_6H_{12}O_6 + O_2 \longrightarrow CO_2 + H_2O \tag{5.3}$$

no attempt is made to balance the number of atoms on each side of the arrow, so these expressions cannot be used for molar calculations. With very complex reactants, to have to balance the equation every time or to show every single product becomes very tedious. Quite often we are interested only in what happens to one particular reactant, and the fate of the other reactants is not so important. In such cases, we use the representation shown in Equation 5.4, where the other reactant, oxygen in this case, is placed on the arrow.

$$C_6H_{12}O_6 \xrightarrow{O_2} CO_2 + H_2O \tag{5.4}$$

▪ Use both these arrow representations to describe what happens to the amino acid glycine, $H_2N-CH_2-COOH$, when it is oxidized in the body.

▪ In the earlier discussion we saw that amino acids were oxidized to carbon dioxide, water and urea. So we can represent this either as:

$$H_2N-CH_2-COOH + O_2 \longrightarrow CO_2 + H_2O + H_2N-CO-NH_2$$

or as

$$H_2N-CH_2-COOH \xrightarrow{O_2} CO_2 + H_2O + H_2N-CO-NH_2$$

We shall use such representations more frequently later in the Course.

## 5.2 Energy conversion

In the last Section we examined how the fuel in our foods, that is glucose, fats and to some extent amino acids, is absorbed and transported to the cells in tissues such as muscles. In such tissues these compounds essentially react with oxygen to release energy. In this Section we shall examine how much energy is obtained in these processes and how efficient the energy conversion is. Then we shall examine in detail how oxygen gets into the body and is transported to the appropriate cells.

### 5.2.1 Counting the calories

The main fuels in the body are sugars and fats, which are oxidized to give carbon dioxide and water. These processes are exothermic. To gain some idea of the overall energy change for a given fuel, we can make estimates based on average bond enthalpies (an experimental approach could also be used, as described in Book 2). For the purposes of this Chapter we shall treat an overall energy change and an overall enthalpy change as similar quantities. To start with, we need a balanced equation for the transformation that we are interested in.

■    Without looking back to Equations 5.1 and 5.2, balance the following equations:

$$C_6H_{12}O_6 + O_2 = CO_2 + H_2O$$

$$C_{13}H_{27}COOH + O_2 = CO_2 + H_2O$$

■    The balanced equations are

$$C_6H_{12}O_6 + 6O_2 = 6CO_2 + 6H_2O \tag{5.1}$$

$$C_{13}H_{27}COOH + 20O_2 = 14CO_2 + 14H_2O \tag{5.2}$$

We shall work together through the calculation for the oxidation of glucose, then you should try the calculation for the fatty acid on your own. First we need to remind ourselves of a couple of features of such calculations:

●    If we are using average bond enthalpies to calculate an enthalpy change, then it is assumed that all reactants and products are in the gas phase. However, in the body glucose is dissolved in aqueous solution, and so we must bear this in mind when we come to compare our estimate with experimental values.

●    The calculation is carried out in molar terms and based on the balanced chemical equation exactly as it is written.

■    The structures of the two reactants in this reaction are given in Figure 5.4. How many of each type of bond are required to be broken to convert the reactants into individual atoms? You can use the model of glucose you made earlier to help you with this – but don't break it up because you will need it again later.

■    In glucose there are five C—C bonds, seven C—O bonds, seven C—H bonds and five O—H bond that need to be broken. Each of the six oxygen molecules contains one O=O bond, thus there are six O=O bonds to be broken.

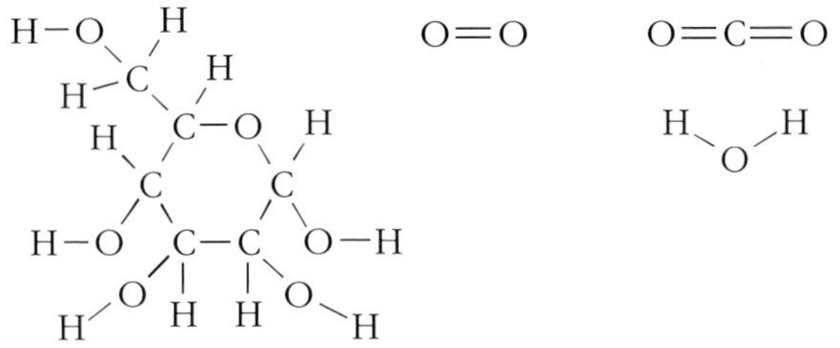

**Figure 5.4**
Structures of the reactants and products in the oxidation of glucose.

■    The structures of the two products in this reaction are also given in Figure 5.4. How many of each type of bond are required to be made to produce the products from their atoms?

■    Each of the six carbon dioxide molecules contains two C=O bonds, thus there are twelve C=O bonds to be made. By similar reasoning, there are twelve O—H bonds to be made.

The average bond enthalpy data are listed in Table 5.1. We shall follow the approach taken in Book 2 and so the calculation will be carried out in three distinct steps as described overleaf.

**Table 5.1** Average bond enthalpies of selected bonds

| Type of bond | Average bond enthalpy |
|---|---|
| single carbon–carbon; C—C | 330 kJ |
| carbon–hydrogen; C—H | 416 kJ |
| oxygen–hydrogen; O—H | 463 kJ |
| single carbon–oxygen; C—O | 327 kJ |
| double oxygen–oxygen; O=O | 498 kJ[a] |
| double carbon–oxygen; C=O | 804 kJ |

[a] Not strictly an average, because it is always the same.

1    The first step is to deal with the bonds that are broken.

| Bonds broken | Enthalpy change |
|---|---|
| 5 × (C—C) | 5 × 330 kJ = 1 650 kJ |
| 7 × (C—O) | 7 × 327 kJ = 2 289 kJ |
| 7 × (C—H) | 7 × 416 kJ = 2 912 kJ |
| 5 × (O—H) | 5 × 463 kJ = 2 315 kJ |
| 6 × (O=O) | 6 × 498 kJ = 2 988 kJ |
|  | Total    12 154 kJ |

2    In the second step we deal with the bonds that are formed.

| Bonds formed | Enthalpy change |
|---|---|
| 12 × (C=O) | 12 × (–804 kJ) = –9 648 kJ |
| 12 × (O—H) | 12 × (–463 kJ) =  –5 556 kJ |
|  | Total    –15 204 kJ |

Already in this step we can see that forming twelve C=O bonds is going to have a marked influence on the overall *exothermic* nature of the oxidation.

3    In the final move we determine the overall enthalpy change by adding together the totals in steps 1 and 2.

$$\Delta H = 12\,154\,\text{kJ} + (-15\,204\,\text{kJ})$$
$$= 12\,154\,\text{kJ} - 15\,204\,\text{kJ}$$
$$= -3\,050\,\text{kJ}$$

As expected, the negative sign confirms this is an exothermic reaction. Thus –3 050 kJ is the estimated enthalpy change on oxidizing one mole of glucose molecules in the gas phase. As already indicated, we can consider this to be similar to the overall energy change.

■    What is the estimated heat released by oxidizing 1.00 g of glucose?

■    We shall follow the method given in Section 6.2 of Book 2. The proposed thermochemical equation is:

$$C_6H_{12}O_6(g) + 6O_2(g) = 6CO_2(g) + 6H_2O(g) \qquad \Delta H = -3\,050\,\text{kJ}$$

The relative molecular mass of glucose of molecular formula $C_6H_{12}O_6$ is $\{(6 \times 12.0) + (12 \times 1.01) + (6 \times 16.0)\}$, which is 180.1.

Thus one mole of glucose molecules has a mass of 180.1 g.

Our calculation based on Equation 5.2 shows that one mole of glucose molecules (180.1 g) releases on oxidation 3 050 kJ of heat.

Thus the estimated heat released, which can be taken to be similar to the energy released, when 1.00 g of glucose is oxidized to give carbon dioxide and water is 3 050/180.1, which is 16.9 kJ.

The experimental value for the combustion of 1.00 g of solid glucose is 15.54 kJ, which is very close to the estimated value.

■ What assumptions have we made in the calculation which may explain the small difference between the two values?

■ The calculation assumed everything was in the gas phase, whereas the experimental value used solid glucose. Secondly, average bond enthalpies were used. The individual bond enthalpies in glucose will be slightly different from the average values.

■ The average value for the heat released per gram of carbohydrate was given in Book 2 as 17 kJ. This value is very similar irrespective of whether the fuel is a monosaccharide, disaccharide or polysaccharide. Why do you think this is so?

■ As we saw in Chapter 2, all carbohydrates are made up of sugar units. These basic building blocks have very similar structures. So on a mass-for-mass basis, all carbohydrates contain roughly the same number of sugar units and thus the same numbers of C—C, C—O, C—H and O—H bonds. Thus, it is not surprising that the heat released per gram is similar.

## Activity 4  Energy released from myristic acid

You should now calculate the energy released when 1.00 g of myristic acid, $C_{13}H_{27}COOH$, reacts with oxygen to give carbon dioxide and water (Equation 5.2). The structures of the reactants and products are given in Figure 5.5.

In fact it is the triglyceride that is used for the fuel in the body, but this even more complex molecule would make the calculation quite hard. The use of the fatty acid in the calculation does not lead to that big a difference in the result.

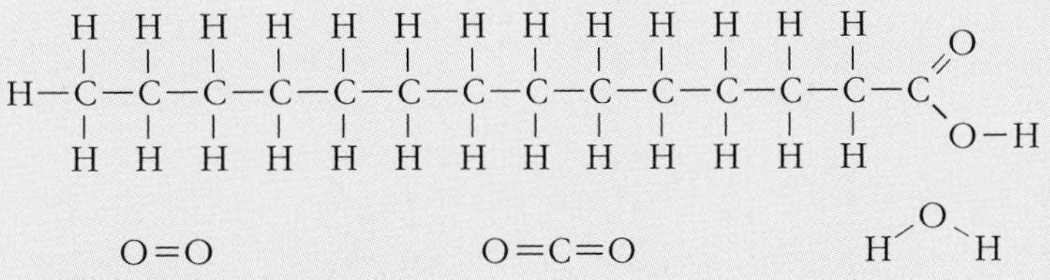

**Figure 5.5**
Structures of the reactants and products in the oxidation of myristic acid

Because the balanced thermochemical equation applies equally well to either the combustion of a nutrient in the air or its oxidation in the body, both processes release the same amount of energy. The path taken between reactants and products does not affect the overall energy released.

Table 5.2 lists the experimental values for the energy released per gram on combustion of various nutrients. Also included are the values for the energy available for use by the body from a gram of nutrient in food. These values are lower than the other values because of incomplete absorption of some nutrients during digestion, so not all the nutrient is oxidized.

**Table 5.2** Average energy released per gram of nutrients.

| Nutrient | Energy released on combustion/kJ | Available energy value/kJ |
| --- | --- | --- |
| carbohydrate | 17 | 17 |
| fat | 40 | 37 |
| protein | 24 | 17 |

■   What do you notice about the size of the energy per gram for the different nutrients?

■   The most striking aspect of Table 5.2 is how much more energy per gram is obtained from fat than from carbohydrate and protein.

This difference in energies explains why 'fat-free' diets are often recommended. The average person needs to eat sufficient food to provide about 11 000 kJ of energy per day. If you eat more food than is needed to provide this energy then it is stored as fat. Thus, you can eat twice as much protein and carbohydrate to achieve this figure as you can fat. Because you are eating twice as much material you do not feel so hungry.

Our estimation of the enthalpy change for these two reactions gives us a clue to why these values are so different. In Book 2, we saw that the key factor in the release of energy on combustion of a fuel is the formation of carbon–oxygen double bonds and oxygen–hydrogen bonds, with relatively high bond enthalpies, at the expense of carbon–carbon and carbon–hydrogen bonds, with relatively low bond enthalpies. The structure of glucose shows that it is already partially oxidized, with fewer carbon–carbon and carbon–hydrogen bonds for oxidation, so it is not surprising that less energy is released per gram.

■   An average person uses about 11 000 kJ of energy per day. Using the energy change for the oxidation of myristic acid calculated in Activity 4, and assuming that the energy available to the body is the same as the energy released, how many moles of molecules of myristic acid are needed each day to provide the energy needs of the average person?

■   On oxidation, each mole of myristic acid molecules releases about 8 400 kJ of energy. If this is the same as the energy available to the body, then 11 000 kJ will be provided by 11 000/8 400 moles, that is about 1.31 mol of the fatty acid.

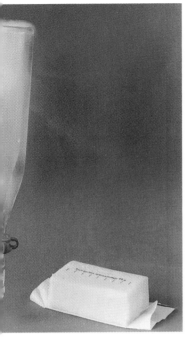

**Figure 5.6**
A pack of lard and a pint
and a half of liquid oxygen.

This calculation shows that 1.31 mol, or about 300 g, of myristic acid, are required to provide the average daily requirement of energy. This is equivalent to a pack of lard (Figure 5.6), not a very healthy or appetizing meal!

▪ Based on Equation 5.2, how much oxygen is needed to provide this daily amount of energy?

▪ Equation 5.2 shows that twenty moles of oxygen molecules, $O_2$, are consumed for each mole of myristic acid, $C_{13}H_{27}COOH$. Because 1.31 mol of myristic acid molecules would need to be consumed each day, then 26.2 mol of $O_2$ molecules would be required.

The relative molecular mass of oxygen is $(2 \times 16.0)$, that is 32.0.

One mole of $O_2$ has a mass of 32.0 g, so 26.2 mol have a mass of $26.2 \times 32.0 = 838$ g of oxygen.

This mass is a truly remarkable figure: three times as much oxygen is required as fat. If we had to take in our oxygen in liquid form it would be equivalent to drinking a pint and a half of oxygen a day (Figure 5.6). Since oxygen is a gas it tends to be the forgotten partner in such oxidation reactions, but as this calculation shows it needs to be provided in large quantities.

---

## Activity 5  Energy in food

Knowing the energy available per gram for the various kinds of nutrient (Table 5.2), we can calculate the energy value of a food, providing its composition is known. For example, the energy content of milk is calculated in Table 5.3. Using a similar tabular method, calculate the energy content per 100 g of the foods in Figure 5.7.

**Table 5.3** Energy content of a pint of milk calculated from its constituents.

| Nutrient | Mass of nutrient per pint | Average available energy per gram of nutrient | Energy available from the nutrient in a pint |
|---|---|---|---|
| protein | 18.9 g | 17 kJ | 321 kJ |
| fat | 22.8 g | 37 kJ | 844 kJ |
| carbohydrate | 26.8 g | 17 kJ | 460 kJ |
| | | Total | 1 625 kJ |

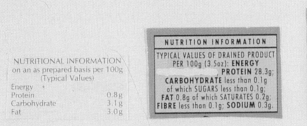

**Figure 5.7**
Labels showing the composition of tinned soup, tuna fish, and prunes. The energy values have been blanked out.

■   Is energy created in the body from nutrients?

■   No. Energy cannot be created in a chemical reaction, it can only be transformed from one form into another. When a fat or sugar reacts with oxygen to give carbon dioxide and water, the various changes the molecules undergo lead to a release of energy.

■   Where do you think this energy ultimately originated from?

■   As we saw in Book 2, all energy contained in food ultimately comes from the Sun.

Plants absorb sunlight and use this energy to make sugars, such as glucose, from carbon dioxide and water. This process is known as **photosynthesis**.

$$6H_2O + 6CO_2 = C_6H_{12}O_6 + 6O_2 \qquad\qquad (5.5)$$

Notice that this is the reverse of a sugar reacting with oxygen to give water and carbon dioxide.

■   What is the enthalpy change for Equation 5.5?

■   We can take it to be opposite to the enthalpy change for the combustion process. Based on our previous estimate for the process, it follows that $\Delta H$ is $+3\,050\,kJ\,mol^{-1}$.

Based on Equation 5.5, we can calculate that for every 1.0 g of sugar formed, 1.1 g of oxygen are also produced. The sugar formed is either stored as starch, which is used to make cellulose, the structural material of plants, or oxidized. The energy released on oxidation is used by the plant to make proteins and fats from simpler materials. If the plant is eaten by an animal, then the animal uses these stores of energy to live and to build up its own stores of fat, carbohydrate and protein. We then come along and eat both plants and animals – but irrespective of the  type of food, the energy still came originally from the Sun.

Eating meat is not a particularly efficient method of using our valuable resource of energy. An animal needs to eat plants with an energy content of 5 kJ to produce meat with an energy content of 1 kJ. The missing 4 kJ of energy is consumed in the various processes needed to keep the animal alive, as well as the chemical processes involved in the conversion of plant material into meat. Thus for every 1 kJ of energy we get from meat we could have got 5 kJ of energy if we could eat the plants themselves. Should grain be used so inefficiently to produce meat for consumption in the West whilst certain areas of the world have insufficient grain?

## 5.3  Oxygen in the right place at the right time

■   Table 5.4 shows the major components of air. Which are the important gases for life?

■   As we have seen, oxygen is required to oxidize food to generate energy, and carbon dioxide is needed for photosynthesis, giving oxygen back again.

**Table 5.4** The major components of dry air (the water content can vary depending on the humidity).

| Component | Percentage composition by volume | Percentage composition by mass |
|---|---|---|
| nitrogen | 78 | 76 |
| oxygen | 21 | 23 |
| argon | 0.93 | 1.3 |
| carbon dioxide | 0.033 | 0.050 |
| neon | 0.0018 | 0.0012 |
| helium | 0.00052 | 0.000072 |
| krypton | 0.00011 | 0.00031 |
| hydrogen | 0.00005 | 0.0000035 |
| methane | 0.00020 | 0.00011 |

In the previous Section, we discussed how oxygen is used in our bodies to oxidize fats, sugars and proteins to provide energy. However, so far we have not discussed how the oxygen gets from the air into the cells where this reaction takes place. Well, as you might expect, the key organ is the lung. When we breathe in, the lungs expand, as shown in Figure 5.8. Thus air enters the body through the nose or mouth.

**Figure 5.8**
These radiographs show how the lungs expand when we breathe in: (a) breath out; (b) breath in.

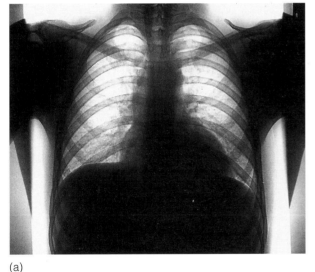
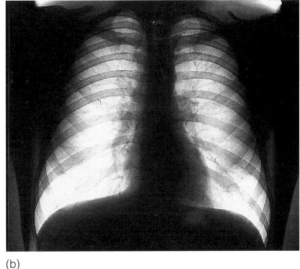

(a)　　　　　　(b)

The structure of the lungs is quite complex and we do not need to go into too much detail. However, the important components are the numerous capillaries on the surface of the lungs, which contain blood that can come into contact with the inhaled air and thus provide a route for oxygen to get into the bloodstream. It can then be transported to the various sites where it is needed for reaction with fats or sugars.

In fact, the oxygen does not simply dissolve in the blood. The oxygen molecules become attached to a large protein-based molecule called

**haemoglobin**, which is dissolved in the blood. This is the form in which the oxygen is transported through the blood vessels to the muscle, where it is transferred to another molecule called myoglobin, which makes it available for reaction with the fat or glucose, as shown in Figure 5.9. Haemoglobin also plays a vital role in the transport and removal of the product of oxidation, carbon dioxide. When the carbon dioxide gets back to the lungs it is released and expelled in the air we breathe out. Haemoglobin and myoglobin are both large proteins that contain an iron atom. The iron is surrounded by four nitrogen atoms arranged in a square. It is at this iron site that the oxygen is attached, as shown in Figure 5.10.

**Figure 5.9**
Schematic diagram of the transport of oxygen through the body (Hb represents haemoglobin and Mb represents myoglobin).

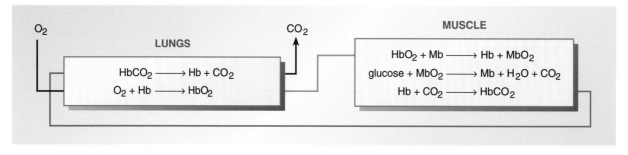

LUNGS

$$HbCO_2 \longrightarrow Hb + CO_2$$
$$O_2 + Hb \longrightarrow HbO_2$$

MUSCLE

$$HbO_2 + Mb \longrightarrow Hb + MbO_2$$
$$glucose + MbO_2 \longrightarrow Mb + H_2O + CO_2$$
$$Hb + CO_2 \longrightarrow HbCO_2$$

**Figure 5.10**
Stereoscopic model showing how oxygen binds to the iron atom in haemoglobin.

■ About 2 g of iron, half of the mass in the body, are bound up in haemoglobin molecules in the bloodstream. Assuming that one molecule of oxygen, $O_2$, is attached to each atom of iron, and that at any one time only half the haemoglobin molecules have oxygen bound, what mass of oxygen is circulating in the bloodstream at any one time?

■ Only half the iron atoms in the haemoglobin in the blood have an oxygen molecule attached at any time. This corresponds to 1 g of iron atoms.

The relative atomic mass of iron is 55.8, thus one mole of iron atoms has a mass of 55.8 g.

1.0 g of iron corresponds to 1/55.8 mol, that is 0.02 mol of iron atoms.

If each of these atoms of iron has one molecule of oxygen attached, then 0.02 mol of oxygen molecules, $O_2$, will be attached

The relative molecular mass of oxygen is $2 \times 16.0$, which is 32.0.

One mole of oxygen molecules has a mass of 32.0 g, thus 0.02 mol of oxygen molecules has a mass of $0.02 \times 32.0$, which is about 0.6 g of oxygen.

### Box 5.1  Meat

Most of the meat we consume comes from the muscles of animals. There are two types of muscle constituent, red fibres and white fibres. Whether meat has a light or dark colour depends on the amount of each type present. Red muscle fibres must sustain long periods of activity so fat is stored around these muscles as an energy source. Oxygen is needed also and so these cells are high in myoglobin, hence the red colour. White fibres are found in muscles that are needed to be active for only a short period of time. These cells use sugar circulating in the blood as a source of energy so there is little fat. They also do not need so much oxygen, so there is less myoglobin and they are lighter in colour. The leg muscles of poultry are continuously used so require high levels of myoglobin, hence the meat is dark and contains large stores of fat. The breast muscles of the bird are used for flight, which in chickens is quite rare, so the levels of myoglobin are low and the meat is pale in colour with little fat.

Oxygen is needed continuously in the body in energy-releasing reactions. Oxygen has no long-term store in the body, unlike fats and sugars, thus it must be continuously provided by the lungs. If the oxygen supply to the body is stopped for more than two or three minutes then the oxygen in the blood is exhausted and some important reactions in the body are halted, resulting in death.

To finish our discussion of how oxygen is transported in the body, we shall examine the structures of myoglobin and haemoglobin in a little more detail. Myoglobin has the structure shown in Figure 5.11. As with all proteins it is a long chain made up of amino acid residues.

- Draw the generalized structure of an amino acid residue.

- The structure is as follows:

$$\sim\!\!\sim\!\!\sim\!\! HN-\underset{\underset{H}{|}}{\overset{\overset{R}{|}}{C}}-\overset{\overset{O}{\|}}{C}-\!\!\sim\!\!\sim\!\!\sim$$

There are twenty or so different side-chains, R. In some amino acids these are polar groups and in others they are non-polar.

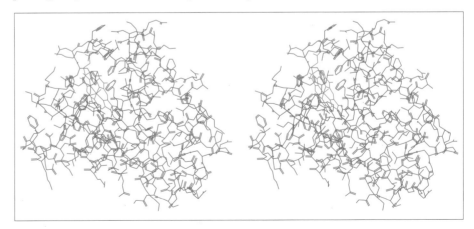

**Figure 5.11**
Stereoscopic framework model of myoglobin. The fragment shown in Figure 5.10, with the iron atom, is highlighted.

In myoglobin, as in many globular proteins, virtually all the amino acid residues that point towards the centre of the myoglobin have non-polar side chains whereas many of the side chains on the outside of the molecule are polar. Thus, myoglobin resembles an oil-drop in an emulsion: the non-polar groups of myoglobin stay in the middle and the polar groups stay on the outside, in contact with the water. The iron atom is at the bottom of a crevice in the molecule – the oxygen doesn't just attach itself to the molecule randomly, it has to fit inside a specially made pocket. Haemoglobin has a similar structure to myoglobin, except that it is made up from four separate protein molecules each similar to myoglobin, as shown in Figure 5.12. It is estimated that, in evolutionary terms, haemoglobin developed from myoglobin about 700 million years ago.

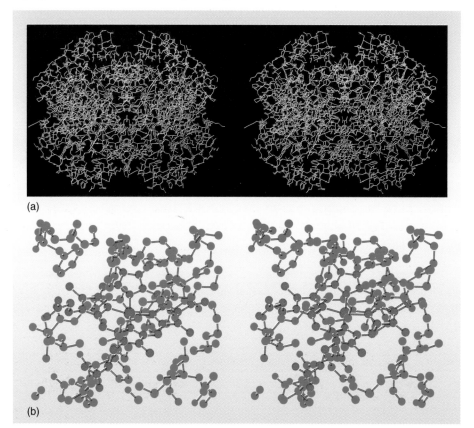

(a)

(b)

**Figure 5.12**
Stereoscopic framework models of (a) haemoglobin and (b) one of the four oxygen-binding sites in haemoglobin. The four separate protein molecules are in different colours in (a). Each sub-unit has an oxygen-binding site (highlighted), one of which is expanded in (b).

Oxygen is attached to haemoglobin in the lungs to form oxyhaemoglobin, which is transported in the blood. The oxygen is released from the oxyhaemoglobin in the muscles:

haemoglobin + oxygen $\rightleftharpoons$ oxyhaemoglobin        (5.6)

this side favoured in muscle        this side favoured in lungs

This is another example of an equilibrium reaction. In the lungs the position of equilibrium of this reaction lies to the right-hand side of the equation, that is the product is favoured. Oxygen reacts with haemoglobin to give oxyhaemoglobin. The oxyhaemoglobin is then transported by the bloodstream to the muscles. In the muscles the position of equilibrium of this reaction changes to the left-hand side of the equation. Thus the reactants are favoured and the oxyhaemoglobin breaks down to give back the reactants, haemoglobin and oxygen. In fact it is the pH that determines the position of balance in this reaction. A higher pH in the blood of the lungs favours the uptake of oxygen, and a lower pH in the muscle favours the release of oxygen.

- What does this mean in terms of the relative hydrogen ion concentrations in the blood of the lungs and the muscle?

- We need a higher pH in the lungs than in the muscle, so the concentration of hydrogen ions should be lower in the lungs than in the muscle.

- When muscles 'burn' fat or carbohydrate, the product is carbon dioxide, which dissolves in water and, as we saw in Chapter 6, can react in the following way:

$$CO_2(aq) + H_2O(l) = H^+(aq) + HCO_3^-(aq) \qquad (5.7)$$

  Will this lead to an increase or decrease in the pH? How will this affect the position of balance of Equation 5.6?

- Reaction 5.7 will lead to an increase in hydrogen ions and a decrease in pH, favouring the release of oxygen in Equation 5.6.

The susceptibility of reaction 5.6 to changes in pH provides a method by which oxygen is supplied to the right place. When the muscles do work they 'burn' fats or carbohydrates, which requires a ready supply of oxygen. The product of this activity is carbon dioxide, which causes the blood in the vicinity of the muscle to be acidic. The associated decrease in pH results in the release of oxygen, which is just what the muscle needs to do more work.

Carbon monoxide can also bind to haemoglobin, in place of oxygen (see Box 5.2).

## Box 5.2 Binding to iron

Carbon monoxide is poisonous to humans because when it is inhaled it binds to the iron of the haemoglobin more strongly than oxygen, as shown in Figure 5.13, and prevents the oxygen from becoming bound. Thus, the level of oxygen in the blood falls and if it becomes too low the important reactions in the body stop, with a terminal effect! In fact, the binding of carbon monoxide changes the colour of haemoglobin from red to pink, which results in the pink colour

**Figure 5.13**
Stereoscopic model showing carbon monoxide binding to the iron atom in haemoglobin.

of victims of carbon monoxide poisoning.

Binding of small molecules to myoglobin also causes the colouration of meat. On standing, the myoglobin on the surface of the meat is denatured and the $Fe^{2+}$ ion is oxidized by the oxygen at the surface to an $Fe^{3+}$ ion. This gives rise to the characteristic colour change of meat from red to brown. The red or pink colour of uncooked bacon and ham is maintained by reaction of nitric oxide, NO, with the iron of the haemoglobin or myoglobin in the meat. The nitric oxide arises from the reduction of sodium nitrite, $Na^+NO_2^-$, which is used as a preservative. The colouration is quite stable, but on cooking the myoglobin is denatured to give a paler pink colour.

As we discussed earlier, the primary structure of a protein is important in determining its shape and its mode of action. Any mistakes in the primary structure can cause problems. Sickle cell anaemia arises when two of the four units that make up the haemoglobin are slightly different from normal. In each of these two units, the protein chain of 146 amino acid residues has the sixth amino acid residue, which came from glutamic acid, replaced by one from valine, as shown in Figure 5.14. This amino acid residue is sited on the surface of the protein. Valine has a hydrocarbon side-chain, which is non-polar, whereas the glutamic acid side-chain contains a COOH group, so is polar. Substitution of the polar glutamic acid by a non-polar valine (such an erroneous replacement is called mutation) reduces the number of polar groups on the surface of the protein. Thus, the protein does not interact with water so well, and this makes it less soluble. This leads to fibrous precipitates, which deform the red blood cells giving them their characteristic sickle shape, as shown in Figure 5.15.

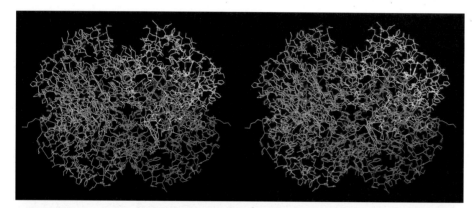

**Figure 5.14**
Stereoscopic framework model of sickle cell haemoglobin. Only the two sub-units coloured green and blue are altered from normal haemoglobin. In each of these chains only one amino acid residue is altered, and these are highlighted in red.

**Figure 5.15**
Deformed red blood cells in sickle cell anaemia.

Not only is the amount of haemoglobin in solution reduced, leading to anaemia, but the small blood vessels become blocked. This impairs the circulation, resulting in the failure of vital organs. The alteration of the side-chain of just one amino acid can have such a dramatic effect!

The frequency of sickle cell anaemia is found to be related to the incidences of malaria, and it is thought that the mutation provides protection against the most lethal form of malaria. People originating from central Africa are most likely to suffer from this hereditary disease. The presence of sickle cell anaemia can now be identified early in pregnancy, by looking for the substitution of glutamic acid by valine in the haemoglobin of the foetus. Parents who are at risk can thus make an informed decision as to whether to terminate the pregnancy.

## Box 5.3 Why don't we use the nitrogen we breath in?

Nitrogen is one of the key elements in amino acids and proteins – in the body there is about 2 kg of nitrogen. But where does this nitrogen come from? Elemental nitrogen, $N_2$, exists in almost limitless quantities in the atmosphere – about 80% of the air, as shown in Table 5.4. Unfortunately, the body is unable to make use of this source in making nitrogen compounds. We have to be supplied with nitrogen that has already been converted into a suitable form, usually as amino acids. Thus we have a rather paradoxical situation, that although we are surrounded by nitrogen, such compounds that contain nitrogen that we can use are scarce. The explanation for this is that nitrogen is fairly unreactive: it is difficult to convert the element into its compounds, a process known as fixation. Such fixation can be carried out commercially but it requires a great deal of energy. Fortunately, **nitrogen fixation** is performed with ease in nature, not by higher plants and animals, but by bacteria and blue-green algae. Some of these micro-organisms, such as *Rhizobium*, invade the roots of leguminous plants, such as clover, beans, peas and alfalfa, to form root nodules, shown in Figure 5.16. A symbiotic relationship exists between the plant and the micro-organism. The plant provides compounds from which the micro-organism can get energy and in return the micro-organism provides the plant with nitrogen compounds. Thus, organic farmers often rotate crops using leguminous plants to provide the soil with nitrogen. About $2 \times 10^{11}$ kg of nitrogen are fixed by micro-organisms each year!

**Figure 5.16**
Root nodules on clover.

## Summary of Chapter 5

This chapter has been concerned with the fate of the products of digestion. We have heard about their conversion into body material and how they are oxidized to release energy.

The reactions in the body are very complex. The simple balanced equations tell us nothing of the complicated reaction mechanisms. Arrows are sometimes used to represent transformations in organic chemistry and biochemistry.

Enthalpy changes that occur when nutrients are oxidized can be calculated using average bond enthalpies. Oxidation of fats releases far more energy than oxidation of carbohydrates, because carbohydrates are already partially oxidized.

Knowing the energy available per gram for each nutrient and the composition of a food, it is possible to calculate the energy content of the food.

Oxygen is attached to haemoglobin in the lungs, transported in the bloodstream, and then released at the muscles.

Sickle cell anaemia arises from the alteration of one amino acid residue in haemoglobin.

**Question 21** Whales are mammals that need to stay under the water for extended periods of time. The concentration of myoglobin in the muscle of a sperm whale is ten times that in human muscles. Why do you think this is?

# Chapter 6
# The chemist as food processor

In this Chapter we examine what the chemist can do to ensure a healthy diet. In particular we look at two foodstuffs, sweeteners and spreading fats. We examine the problems of using the 'natural' material and discuss ways in which the chemicals in the food can be modified to provide safer alternatives.

## 6.1  Towards a sweeter tomorrow

Sucrose, more commonly called sugar, is a common additive to our diet. It may be added as a pure compound to coffee and tea, or it may be already added in the preparation of a foodstuff, such as baked beans or cereal. The reason it is there is to improve the taste. Most people like the taste of sweet things and, until recently, sucrose has been the standard sweetener. There are many reasons why we may crave sweet-tasting foods, but essentially it results from evolution. Sucrose is a ready form of energy and thus it is advantageous for us to eat foods that are sweet. However, eating too much sweet food has associated problems: first, dental disorders, and second, weight gain, which can lead to further health problems. In this Section we shall look at how sugar is manufactured, then look at some of the disorders associated with eating too much sugar. We shall finish with an examination of alternative sweeteners and in particular how synthetic sweeteners are developed.

### 6.1.1  Sugar manufacture

Ordinary sugar is one of the chemically purest compounds that we can eat. This compound is present in many plants but there are two main sources used for isolation - sugar-cane, which is grown in tropical countries, and sugar-beet, which is grown in more temperate zones. In the UK about 60% of our sugar comes from sugar-beet. The beet is first shredded then the sugar is extracted using hot water. This gives a solution containing about 14% sucrose, together with a range of impurities. These impurities are removed by adding calcium hydroxide to the solution, which precipitates citric, tartaric and oxalic acids as their insoluble calcium salts. A clear solution is left, which is predominantly sucrose. Water is then evaporated from the solution.

■  What effect will the evaporation have on the concentration of sugar? What will happen after the concentration has reached the solubility of sugar?

■  As the water is removed so the concentration of sucrose increases because we have the same amount of solute but a smaller volume of solution. After the concentration reaches the solubility of sucrose, solid sucrose will crystallize out of solution.

The solid sucrose is filtered off from the remaining syrup, called molasses. This solid contains about 96% sucrose. The molasses is used for the manufacture of rum and industrial alcohol.

Sucrose can be obtained from sugar-cane in the same way. Sugar-cane is a giant grass of which sucrose is about 15% by mass. As with sugar-beet, the cane is crushed and extracted with water to give an aqueous solution, which is treated as before. Sugar-cane is a richer source of sugar: three to eight tonnes of sugar can be obtained from an acre of sugar cane whereas only two tonnes can be obtained from an acre of sugar beet.

The raw solid sugar obtained from cane and beet is still impure and needs further refining. The raw sugar is mixed with a sugar syrup to produce a semi-solid of syrup and crystals. The more soluble impurities in the raw solid dissolve in the water in the sugar syrup whereas the sucrose remains as crystals. Filtration again gives back the solid, which is washed with water to remove any adhering syrup.

■    Can you see a problem with washing the sugar crystals with water?

■    Washing with water will cause some of the solid sugar to dissolve in the water along with the syrup. This sugar can be recovered by evaporation of the water.

The crystals are then dissolved in water, and the solution is passed through a bed of charcoal, which removes any coloured impurities. The fine liquor, as it is known, is then concentrated by evaporation so that pure sucrose crystallizes out of solution. The remaining sugar syrup is then used for washing raw sugar as described earlier. Eventually, this syrup contains too many impurities so it is used to manufacture golden syrup or concentrated to give soft brown sugar.

### 6.1.2  The problems of eating too much sugar

As mentioned earlier, eating too much sugar provides too much energy and the body stores it first as glycogen then as fat, causing us to become overweight. The problem is that an individual eats the sugar because it tastes nice, not to take in more energy. As described in the next Section, the answer is to eat food that contains an artificial sweetener that satisfies our taste-buds, but does not increase our weight.

A second problem associated with eating too much sucrose is tooth decay. The relationship between tooth decay and sugar is well established. Teeth are commonly coated with a soft layer of bacteria called plaque. These bacteria convert sugars into carboxylic acids and it is these acids that attack teeth. Very shortly after we eat sugary things, acids are produced and the more sugar we eat the more acid is produced. Saliva neutralizes the acid to some extent but, if too much sugar is eaten, the pH becomes too low for neutralization by saliva. Much of the structural material of teeth is hydroxyapatite, $Ca_5(PO_4)_3(OH)$. In the mouth, the $OH^-$ of the hydroxyapatite reacts with the $H^+$ in the acid to give water.

$$OH^-(aq) + H^+(aq) = H_2O(l)$$

Removal of the hydroxide ion weakens the tooth structure, which eventually leads to tooth decay. The inclusion of fluoride, usually in the form of sodium fluoride, in the diet, results in a replacement of the hydroxide ion in the hydroxyapatite to form an acid-resistant fluoroapatite, $Ca_5(PO_4)_3F$, which doesn't react with the acid produced by the plaque and resists decay.

### 6.1.3 Synthetic sweeteners

One way to avoid tooth decay and getting fat from eating too much sucrose is to cut down your sugar intake. However, this would lead to less palatable foods. To encourage people to eat healthily, yet still enjoy sweet-tasting foods, a range of synthetic sweeteners that provide the satisfying taste without the extra calories has been developed.

Suppose you were put in charge of a new project to discover alternatives to sucrose. Spend a few moments thinking about how you would go about it. What particular tests or measurements would need to be set up to aid you in your quest?

For the rest of this Section we shall describe one possible way of attacking this problem. We shall illustrate it with examples of existing synthetic sweeteners.

***Define what you mean by sweetness and devise some scale for measuring it.***

If we are to discover new sweeteners in a logical fashion, then we need to define what we mean by sweetness and create some sort of scale by which we can compare the sweetness of different compounds. Unfortunately, in this case, there are no laboratory instruments that can be used to measure sweetness. Taste, like many of our senses, is difficult to define objectively. We have taste-buds on our tongues that respond to sucrose, but the brain interprets that response in a subjective way. Try to describe what you mean by sweetness without some comparison with other tastes! In the end, we have to rely on the human tongue as our measuring instrument. As a general laboratory rule we should never taste chemicals; however, flavour compounds must be tasted, but only after they have been shown to be safe. Since taste will vary from person to person, to avoid individual 'tastes', a large group of people should be surveyed. One way of doing this is to take a particular aqueous solution of sucrose as the standard, and then to vary the concentration of the material under test until it has an equivalent sweetness to the standard sucrose solution, as judged by a tasting panel. The relative concentrations then give a measure of the effectiveness of the sweetener – the sweetness value.

■ Suppose a $0.02 \, mol \, l^{-1}$ solution of our sweetener under test had the same sweetness as a $0.1 \, mol \, l^{-1}$ solution of sucrose. Would the test compound be more or less sweet than sucrose?

■ Because, on a molar basis, less of the test compound was needed than of sucrose to achieve the same taste, then the test compound is more sweet.

As the concentration of sucrose is five times more than that of the test compound, we say the test compound is five times more sweet than sucrose and it has a sweetness value of 5. Table 6.1 gives a list of compounds and their sweetnesses as defined by such a panel. Any test that relies on human response will be subjective and thus have an associated error. So, we should not treat the numbers with too much confidence, but such numbers do allow a relative measure of different materials to be defined.

**Table 6.1** Relative sweetnesses of various compounds: the values for naturally occurring compounds (left) are on a molar basis, and those for synthetic compounds (right) are on a mass basis.

| Compound | Sweetness relative to sucrose | Compound | Sweetness relative to sucrose |
|---|---|---|---|
| sucrose | 1.00 | cyclamate | 30 |
| glucose | 0.42 | aspartame | 200 |
| fructose | 0.90 | saccharin | 350 |
| lactose | 0.16 | acesulfame | 130 |
| | | P-4000 | 4000 |

■ How sweet are the sugars glucose, fructose and lactose compared with sucrose?

■ Most sugars are considerably less sweet than sucrose.

■ What kind of sweetness value should a potential sweetener have?

■ A sweetener should have a large value so that only a small amount needs to be added to a food to achieve the required sweetness, without affecting the other properties of the food.

This is demonstrated by the popular sweetener saccharin, which is 350 times more sweet than sucrose. One problem associated with this method of measuring sweetness is that no sweetener ever tastes quite the same as sucrose (Figure 6.1). For example, saccharin has a bitter, metallic after-taste, so it is hard to judge exactly its level of sweetness.

### How can we predict which compounds will be sweet?

Once we had established our method of measuring sweetness, if we were starting this project from scratch we probably would have first tested the natural sugars, then moved on to other compounds. How would we choose which of the millions of compounds to test? Historically, the discovery of synthetic sweeteners was rather hit and miss – a lot can be put down to luck or even bad laboratory practice. For example, saccharin was discovered by Constantin Fahlberg in 1879, after he accidently spilled some on his hand. Cyclamate was discovered in 1937 when Michael Sveda noticed its sweet taste on a cigarette he had temporarily set down on a laboratory bench. James Schlatter discovered aspartame in 1965 when he accidently got some on his hand and noticed its sweet taste when he licked his finger to pick up a piece of paper. In all these cases the compound was made for other reasons, and the sweet taste was a bonus.

More recently there has been a more logical strategy for sweetener discovery. The taste buds on the tongue are responsible for detecting sweetness (Figure 6.2). If we can find out how they work then we can start to design molecules with the required properties. It has been shown that the taste buds contain cavities called **receptor sites**.

**Figure 6.1**
A synthetic substitute for sucrose. Many such products contain blends of more than one sweetener, in an effort to mimic the taste of sucrose.

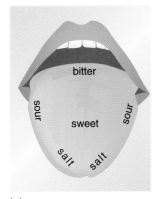

(a)

**Figure 6.2**
(a) Taste buds on different parts of the tongue detect different types of taste;
(b) an electron micrograph of the tongue surface: the taste buds are contained in the pink areas (magnification x 170).

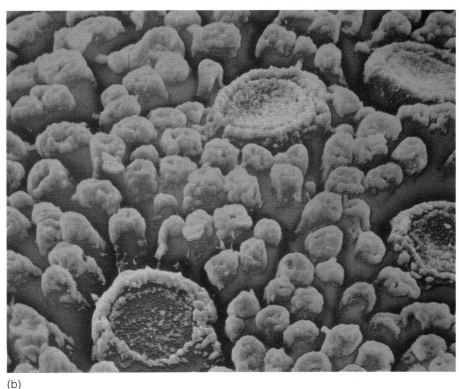

(b)

These receptor sites behave like the active sites in enzymes, in that they bind only specific molecules.

It is a fairly general rule that molecules are bound to receptors by the types of force that we discussed in Book 1. For example, if a receptor has an OH on the surface it could form a hydrogen bond to an oxygen or nitrogen atom in the binding molecule. This is shown schematically in Figure 6.3.

Attraction between oppositely charged atoms, as shown in Figure 6.4, is also significant in the context of receptor binding (although still weak compared with covalent bonds). Dipole–dipole interactions are also possible but much weaker, and London forces can also help binding. If there is a receptor with a large hydrocarbon region and a reactant molecule also with a long hydrocarbon chain, it may well happen that the two areas line up side-by-side, as a result of London forces.

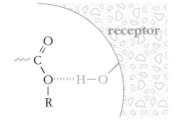

**Figure 6.3**
Hydrogen bonding in a receptor.

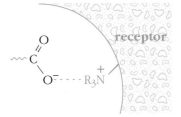

**Figure 6.4**
Attraction between ions in a receptor.

Each of these interactions is relatively weak (from 3 to 10% of the strength of a covalent bond) but a molecule can be held quite tightly in a receptor *if it is bound at more than one site*. The binding of a molecule to a receptor in at least two places, as shown in Figure 6.5, ensures that only molecules with appropriate geometries and types of atom can fit the receptor.

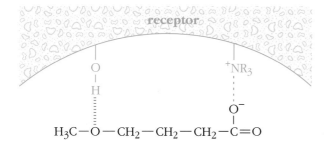

**Figure 6.5**
Binding at more than one site in a receptor.

When a molecule binds to a receptor a message is sent to the brain via the nervous system. In fact, as Figure 6.2a shows, there is a range of different receptors in the mouth that each detect a different kind of taste, such as sweetness, bitterness, sourness, etc. When a meal is eaten, most of the molecules will not be able to fit in the receptors so will not trigger any signals to the brain. However, if the right type of flavour molecule is present it will fit the receptor and a message will be sent. A particular type of food will contain a range of these flavour molecules present in different amounts, so each set of flavour receptors will be sending messages to the brain to different extents, giving rise to the flavour peculiar to that type of food. We shall examine the ideas of flavour and smell in more detail in Book 4.

It seems that the rational design of sweeteners simply requires us to discover the structure of the receptor site for sweetness, so that we can determine what type of molecule will fit. Unfortunately, this is not as simple as it sounds, because the protein that makes up the receptor will be present to only a small extent and mixed in with a whole range of other proteins on the tongue. Furthermore, trying to remove such a molecule from its environment on the tongue for study in the laboratory will simply lead to denaturation.

Although we can't get hold of the lock we do know what kind of key fits it. By examining the structures of a whole range of sweeteners, together with their potency, common structural elements can be identified.

This has led to a model of the chemical interactions by which sweet-tasting molecules bind to the taste receptor. First, the substance must be able to form two hydrogen bonds, as shown in Figure 6.6. In one hydrogen bond the substance shares its hydrogen with another atom on the receptor, and in the other hydrogen bond the shared hydrogen comes from the receptor. It seems to be important that the distance between the hydrogen on A and the atom B has a particular value, close to 300 pm. $\alpha$ Glucose has this arrangement, as shown in Figure 6.7. However, this in itself is not enough for a compound to taste sweet: there also needs to be a non-polar group at a particular distance from AH and B, as shown in Figure 6.8. This non-polar group could be a $-CH_2-$, as in fructose or sucrose, or part of a benzene ring, as in saccharin and aspartame (Figure 6.9).

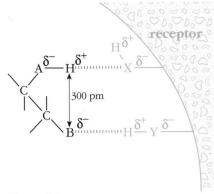

**Figure 6.6**
The binding of a sweet-tasting molecule to a receptor.

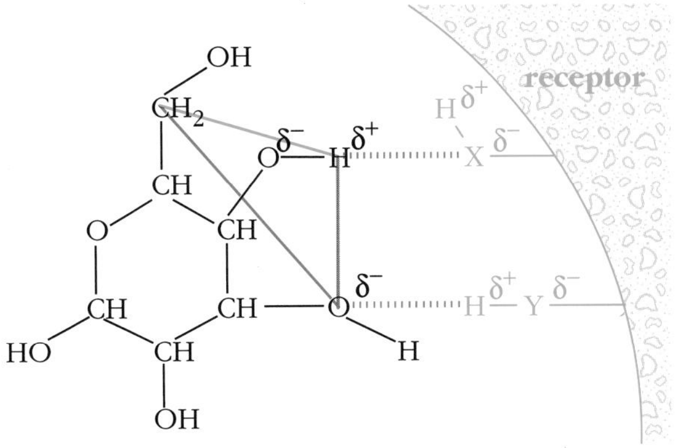

**Figure 6.7**
How α glucose may form hydrogen bonds to a receptor. The coloured lines relate to those in Figure 6.8.

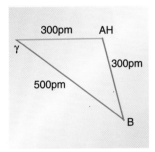

**Figure 6.8**
The relative positions of the two polar groups AH and B and the non-polar group (designated γ (gamma)) involved in binding sweet-tasting molecules to a receptor.

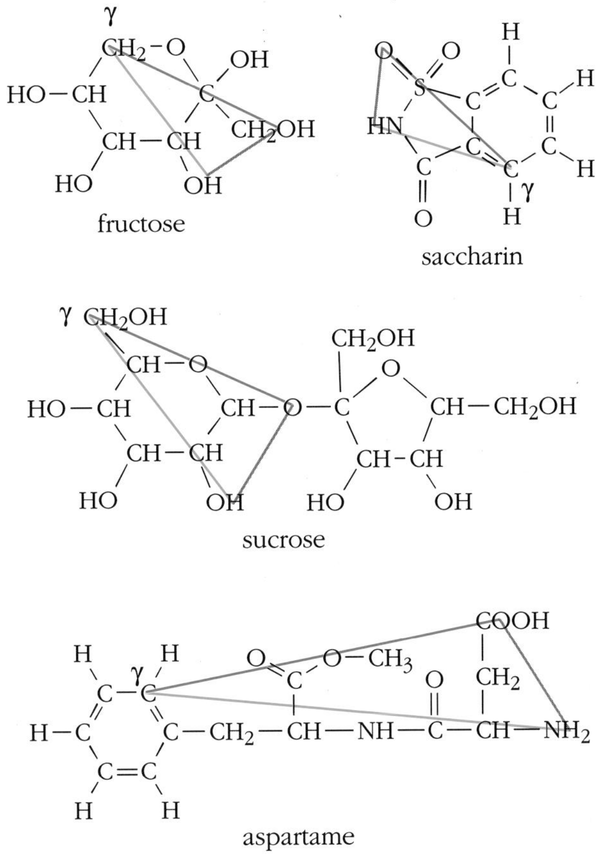

fructose

saccharin

sucrose

aspartame

**Figure 6.9**
The AH, B and γ binding sites in fructose, sucrose, saccharin and aspartame. The coloured lines relate to those in Figure 6.8 and the corresponding distances (they are not to scale because these are flat representations of three-dimensional structures).

## Activity 6  Measuring glucose

Use your model of the α form of glucose to confirm that the distances between the various centres are as shown in Figure 6.8. Use a ruler to measure the distances, and assume that 1 cm = 38 pm.

Armed with a knowledge of the key features of sweet-tasting molecules, it is possible to design new compounds that have similar dimensions. However, it must be stressed that although all sweet-tasting molecules have these features, the presence of such groups in a molecule does not guarantee that the molecule is a *good* sweetener. Other factors may come into play that reduce the binding of the molecule to the receptor. This rational design of biologically active molecules is extended later in this Book, and in Book 4, which discusses the use of computers to create such models.

We shall finish our discussion of replacements for sucrose with a brief review of artificial sweeteners currently in use. By 1900, saccharin had an annual production of about 200 tonnes, and shortages of sucrose during the two world wars led to its further widespread use. As mentioned earlier, it does have a bitter aftertaste, but this can be masked if it is combined with other sweeteners (Figure 6.1). Saccharin has no food value, and at various times doubts have been raised about its safety. In 1977 in Canada, it was removed from food and beverages because it was thought to be unsafe. Because no safer alternative sweetener was available, this action virtually destroyed the Canadian diet soft drink industry until aspartame became available in 1981. In fact, toxicological tests are inconclusive, and in most countries saccharin has a clean bill of health. The same is not true of cyclamate, which has a superior taste to saccharin. However, a single carcinogenicity test, involving feeding cyclamate to rats for two years, showed that they developed bladder tumours (Figure 6.10). It was therefore banned in the UK and the USA.

**Figure 6.10**
Do not feed this to rats!

Nevertheless, not everybody believed these data and so cyclamate is still available in some countries, including France and Holland. This again reflects the subjective way in which such tests are interpreted and the risks assessed.

Aspartame, or Nutrasweet (Figure 6.9), is the newest sweetener to be used on a large scale. Tests have shown it to be safe, and it has an excellent taste profile. It is particularly suitable for use with a wide range of foods because it tastes a lot like sucrose and blends well with other flavours.

*Omit this question as there aren't enough atoms in kit to make molecule of acesulfame.*

**Question 22** Acesulfame K goes by the trade name Sunett. It is used in soft drinks, desserts and puddings, as well as being sold as a sweetener for tea. Over 2 000 products worldwide contain it.

Use the model kit to make a model of acesulfame K. You will need five white centres, four black centres, four red centres, one blue centre with five holes, and one purple centre with four holes.

First, join two black carbon centres by two flexible bonds to form a carbon–carbon double bond. To one of these carbons add a third carbon by a short bond. To this latter carbon attach three white hydrogens by short bonds. To the other carbon of the double bond attach a hydrogen by a short bond and a fourth carbon by a short bond. The hydrogen should be *cis* to the CH₃ and the carbon *trans*. To this latter carbon attach a red oxygen via two flexible bonds to form a carbon–oxygen double bond. This should give you the model shown in Figure 6.11a.

Now take a blue nitrogen with five holes. Locate the three holes that are separated by 120° in a plane, and attach a hydrogen to one hole. Attach the carbon of the carbon–oxygen double bond to one of the three holes on the nitrogen. Take a purple centre with four holes and join this to the third hole of the nitrogen. This purple centre will represent the sulfur atom. It is quite difficult to model the double bonds from sulfur to oxygen, so just join two red oxygens to the purple centre by short bonds. Finally, complete the ring by joining a red oxygen to the purple sulfur and the carbon of the original carbon–carbon double bond to give the model shown in Figure 6.11b.

Use a ruler to obtain the distances between the binding sites 2 and 3 and 1 and 3 as shown in Figure 6.11c. Use the same conversion factor as before: 1 cm = 38 pm.

(a)

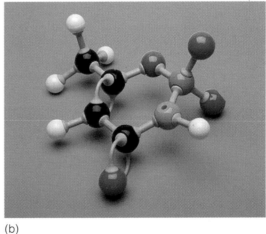

(b)

(c)

**Figure 6.11**
(a) Partial model of acesulfame K;
(b) complete model of the structure of acesulfame K;
(c) the structure of acesulfame, which binds through the sites 1 (γ), 2 (B) and 3 (AH).

**Question 23** Aspartame is not particularly good for cooking because it is prone to hydrolysis. What are the products of hydrolysis of aspartame? Why are the products not sweet-tasting?

## 6.2 The chemistry of fats and oils

In this Section we take a final look at the ways in which a knowledge of chemistry can help provide healthier foods: this time, fats and oils. Despite what you may think, these are some of the simplest molecules that make up our diet. A great deal of work has gone into analysing the chemicals in fats and oils, and using chemistry to modify their properties. We shall start by examining the structures of saturated and unsaturated fats and oils, and see what features make them good or bad for us.

### 6.2.1 Unsaturates – is it a mono or a poly?

- The label on a particular brand of real dairy ice cream states $100\,g$ contains $11.2\,g$ of fat, of which $7.2\,g$ are saturate and $0.2\,g$ polyunsaturate. What is the rest of the fat?

- If $7.2\,g$ are saturated fats, then $4.0\,g$ must be unsaturated fats. If $0.2\,g$ of this is polyunsaturated fats, then $3.8\,g$ must be monounsaturated fats.

As we discussed earlier, fats and oils are mixtures of triglycerides formed from the reaction of three fatty acid molecules with glycerol, as shown in Equation 6.1 for saturated fatty acids.

$$
\begin{array}{l}
CH_2-OH \\
| \\
CH-OH \quad + \ 3CH_3(CH_2)_nCOOH \ \longrightarrow
\end{array}
\quad
\begin{array}{l}
\ \ \ \ \ \ \ \ \ \ \ \ \ \ \ \ \ \ \ O \\
\ \ \ \ \ \ \ \ \ \ \ \ \ \ \ \ \ \ \ || \\
CH_2-O-C-(CH_2)_n-CH_3 \\
| \qquad\qquad\ O \\
| \qquad\qquad\ || \\
CH-O-C-(CH_2)_n-CH_3 \quad + \ 3H_2O \qquad (6.1)\\
| \qquad\qquad\ O \\
| \qquad\qquad\ || \\
CH_2-O-C-(CH_2)_n-CH_3
\end{array}
$$

- If the fat is formed from a range of different fatty acids, will the three fatty acids that lead to a single triglyceride molecule be identical?

- Possibly, but not necessarily. The triglyceride can be made from up to three different fatty acids. Given the fat is made from a mixture of fatty acids it is likely that most of the triglycerides will be derived from more than one type of fatty acid. However, the way the fatty acids are incorporated in triglyceride molecules is not random and will depend on the organism that made the fat.

- When we talk of a mixture being 50% saturated fats, do you think we mean that 50% of the triglyceride molecules are derived from *only* saturated fatty acids?

- No. Fats contain a range of triglyceride molecules. Although each will be derived from three fatty acids, there will be a variety of combinations of the different fatty acids. All three, two out of three, one out of three or none of the fatty acids used to make a triglyceride could be saturated, the others being unsaturated.

When we talk of a mixture being 50% saturated fats we mean that the overall mixture of triglycerides is derived from fatty acids, 50% of which are saturated. To make things simpler, when discussing the structure of saturated and unsaturated fats we shall focus on the fatty acid esters (Figures 6.12), that is we can concentrate on just one of the fatty acid tails. So when we talk about saturated and unsaturated fatty acid esters, we assume that they are part of a triglyceride that contains two other fatty acid esters, or tails.

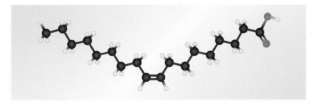

**Figures 6.12**
The general structure of fatty acid esters.

We noted in Chapter 1 that there may be a relation between high incidences of chronic heart disease and the intake of saturated fats. Figure 2.6 shows that this means we ought to eat less butter, lard and hard margarine, which are high in saturates, and eat more soft margarine, fish and plant oils, which are high in unsaturates. We shall now examine some of these unsaturated fats in detail.

### Monounsaturated fatty acid esters

By definition, monounsaturated fatty acid esters contain only one carbon–carbon double bond in their hydrocarbon chain. The carbon–carbon double bond is called the alkene functional group (see Box 6.1). An example of a monounsaturated fatty acid is oleic acid (Figure 6.13).

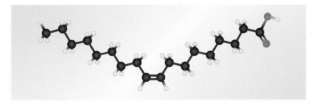

**Figure 6.13**
Ball-and-stick representation of oleic acid.

■   Oleic acid is a *cis* isomer, because the hydrogen atoms on the two carbon atoms of the double bond are on the *same* side of the double bond. Draw out the *trans* isomer of oleic acid.

■   The *trans* isomer is known as elaidic acid; its structure is shown in Figure 6.14. The hydrogens on the two carbon atoms of the double bond are on *opposite* sides of the double bond.

Unlike single bonds, rotation is not possible about double bonds, so *cis* and *trans* isomers cannot be easily interconverted. Compounds that have the same molecular formula and the same order in which the atoms are joined, but differ only in the spatial orientation of the atoms, are known as stereoisomers.

**Figure 6.14**
Ball-and-stick representation of the *trans* isomer of oleic acid, elaidic acid.

Stereoisomerism can have dramatic effects on the properties of a fat. As with other chemicals, the melting temperature of a fat depends on how well the triglyceride molecules pack together. The better they pack the closer they get, and the greater the forces between the molecules. The better the packing the higher melting temperature, since more energy is needed to break down the forces between the molecules. Table 6.2 shows that stearic and elaidic acid both have melting temperatures well above room temperature, implying that insertion of a *trans* double bond does not drastically change the way the molecules pack together.

**Table 6.2** Melting temperatures of triglycerides.

| Carboxylic acid | Comments on structure | Melting temp | Triglyceride | Melting temp |
|---|---|---|---|---|
| lauric acid | 12-carbon sat. | 44.2 °C | 3 lauric acids | 34 °C |
| myristic acid | 14-carbon sat. | 54.1 °C | 3 myristic acids | 44 °C |
| palmitic acid | 16-carbon sat. | 62.7 °C | 3 palmitic acids | 56 °C |
| stearic acid | 18-carbon sat. | 69.6 °C | 3 stearic acids | 64 °C |
| elaidic acid | 18-carbon unsat. 1 *trans* C=C | 43.7 °C | – | – |
| oleic acid | 18-carbon unsat. 1 *cis* C=C | 10.5 °C | 3 oleic acids | −13 °C |
| linoleic acid | 18-carbon unsat. 2 *cis* C=C | −5.0 °C | – | – |
| linolenic acid | 18-carbon unsat. 3 *cis* C=C | −11.0 °C | – | – |

Presumably, the presence of a *trans* double bond does not greatly change the shape of a molecule of a fatty acid, compared with the corresponding saturated compound. However, the presence of a *cis* double bond introduces a kink into the structure (Figure 6.15). Because of the kink the chains do not pack together quite so efficiently as those of the saturated compounds, and so the melting temperature is correspondingly lower. The monounsaturated fatty acids most commonly found in higher organisms have the double bond between the ninth and tenth carbon atoms (counting down the chain from the carboxylic acid group).

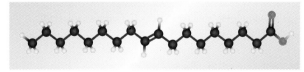

(a)

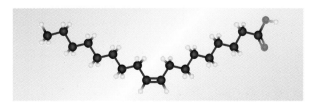

(b)

**Figure 6.15**
The effect of the presence of a *cis* (b) rather than a *trans* (a) double bond in a fatty acid hydrocarbon chain.

## Box 6.1 Alkenes

An example of an alkene is propene, which is probably more familiar to you when it is polymerized in polypropylene:

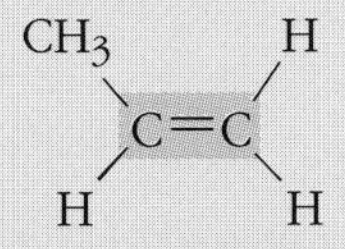

The alkene functional group, which is a carbon–carbon double bond, is highlighted in blue.

Other examples of alkenes are ethene and β-carotene:

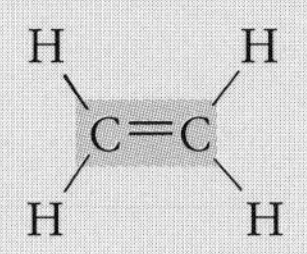

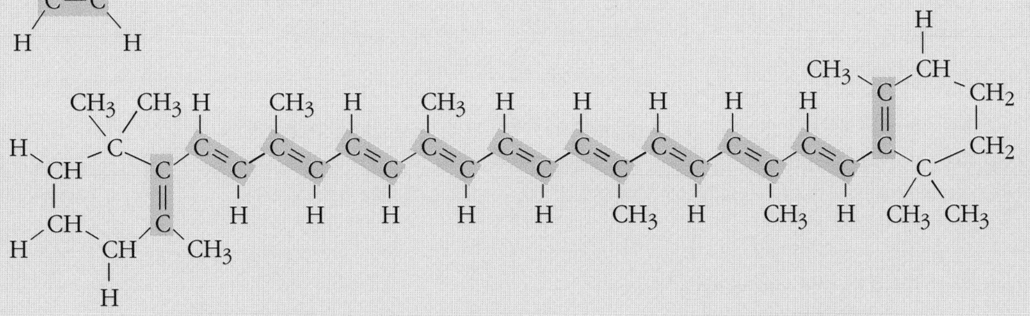

Ethene is the monomer that leads to polyethene. It is important in ripening fruit. Bananas give out a great deal of ethene and can be used to encourage the ripening of apples, tomatoes and avocados. β-Carotene, which contains eleven C=C double bonds, gives carrots their orange colour. It is also a major dietary source of vitamin A.

The generalized structure of alkenes, where $R^1$, $R^2$, $R^3$ and $R^4$ are other parts of the molecule, is:

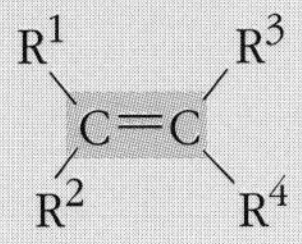

In propene $R^1$ is $CH_3$ and $R^2$, $R^3$ and $R^4$ are hydrogen.

### Polyunsaturated fats

As the name implies, polyunsaturated fatty acid esters are fatty acid esters with more than one double bond in a fatty acid chain. Some examples are given in Figure 6.16.

$$CH_3-CH_2-CH_2-CH_2-CH_2-CH=CH-CH_2-CH=CH-(CH_2)_7-COOH$$
linoleic acid

$$CH_3-CH_2-CH=CH-CH_2-CH=CH-CH_2-CH=CH-(CH_2)_7-COOH$$
linolenic acid

**Figures 6.16**
Two polyunsaturated fatty acids.

■ Do you think the triglyceride made from three oleic acids is a polyunsaturated fat? After all, the molecule contains three double bonds in the hydrocarbon chains.

■ No. The polyunsaturation refers to the fact that there is more than one double bond in a *single* fatty acid ester rather than in the triglyceride molecule as a whole.

In nature, the double bonds are predominantly *cis*, leading to kinks in the chains. In most polyunsaturated fatty acids one of the double bonds is usually found between the ninth and tenth carbon atoms, the other double bonds lying farther away from the COOH group.

As well as being nutritionally better for you than saturated fats, some of the polyunsaturated fatty acids (PUFA) are particularly important. In the late 1980s and early 1990s there was a trend towards fat-free diets. However, a truly fat-free diet could prove fatal. Fats are the only source of some essential fatty acids that the body needs for its operation, but which it cannot make itself. The most important of these is linoleic acid (Figure 6.16), which is found in large amounts in oil from corn, soya bean and sunflower seeds. We need somewhere between 2 and 10 g of linoleic acid per day. However, human deficiency is very rare. This compound is the starting material for the synthesis in the body of a range of important hormones known as prostaglandins, which are involved in inflammation and the contraction of smooth muscle. Another possible essential fatty acid is linolenic acid. The reason why it is referred to as a 'possible' essential fatty acid is because the amounts needed by the body are so small that it is difficult to determine whether it is essential or not. It may turn out that the body can make it from other fatty acids.

## 6.2.2 Isolation and refining of vegetable oils

We now turn our attention to how vegetable oils are extracted and purified ready for eating. Butter is manufactured from milk (cream) and lard is obtained by rendering (melting) pig's fat. Similarly whale and fish oil are obtained by rendering, or drying the fish, and extracting the fat with solvent. However, by far the most important sources of oils and fats are vegetables, so we shall spend some time examining how they are extracted and purified. Most vegetable oils are extracted from seeds, kernels or nuts either by mechanical pressure or by solvent extraction. This latter method uses the principle of 'like dissolves like'.

■   From what you know about the nature of oils and fats, what kind of solvent should be employed to extract fats?

■   Oils are non-polar. They do not dissolve in water, and so non-polar solvents should be used. In fact, hexane is normally employed.

After the seed or nut has been ground, it is shaken with the solvent, which dissolves the oil, leaving a solid residue. After filtration, the liquid solution is heated and the solvent evaporates, leaving the oil.

Once the crude oil has been extracted it is ready for refining. Most vegetable oils contain moisture, free fatty acids, colouring matter, resins, gums, and sometimes even vitamins. These impurities affect the flavour and odour of the oil. The refining process that removes these impurities involves a number of stages, as outlined below.

### *Degumming*

Some vegetable oils contain solid particles in suspension, which are removed by adding a little water and heating to about 70 °C. The mixture is then centrifuged, which involves spinning the oil round at high speed, so that the more dense particles, such as the gum formed with the water, are thrown to the bottom of the vessel, leaving an upper layer of clear oil.

### Neutralization

▨ What happens when water reacts with a triglyceride?

■ Hydrolysis occurs (Equation 6.2) to give, eventually, the free fatty acids and glycerol. This process occurs when fats are broken down in digestion. However, in the body the process is aided by enzymes.

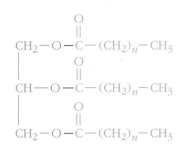

$$CH_2-O-C-(CH_2)_n-CH_3 \atop CH-O-C-(CH_2)_n-CH_3 \atop CH_2-O-C-(CH_2)_n-CH_3 \; + \; H_2O \longrightarrow CH_2-OH \atop CH-O-C-(CH_2)_n-CH_3 \atop CH_2-O-C-(CH_2)_n-CH_3 \; + \; CH_3-(CH_2)_n-C{\scriptstyle O \atop OH} \quad (6.2)$$

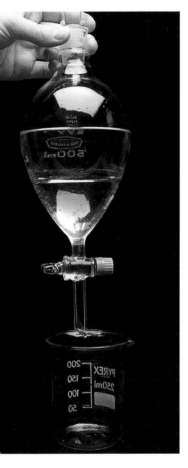

**Figure 6.17**
Demonstration of how an aqueous layer and an oily layer can be separated.

Although hydrolysis of oils and fats occurs very slowly in the absence of enzymes, none the less, depending on the history of the oil, substantial amounts of free fatty acids can be present. These can be removed by adding a solution of sodium hydroxide.

▨ What is the result of reaction between a fatty acid and sodium hydroxide?

■ A neutralization reaction occurs; that is, the acid and the base react together to give an ionic compound and water.

In chemical terms this can be represented as:

$$RCOOH + NaOH = RCOO^-Na^+ + H_2O$$

RCOOH is an acid because, as we saw earlier, it can donate $H^+$ ions.

▨ The ionic compound, $CH_3(CH_2)_nCOO^-Na^+$ is soluble in water, so how can it be removed from the oil?

■ Addition of water to the oil will give two separate layers. Because the salt is soluble in water and the oil is not, the salt moves out of the oil into the water layer.

These two layers can be separated, as shown in Figure 6.17, and the free fatty acid is essentially removed from the oil. Further washing of the oil with water removes any remaining traces of the ionic compound. The oil can then be dried with a solid that absorbs water such as magnesium sulfate. (Yes – liquids can be dried, since in chemical terms drying means the removal of water!)

### Bleaching and decolorization

For aesthetic reasons, most edible oils are required to be colourless. However, many crude oils are coloured because they contain natural pigments extracted from the plant. This coloured material can be removed by selectively adsorbing the molecules that cause the colour onto the surface of a solid. In practice, the oil is mixed with about 0.2–2.5% of clay. If the solid is filtered off, the coloured material is removed and the oil is colourless.

### Deodorization

Almost all edible fats are deodorized before they are consumed. The oil is heated in a tank under vacuum and steam is passed through the hot oil. The volatile odoriferous substances evaporate from the oil. This process is known as steam distillation and is carried out using either a batch process or a continuous flow process. In a **batch process** the fat is introduced into a large vessel and heated with steam for between three to eight hours. After this time the oil is cooled and then discharged from the vessel leaving the vessel ready to be charged with more fresh oil. So, as the name implies, each batch of oil is treated separately. In a **continuous flow process** the oil flows slowly through a series of processes, as shown in Figure 6.18. The length of time that the oil is treated with steam depends on the rate at which it flows from one vessel to the next. Because it is a continuous system the process does not need to be stopped and started. The untreated oil enters one end and the deodorized oil exits from the other. At this stage the oil is fairly pure and ready for use in cooking, although it is often blended with other oils to get the right properties. The oil can be also converted into a solid – margarine.

**Figures 6.18**
Flow diagram for the deodorization of oil.

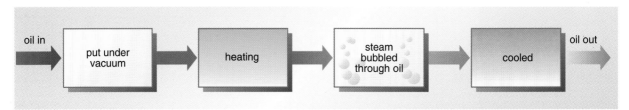

### 6.2.3 Spreading fats

Although butter and margarine are made from fats they also contain a good deal of water. An average butter contains about 15% water and margarine can contain up to 20% by mass of water.

- Both margarine and butter are emulsions. What kind of emulsion do you think they are, oil in water or water in oil?

- Since there is about 80% fat and 20% water by mass, the water is dispersed as tiny droplets in the fat.

- How do you think such an emulsion is stabilized?

- An emulsifier is added to stabilize the emulsion.

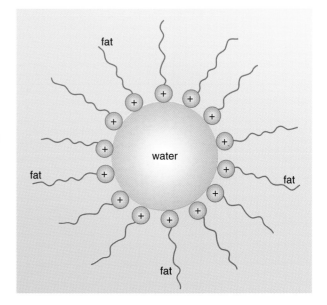

**Figure 6.19**
Emulsification of water in a fat.

Monoglycerides and lecithin are often used as emulsifiers. As we saw in Question 17, the emulsifier contains two types of environment, a polar region that interacts with the water and a non-polar region that interacts with the fat, as shown in Figure 6.19.

Margarine is made by mixing a fat and an emulsifier with fat-free milk to provide the water. Margarine has a minimum of 80% fat by mass, whereas low fat spreads contain 40–80%. The rest is water, still emulsified in the fat. So when we pay extra for a low fat spread we are paying for more water! Several different types of fat or oil are blended together to get margarine of the right consistency. The blend may contain animal, vegetable and fish oils and fats, depending on cost and availability. The oil or fat should have a bland taste and a wide temperature range at which it is spreadable. Unfortunately, solid fats with the correct consistency generally come from animals, so they are relatively expensive and there is insufficient for demands.

Consider the following three points and see if you can deduce how we can obtain spreading fats from plant materials.

1   The oils obtained from plants are cheap and plentiful; however, they are generally liquids, so vegetable oils cannot be used directly to make margarine.

2   Vegetable oils are liquids because they contain a large number of unsaturated fatty acid esters. Most unsaturated fatty acid esters involve *cis* double bonds, so the chains of carbon atoms are kinked. This means they do not pack together very well and so the triglyceride has a lower melting temperature. At room temperature a triglyceride with a high degree of unsaturation will be an oil. However, as we saw in Table 6.2, a saturated fatty acid ester with the same number of carbon atoms in the chain may pack together very well because the chain is not kinked, so the corresponding saturated triglycerides will be solid.

3   Using a metal catalyst it is possible to add hydrogen to an unsaturated fatty acid ester to make a saturated fat with the same number of carbon atoms.

The addition of hydrogen to an unsaturated oil will lead to some saturated fatty acid esters, which have higher melting temperatures. Thus more of the fat will crystallize. If this crystallization occurs to a sufficient extent a solid fat will be produced with the right consistency that can be emulsified with water.

This solution to the problem was discovered at the beginning of the 19th century and has developed into a modern industrial sector that produces 330 000 tonnes of margarine per year.

### 6.2.4 Reactions of unsaturated fatty acid esters

As we saw in Chapter 4, the functional group approach depends on the fact that saturated hydrocarbon chains are relatively inert to many chemical reactions, so the hydrocarbon chains in saturated fatty acid esters do not undergo many reactions. However, because unsaturated fatty acid esters contain an alkene functional group, these fats can undergo a number of reactions specific to double bonds. The most important reaction, which is characteristic of all double bonds, is an addition reaction (Box 6.2).

## Box 6.2 Addition reactions

An addition reaction is a general term used for the reaction where two atoms or groups of atoms are added across a double bond. Some typical addition reactions involving simple alkenes are as follows:

$$Br-Br \ + \ \underset{H \quad\quad H}{\overset{H \quad\quad H}{C=C}} \longrightarrow Br-\underset{\underset{H}{|}}{\overset{\overset{H}{|}}{C}}-\underset{\underset{H}{|}}{\overset{\overset{H}{|}}{C}}-Br$$

$$H-Cl \ + \ \underset{H \quad\quad H}{\overset{H \quad\quad H}{C=C}} \longrightarrow H-\underset{\underset{H}{|}}{\overset{\overset{H}{|}}{C}}-\underset{\underset{H}{|}}{\overset{\overset{H}{|}}{C}}-Cl$$

The general equation for an addition reaction is

$$X-Y \ + \ \underset{H \quad\quad H}{\overset{H \quad\quad H}{C=C}} \longrightarrow X-\underset{\underset{H}{|}}{\overset{\overset{H}{|}}{C}}-\underset{\underset{H}{|}}{\overset{\overset{H}{|}}{C}}-Y$$

The atoms X and Y may be the same (for example $Br_2$) or different (for example HCl).

Hydrogenation is the addition of hydrogen across a double bond to give a hydrocarbon. This time we use the generalized form of an alkene:

$$H-H \ + \ \underset{R^2 \quad\quad R^4}{\overset{R^1 \quad\quad R^3}{C=C}} \ = \ H-\underset{\underset{R^2}{|}}{\overset{\overset{R^1}{|}}{C}}-\underset{\underset{R^4}{|}}{\overset{\overset{R^3}{|}}{C}}-H \qquad (6.3)$$

In the presence of an acid catalyst, water can undergo an addition reaction with a double bond:

$$H_2O \ + \ \underset{R^2 \quad\quad R^4}{\overset{R^1 \quad\quad R^3}{C=C}} \ \xrightarrow[\text{catalysis}]{\text{acid}} \ H-O-\underset{\underset{R^2}{|}}{\overset{\overset{R^1}{|}}{C}}-\underset{\underset{R^4}{|}}{\overset{\overset{R^3}{|}}{C}}-H$$

The terms saturated and unsaturated arise from the fact that unsaturated compounds contains double bonds, which can react with reagents such as hydrogen. However, saturated compounds do not react – they are full up, or saturated, with hydrogen.

Margarine production involves hydrogenation, the addition of hydrogen across a double bond in the presence of a metal catalyst, as shown in Box 6.2 (Equation 6.3).

■ Draw out the reaction between oleic acid ester and hydrogen, $H_2$. What is the product?

■ This reaction is the conversion of the unsaturated fatty acid ester from oleic acid into the saturated fatty acid ester from stearic acid:

$$CH_3-(CH_2)_7-CH=CH-(CH_2)_7-COOR \ + \ H_2 \longrightarrow CH_3-(CH_2)_7-\underset{\underset{}{|}}{\overset{\overset{H}{|}}{CH}}-\underset{\underset{}{|}}{\overset{\overset{H}{|}}{CH}}-(CH_2)_7-COOR$$

or

$$CH_3-(CH_2)_{16}-COOR$$

So the unsaturated fats are converted into saturated fats and the melting temperature increases. The metal catalyst is usually platinum, palladium or nickel.

■ In general terms, how does a catalyst make a reaction go faster?

■ The catalyst provides an alternative faster reaction mechanism.

Like enzymes, the metal provides an environment where the reaction can take place. Just like enzyme catalysis, there are three stages, as shown in Figure 6.20. The first stage is the attachment of the reactants, hydrogen and the unsaturated compound, to the surface of the metal. This process is known as adsorption (not *ab*sorption) and takes place only at certain preferred areas of the solid surface, known as active centres, such that the two reactants are brought close together. The adsorption process involves forming bonds between the reactants and metal atoms on the surface of the metal, leading to a loosening of the H—H and C=C bonds. This weakening of the bonds enables the reactants to combine more readily. This is the second stage of the reaction, in which the products are formed. The last stage, which involves the product detaching from the surface, is known as desorption. This leaves the metal surface free to catalyse further reaction.

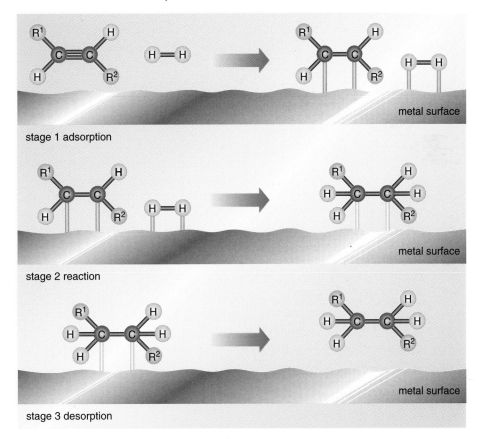

**Figures 6.20**
Hydrogenation catalysed at the surface of a metal.

Such catalysts, where reaction occurs at the surface of the metal, are one example of a general class known as heterogeneous catalysts. They are used a great deal in industry for a variety of reactions, and a wide range of metals is employed.

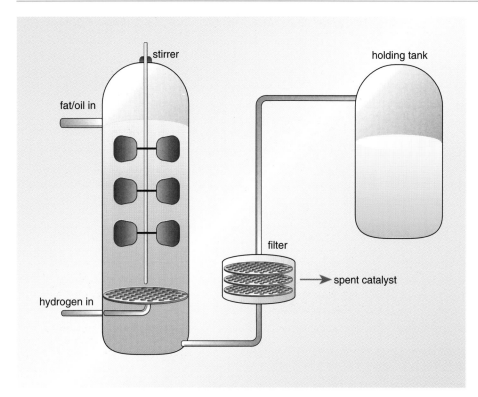

**Figures 6.21**
Flow diagram of margarine production.

Figure 6.21 shows a typical diagram of how this is carried out in industry. Finely divided nickel is added in small quantities to the refined unsaturated oil, which is stirred in large closed steel vessels called converters. The other reactant, hydrogen, is pumped in at the bottom of the converter. The reaction takes place at temperatures of above 170 °C and at high pressures, about 200–700 kPa (2–6 atm). Although the reaction mixture needs heating at first to get it up to temperature, the reaction is exothermic so further heating is not required. The reaction takes between one and four hours, depending on the degree of hydrogenation required. At the end of the reaction the converter is cooled, but not so much that the oil solidifies. The oil is filtered, to remove the solid nickel particles. Since the final product will be a solid at room temperature, these manipulations need to be carried out at a sufficiently high temperature for the oil to remain fluid.

Figure 6.22 shows another interpretation of the process of margarine production. You should now be in a better position to judge the fairness of such a view.

# TYPICAL PROCESS FOR MANUFACTURING MARGARINE.

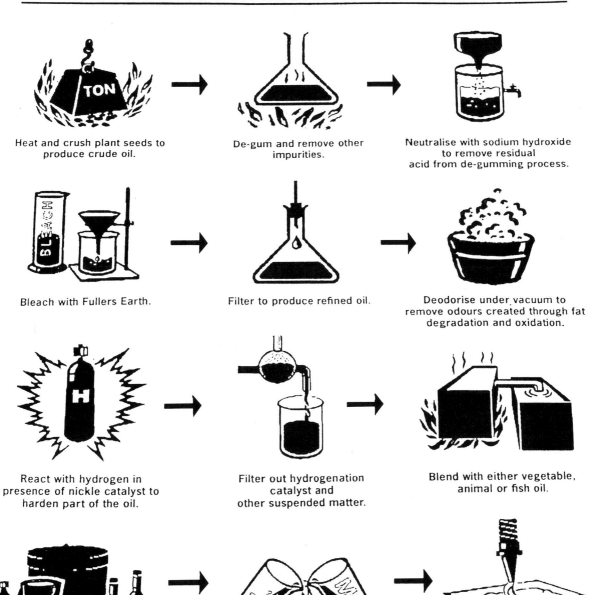

Heat and crush plant seeds to produce crude oil.

De-gum and remove other impurities.

Neutralise with sodium hydroxide to remove residual acid from de-gumming process.

Bleach with Fullers Earth.

Filter to produce refined oil.

Deodorise under vacuum to remove odours created through fat degradation and oxidation.

React with hydrogen in presence of nickle catalyst to harden part of the oil.

Filter out hydrogenation catalyst and other suspended matter.

Blend with either vegetable, animal or fish oil.

add whey, colouring, flavouring and vitamins.

Add Lecithin and Monoglycerine to emulsify.

Extrude into plastic tub.

**Figure 6.22**
Illustration from an advert to promote butter.

## Summary of Chapter 6

This Chapter has been concerned what we chemists can do to ensure a healthier diet.

Sugar (sucrose) is extracted from sugar-cane or sugar-beet, then purified by crystallization.

The sweetness value of a synthetic sweetener can be determined by a panel of tasters who establish what concentration of sweetener is comparable with a standard solution of sucrose.

Synthetic sweeteners can be designed by identifying common structural elements in existing sweeteners.

Fats and oils can be isolated by solvent extraction, degumming, neutralization, bleaching and deodorization.

Addition is a reaction common to most carbon–carbon double bonds. It involves a reaction in which two atoms or groups of atoms are added across a double bond.

Hydrogenation involves the addition of hydrogen to a double bond using a metal catalyst. Thus, two unsaturated carbons are converted into saturated carbons.

Margarine is manufactured from oils by hydrogenation. The presence of more saturation raises the melting temperature of the triglycerides so the oil becomes more solid.

**Question 24** Predict the products of the following reactions of oleic acid.

$$CH_3-(CH_2)_7-CH{=}CH-(CH_2)_7-COOH \quad + \quad HCl \quad \longrightarrow \quad ?$$

$$CH_3-(CH_2)_7-CH{=}CH-(CH_2)_7-COOH \quad + \quad H_2O \quad \xrightarrow[\text{catalysis}]{\text{acid}} \quad ?$$

**Question 25** What is the problem in predicting what will happen when one mole of molecules of linoleic acid reacts with one mole of hydrogen molecules, $H_2$?

$$CH_3-(CH_2)_4-CH{=}CH-CH_2-CH{=}CH-(CH_2)_7-COOH \quad + \quad H_2 \quad \longrightarrow \quad ?$$

linoleic acid

# Objectives for Book 3 Part 1

After you have studied Book 3 Part 1 you should be able to do the following:

1       Understand the meaning of the words emboldened in the text.

2       Describe briefly the types of chemical that are needed to maintain a healthy body and the relationship between diet and health.

3       Recognize fats, proteins and carbohydrates and comment on their structures and properties.

4       Describe the functional group approach; given a table of functional groups, identify functional groups and R groups in a given organic molecule.

5       Recognize simple organic reactions such as condensation, hydrolysis and addition; given a product or reactant, identify the corresponding reactant or product of one of these reactions.

6       Describe briefly the structure, function and mechanism of action of enzymes.

7       Describe and provide an explanation of the solubility of carbohydrates, fatty acids, fats and gases in water.

8       Use the Brønsted definition to identify acids and bases. Explain the basis of the pH scale and the difference between strong and weak acids.

9       Understand the importance of three-dimensional shape in organic molecules and in particular its role in binding to a receptor or an enzyme.

10      Given a purification procedure, explain the basis of the various steps used to extract a chemical from a natural source.

11      Understand the relationship between food and energy and life. Perform simple calculations to estimate the energy associated with a particular foodstuff.

# Comments on Activities

## Activity 1

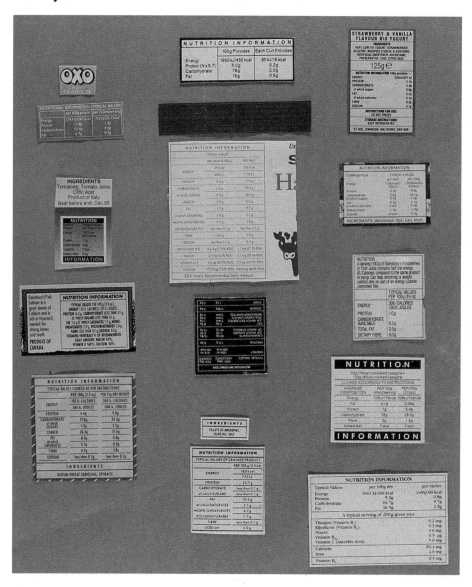

**Figure A1**
Nutritional information listed on the wrappings of a variety of foods.

Figure A1 shows the nutritional contents of a range of foods, as described on their wrappings. The foods I looked at listed the nutritional information in a number of ways, but there were some common headings. Based on my chemical knowledge I have grouped them together according to the type of chemical (Table A1). Although you would not be expected to list them in this way at the moment, I hope you will understand this classification by the time you have finished the first half of this Book.

**Table A1**  Common headings for the nutritional content of food.

| Main heading | Possible subheadings |
| --- | --- |
| energy | |
| protein | |
| carbohydrates | of which sugars<br>added sugar<br>available carbohydrate<br>starch<br>fibre |
| fat | of which saturates<br>of which monounsaturates<br>of which polyunsaturates |
| vitamins | thiamine, riboflavin, niacin, folic acid, vitamin $B_{12}$,<br>vitamin C, vitamin D |
| minerals | salt<br>sodium<br>calcium<br>iron |

You may have included additives such as flavourings or preservatives in your list, after all they often appear on the *contents* of a packet. However, they have no nutritional value so do not appear in the nutritional information on the wrapping. They are there simply to make the food more palatable or to help it keep better.

## Activity 3

As we saw in Book 2, an acid can be defined as a substance that yields hydrogen ions, $H^+(aq)$, in aqueous solution, and a base is a substance that yields hydroxide ions, $OH^-(aq)$, in aqueous solution.

The acidity of the stomach arises from the presence of hydrochloric acid, HCl, which ionizes in water into separate ions, $H^+(aq)$ (since it is an acid) and $Cl^-(aq)$.

Assuming that the milk of magnesia dissolves to give $Mg^{2+}(aq)$ and $OH^-(aq)$ ions it can be defined as a base.

Acids and bases react together to give water, and we could write the balanced equation:

$$Mg^{2+}(aq) + 2OH^-(aq) + 2H^+(aq) + 2Cl^-(aq) = Mg^{2+}(aq) + 2Cl^-(aq) + 2H_2O(l) \quad (A1)$$

However, the simplest kind of chemical equation is one that gives us the *bare essentials of the chemical changes that occur.* In Equation A1, the ions $Mg^{2+}(aq)$ and $Cl^-(aq)$ appear on both sides of the equation. This means that they are not changed by the reaction. Thus if they are removed from *both* sides of the equation, it will still remain balanced, and still correctly describe the chemical change that has occurred:

$$2H^+(aq) + 2OH^-(aq) = 2H_2O(l)$$

which can then be written as

$$H^+(aq) + OH^-(aq) = H_2O(l)$$

This is the standard equation for a neutralization reaction in which the $H^+(aq)$ from the acid reacts with the $OH^-(aq)$ from the base to form our old friend water. When we take milk of magnesia this consumes some of the hydrogen ions, removing the excess acid in the stomach that causes the indigestion.

In fact, $Mg(OH)_2$ is fairly insoluble in water and so we take it as a suspension. In this case a better equation to describe the neutralization is:

$$Mg(OH)_2(s) + 2H^+(aq) = Mg^{2+}(aq) + 2H_2O(l)$$

The insoluble magnesium trisilicate my father took reacted in the same way.

## Activity 4

First, we need to estimate the enthalpy change for the reaction:

$$C_{13}H_{27}COOH(g) + 20O_2(g) = 14CO_2(g) + 14H_2O(g)$$

If we are using average bond enthalpies to calculate an enthalpy change then it is assumed that all reactants and products are in the gas phase. However, myristic acid, $C_{13}H_{27}COOH$, is a liquid at body temperatures and so we must bear this in mind if we compare our estimate with experimental values.

*Bonds to be broken in the reactants*

In myristic acid there are 27 C—H bonds, 13 C—C bonds, one C=O double bond, one C—O bond and one O—H bond that need to be broken. Each of the 20 oxygen molecules contains one O=O double bond, thus there are 20 O=O bonds to be broken.

*Bonds to be formed in the products*

Each of the 14 carbon dioxide molecules contains two C=O double bonds, thus there are 28 C=O bonds to be made. By a similar reasoning, there are 28 O—H bonds to be made.

First we need to remind ourselves of one or two features of such calculations:

1   The first step is to deal with the bonds that are broken

| Bonds broken | Enthalpy change |
|---|---|
| $13 \times$ (C—C) | $13 \times 330$ kJ = 4 290 kJ |
| $1 \times$ (C—O) | $1 \times 327$ kJ = 327 kJ |
| $1 \times$ (C=O) | $1 \times 804$ kJ = 804 kJ |
| $27 \times$ (C—H) | $27 \times 416$ kJ = 11 232 kJ |
| $1 \times$ (O—H) | $1 \times 463$ kJ = 463 kJ |
| $20 \times$ (O=O) | $20 \times 498$ kJ = 9 960 kJ |
|  | Total     27 076 kJ |

2   In the second step we deal with the bonds that are formed.

| Bonds formed | Enthalpy change |
|---|---|
| $28 \times$ (C=O) | $28 \times (-804$ kJ) = -22 512  kJ |
| $28 \times$ (O—H) | $28 \times (-463$ kJ) = -12 964 kJ |
|  | Total     -35 476 kJ |

3   In the final move we determine the overall enthalpy change by adding together the 'totals' in 1 and 2 above.

$$\Delta H = 27\,076\,kJ + (-35\,476\,kJ)$$
$$= 27\,076\,kJ - 35\,476\,kJ$$
$$= -8\,400\,kJ$$

Thus the proposed thermochemical equation is:

$$C_{13}H_{27}COOH(g) + 20O_2(g) = 14CO_2(g) + 14H_2O(g) \quad \Delta H = -8\,400\,kJ$$

Now we can work out the heat released per gram.

The relative molecular mass of myristic acid of molecular formula $C_{14}H_{28}O_2$ is $\{(14 \times 12.0) + (28 \times 1.01) + (2 \times 16.0)\}$, which is 228.3.

Thus one mole of myristic acid molecules has a mass of 228.3 g.

Our calculation shows that one mole of myristic acid molecules (228.3 g) releases 8 400 kJ of heat.

Thus the estimated heat released when 1.00 g of myristic acid is oxidized to give carbon dioxide and water is 8 400/228.4, which is 36.8 kJ, which can be taken to be similar to the energy released.

### Activity 5

Tables A2, A3 and A4 show the calculations for the soup, tuna fish, and prunes, respectively.

**Table A2**  Energy content of chicken and mushroom soup, calculated from the constituents.

| Nutrient | Mass of nutrient per 100 g | Average available energy per gram of nutrient | Energy available from the nutrient in 100 g |
|---|---|---|---|
| protein | 0.8 g | 17 kJ | 14 kJ |
| fat | 3.1 g | 37 kJ | 115 kJ |
| carbohydrate | 3.0 g | 17 kJ | 51 kJ |
| | | | Total 180 kJ |

**Table A3**  Energy content of tuna fish, calculated from the constituents.

| Nutrient | Mass of nutrient per 100 g | Average available energy per gram of nutrient | Energy available from the nutrient in 100 g |
|---|---|---|---|
| protein | 28.3 g | 17 kJ | 481 kJ |
| fat | 0.8 g | 37 kJ | 30 kJ |
| carbohydrate | 0.1 g | 17 kJ | 2 kJ |
| | | | Total 513 kJ |

**Table A4** Energy content of prunes, calculated from the constituents.

| Nutrient | Mass of nutrient per 100 g | Average available energy per gram of nutrient | Energy available from the nutrient in 100 g |
|---|---|---|---|
| protein | 1.1 g | 17 kJ | 19 kJ |
| fat | 0.0 g | 37 kJ | 0 kJ |
| carbohydrate | 23.3 g | 17 kJ | 396 kJ |
| | | | Total 415 kJ |

## Activity 6

Figure A2 shows the model with a ruler. The distance between the oxygen and the hydrogen depends on the rotation about the O—C bond. However, the most stable position is when the hydrogen is pointing directly away from the plane of the ring, when the distance to the oxygen is about 8 cm (Figure A2a). This corresponds to an interatomic distance of about 300 pm. Thus glucose can achieve the required distance of 300 pm. The distance from the oxygen to the $CH_2$ (the $\gamma$ group) was about 13 cm (Figure A2b), which corresponds to about 500 pm, again in agreement with Figure 6.8. The distance between the $CH_2$ and the hydrogen was also measured as roughly 8 cm.

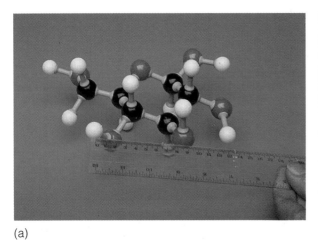

(a)

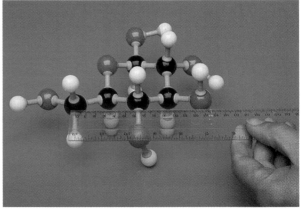

(b)

**Figure A2**
Distances measured on the model of glucose.

# Answers to Questions

**Question 1** Table 1.1 shows that in the average 70 kg person there are 45.5 kg of oxygen, 12.6 kg of carbon and 7.0 kg of hydrogen.

45.5 kg of oxygen correspond to $45.5 \times 10^3/16.0$ mol of oxygen atoms, which is $2.84 \times 10^3$ mol.

12.6 kg of carbon correspond to $12.6 \times 10^3/12.0$ mol of carbon atoms, which is $1.05 \times 10^3$ mol.

7.0 kg of hydrogen correspond to $7.0 \times 10^3/1.01$ mol of hydrogen atoms, which is $6.9 \times 10^3$ mol.

In terms of mass, oxygen is the most abundant element of the three and hydrogen the least. However, in terms of the number of moles, hydrogen is the most prevalent. This emphasizes why we must always quote the basis on which the percentage is calculated.

**Question 2** Sugar is a food you may consume that contains only one nutrient. If you look on a bag of sugar it lists only carbohydrate, with no fat or protein. Another food you may have identified is table salt, which provides only minerals.

**Question 3** Figure 1.2 shows that if you eat only biscuits you consume mainly carbohydrates, which will provide energy but do not help with growth and repair or control of body processes. Thus, after a while on this diet, you may well become ill. Of course this depends on which biscuits you eat, because those containing fruit could also provide some minerals and vitamins. Nevertheless, this is not a diet to be recommended!

**Question 4** Table 1.8 shows that each minute of brisk walking uses up 21 kJ of energy. A Mars bar provides 1 200 kJ of energy, so you would need to walk for 1 200/21, that is 57 minutes to use up this energy.

**Question 5** A compound is chemically pure if it is impossible to detect contaminants, or if their level is such that the substance behaves as if it were pure. Lemonade clearly contains carbon dioxide, and the fact that it fizzes when the bottle is opened shows it does not behave like pure water. Milk is opaque, so it must contain other compounds and does not behave like pure water, which is transparent. Some table salt is pure in that it contains only sodium chloride. Other types of table salt have anti-caking agents added, so they would not be chemically pure. Black coffee is not pure because the water contains compounds from the ground coffee beans that give it a dark colour.

**Question 6** In Figure A3 the ester groups are highlighted in blue.

**Figure A3**
The ester groups of the three compounds.

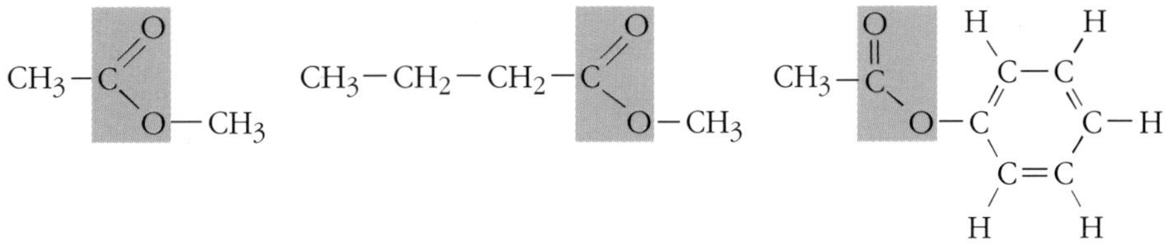

Equation A3 shows the generalized equation for the formation of esters.

$$R^1-OH \; + \; R^2-\overset{\displaystyle O}{\underset{\displaystyle OH}{C}} \; = \; R^2-\overset{\displaystyle O}{\underset{\displaystyle O-R^1}{C}} \; + \; H_2O \tag{A3}$$

Equations A4 to A6 show how each ester would be formed using this reaction.

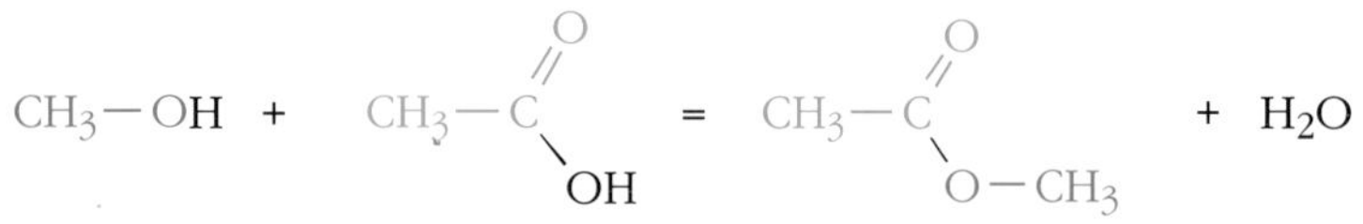

$$CH_3-OH \; + \; CH_3-\overset{\displaystyle O}{\underset{\displaystyle OH}{C}} \; = \; CH_3-\overset{\displaystyle O}{\underset{\displaystyle O-CH_3}{C}} \; + \; H_2O \tag{A4}$$

$$CH_3-OH \; + \; CH_3-CH_2-CH_2-\overset{\displaystyle O}{\underset{\displaystyle OH}{C}} \; = \; CH_3-CH_2-CH_2-\overset{\displaystyle O}{\underset{\displaystyle O-CH_3}{C}} \; + \; H_2O \tag{A5}$$

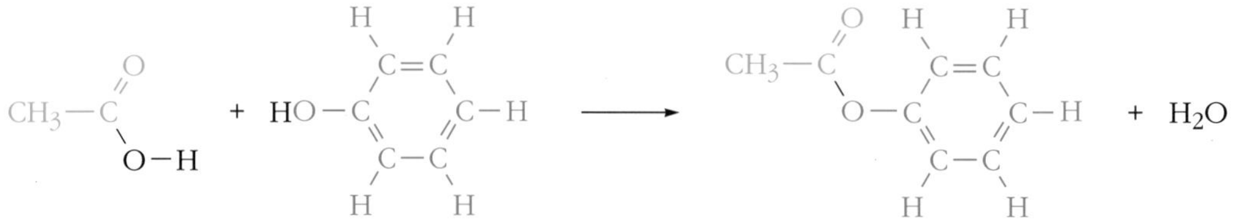

$$\tag{A6}$$

**Question 7**  Ethylene glycol reacts with two moles of fatty acid molecules to give molecules containing two ester groups, as shown in Equation A7.

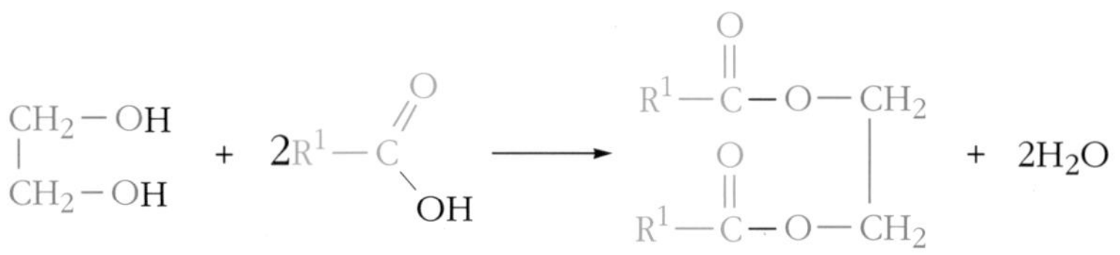

$$\begin{matrix} CH_2-OH \\ | \\ CH_2-OH \end{matrix} \; + \; 2R^1-\overset{\displaystyle O}{\underset{\displaystyle OH}{C}} \; \longrightarrow \; \begin{matrix} R^1-\overset{O}{\overset{||}{C}}-O-CH_2 \\ | \\ R^1-\overset{O}{\overset{||}{C}}-O-CH_2 \end{matrix} \; + \; 2H_2O \tag{A7}$$

As there are two fatty acids to choose from, a mixture of diesters is formed: **A1**, **A2**, and **A3**. Notice that **A4** is the same as **A3**: if the molecule **A3** is rotated it can be superimposed on **A4**.

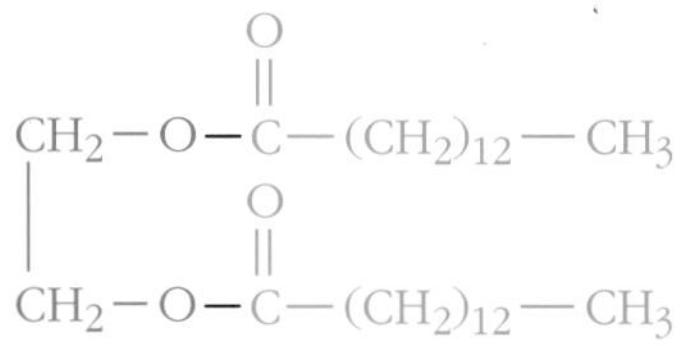

$$\begin{matrix} CH_2-O-\overset{O}{\overset{||}{C}}-(CH_2)_{12}-CH_3 \\ | \\ CH_2-O-\overset{O}{\overset{||}{C}}-(CH_2)_{12}-CH_3 \end{matrix}$$

**A1**

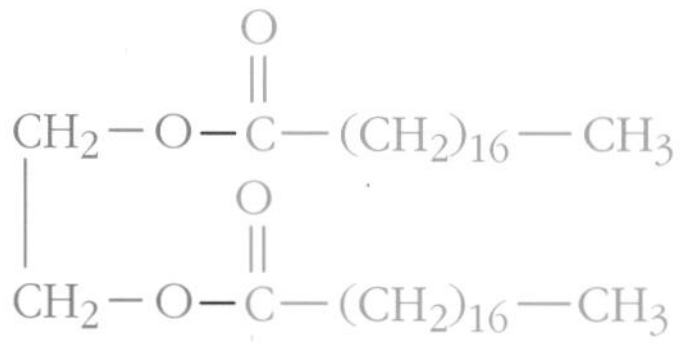

$$\begin{matrix} CH_2-O-\overset{O}{\overset{||}{C}}-(CH_2)_{16}-CH_3 \\ | \\ CH_2-O-\overset{O}{\overset{||}{C}}-(CH_2)_{16}-CH_3 \end{matrix}$$

**A2**

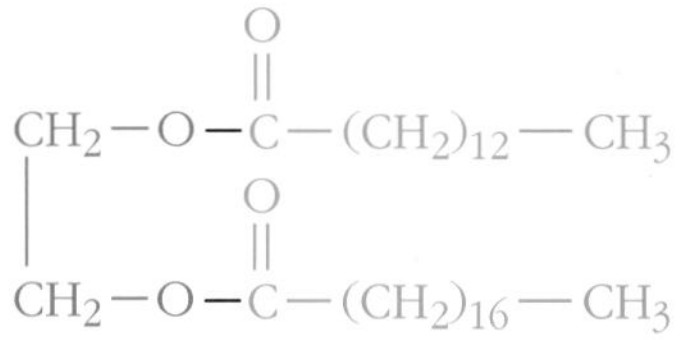

$$\begin{matrix} CH_2-O-\overset{O}{\overset{||}{C}}-(CH_2)_{12}-CH_3 \\ | \\ CH_2-O-\overset{O}{\overset{||}{C}}-(CH_2)_{16}-CH_3 \end{matrix}$$

**A3**

$$\begin{matrix} CH_2-O-\overset{O}{\overset{||}{C}}-(CH_2)_{16}-CH_3 \\ | \\ CH_2-O-\overset{O}{\overset{||}{C}}-(CH_2)_{12}-CH_3 \end{matrix}$$

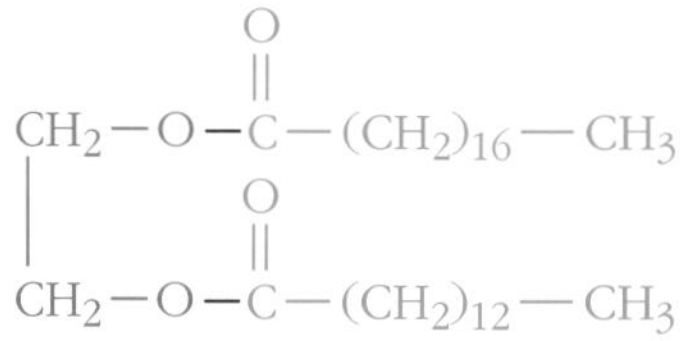

**A4**

**Question 8** Equations A8 to A10 show the reaction of each amino acid to give a chain containing four leucine amino acid residues. Notice the chain still has a carboxylic acid group and an amino group for further reaction.

$$
\begin{array}{ccc}
\text{CH}_3\diagdown\;\diagup\text{CH}_3 & & \text{CH}_3\diagdown\;\diagup\text{CH}_3 \\
\text{CH} & & \text{CH} \\
| & + & | \\
\text{CH}_2 & & \text{CH}_2 \\
| & & | \\
\text{H}_2\text{N—CH—COOH} & & \text{H}_2\text{N—CH—COOH}
\end{array}
\longrightarrow
\begin{array}{c}
\text{CH}_3\diagdown\;\diagup\text{CH}_3 \quad \text{CH}_3\diagdown\;\diagup\text{CH}_3 \\
\text{CH} \qquad\qquad \text{CH} \\
| \qquad\qquad | \\
\text{CH}_2 \qquad\qquad \text{CH}_2 \\
| \qquad\qquad | \\
\text{H}_2\text{N—CH—C—NH—CH—COOH} \\
\quad\;\; \| \\
\quad\;\; \text{O}
\end{array}
\; + \; \text{H}_2\text{O} \qquad \text{(A8)}
$$

$$
\begin{array}{c}
\text{CH}_3\diagdown\;\diagup\text{CH}_3 \quad \text{CH}_3\diagdown\;\diagup\text{CH}_3 \\
\text{CH} \qquad\qquad \text{CH} \\
| \qquad\qquad | \\
\text{CH}_2 \qquad\qquad \text{CH}_2 \\
| \qquad\qquad | \\
\text{H}_2\text{N—CH—C—NH—CH—COOH} \\
\quad\;\; \| \\
\quad\;\; \text{O}
\end{array}
\; + \;
\begin{array}{c}
\text{CH}_3\diagdown\;\diagup\text{CH}_3 \\
\text{CH} \\
| \\
\text{CH}_2 \\
| \\
\text{H}_2\text{N—CH—COOH}
\end{array}
$$

$$\text{(A9)}$$

$$
\longrightarrow
\begin{array}{c}
\text{CH}_3\diagdown\;\diagup\text{CH}_3 \quad \text{CH}_3\diagdown\;\diagup\text{CH}_3 \quad \text{CH}_3\diagdown\;\diagup\text{CH}_3 \\
\text{CH} \qquad\qquad \text{CH} \qquad\qquad \text{CH} \\
| \qquad\qquad | \qquad\qquad | \\
\text{CH}_2 \qquad\qquad \text{CH}_2 \qquad\qquad \text{CH}_2 \\
| \qquad\qquad | \qquad\qquad | \\
\text{H}_2\text{N—CH—C—NH—CH—C—NH—CH—COOH} \\
\quad\;\; \| \qquad\qquad \| \\
\quad\;\; \text{O} \qquad\qquad \text{O}
\end{array}
\; + \; \text{H}_2\text{O}
$$

$$
\begin{array}{c}
\text{CH}_3\diagdown\;\diagup\text{CH}_3 \quad \text{CH}_3\diagdown\;\diagup\text{CH}_3 \quad \text{CH}_3\diagdown\;\diagup\text{CH}_3 \\
\text{CH} \qquad \text{CH} \qquad \text{CH} \\
| \qquad | \qquad | \\
\text{CH}_2 \qquad \text{CH}_2 \qquad \text{CH}_2 \\
| \qquad | \qquad | \\
\text{H}_2\text{N—CH—C—NH—CH—C—NH—CH—COOH} \\
\quad\;\; \| \qquad\qquad \| \\
\quad\;\; \text{O} \qquad\qquad \text{O}
\end{array}
\; + \;
\begin{array}{c}
\text{CH}_3\diagdown\;\diagup\text{CH}_3 \\
\text{CH} \\
| \\
\text{CH}_2 \\
| \\
\text{H}_2\text{N—CH—COOH}
\end{array}
$$

$$\text{(A10)}$$

$$
\longrightarrow
\begin{array}{c}
\text{CH}_3\diagdown\;\diagup\text{CH}_3 \quad \text{CH}_3\diagdown\;\diagup\text{CH}_3 \quad \text{CH}_3\diagdown\;\diagup\text{CH}_3 \quad \text{CH}_3\diagdown\;\diagup\text{CH}_3 \\
\text{CH} \qquad \text{CH} \qquad \text{CH} \qquad \text{CH} \\
| \qquad | \qquad | \qquad | \\
\text{CH}_2 \qquad \text{CH}_2 \qquad \text{CH}_2 \qquad \text{CH}_2 \\
| \qquad | \qquad | \qquad | \\
\text{H}_2\text{N—CH—C—NH—CH—C—NH—CH—C—NH—CH—COOH} \\
\quad\;\; \| \qquad\qquad \| \qquad\qquad \| \\
\quad\;\; \text{O} \qquad\qquad \text{O} \qquad\qquad \text{O}
\end{array}
\; + \; \text{H}_2\text{O}
$$

**Question 9** Figure A4 shows the possibility of hydrogen bonding. Figure A5 shows the possible formation of a cystine bridge. There is also the possibility of London forces between the hydrocarbon chains.

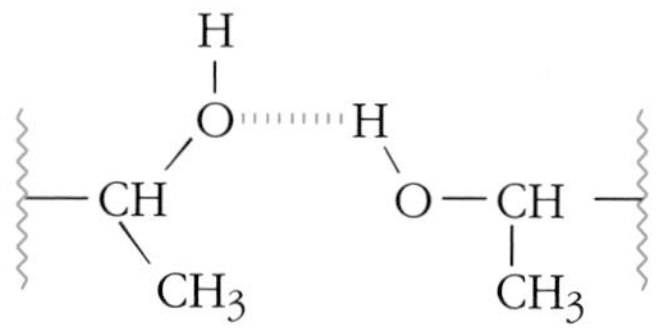

**Figure A4**
Hydrogen bonding; the protein backbone is shown schematically.

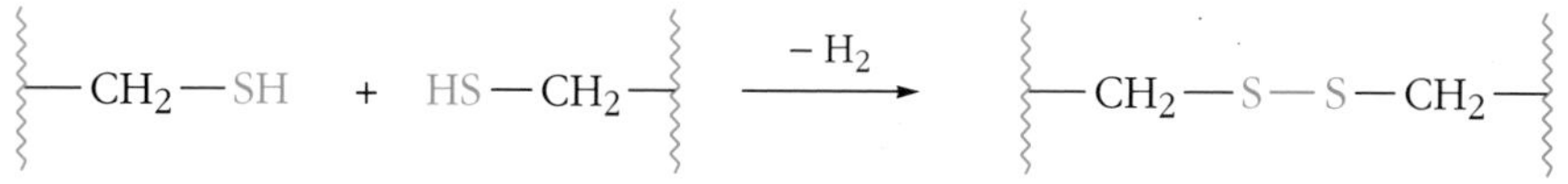

**Figure A5**
Cystine bridge formation; the protein backbone is shown schematically.

**Question 10** The oxygen atom that links the glucose units together is not in the plane of the left-hand ring, so it is an α linkage. Comparison of this structure with the two alternatives, Figures 2.23 and 2.24, confirms that maltose is like the α form of glucose.

**Question 11** Both structures are based on glucose rings joined via a β linkage. The only difference is that in chitin one of the OH groups of each ring has been converted into an amide, in blue in Figure A6.

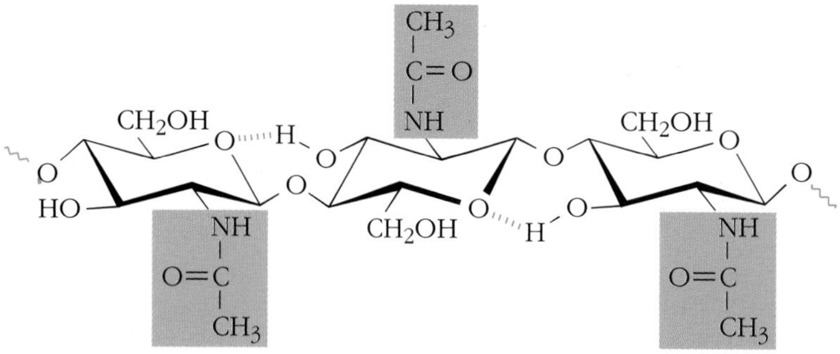

**Figure A6**
The structure of chitin.

**Question 12** When meat loses water on defrosting, some of the water-soluble vitamins are lost. When fats drip off meat during the roasting process, some fat-soluble vitamins are lost.

**Question 13** Milk is rich in lactose. The enzyme that breaks down lactose is lactase; without lactase, lactose will pass through the digestive system. Unfortunately, the bacteria that live in the intestine break the lactose down into lactic acid, which leads to flatulence, discomfort and diarrhoea. Thus, people with this deficiency tend not to drink much milk!

**Question 14** Because there is only so much alcohol dehydrogenase in the body, the ethanol competes with the ethylene glycol for the enzyme. Drinking large amounts of ethanol keeps the enzyme busy oxidizing ethanol and thus stops the oxidation of ethylene glycol. The ethylene glycol is thus excreted unchanged. Ethanol is also the antidote for methanol poisoning.

**Question 15** Compound **4.4** contains two OH groups and a COOH group, and so will dissolve in hot water. Caffeine also contains groups that can form hydrogen bonds (Figure A7). As we saw earlier, cellulose will not dissolve.

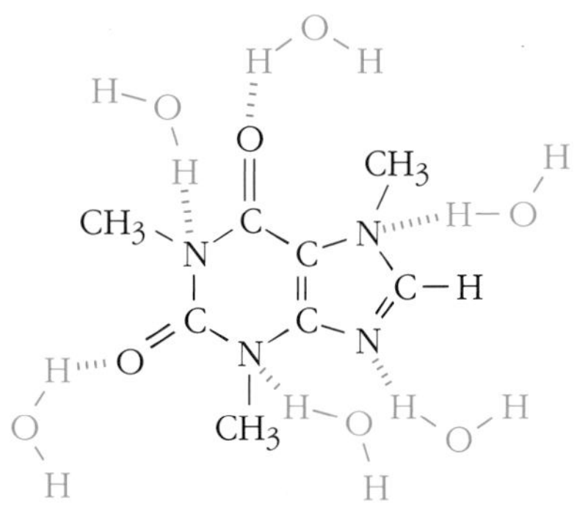

**Figure A7**
Hydrogen bonding between caffeine and water molecules.

**Question 16** When cold water is added to gelatin and the mixture is heated, the OH groups on the chain form hydrogen bonds to the water molecules. Thus the solid will 'dissolve'. Nevertheless, because gelatin has a thickening action, there must still be some interactions between the chains so that there is a three-dimensional gelatin network.

**Question 17** Figure A8 shows how a water drop may be stabilized in an oil. On the surface of the water drop, the non-polar hydrocarbon portion of the emulsifying agent interacts with the oil, whereas the polar portion of the emulsifier interacts with the water.

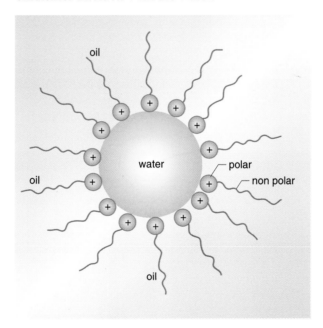

**Figure A8**
Stabilization of a water drop in an oil by an emulsifying agent.

**Question 18** Baking soda reacts with an acid to generate carbon dioxide, which effectively puffs the cake up:

$$H^+(aq) + HCO_3^-(aq) = H_2O(l) + CO_2(g)$$

Clearly, the baking soda needs an acid (and water) for this to occur, and this must come from the cake mixture. Acidic ingredients commonly used are yogurt, sour cream, lemon, pineapple or vinegar.

**Question 19** If the concentration of hydrogen ions is written as $1 \times 10^{-n}$ mol l$^{-1}$, then the pH value is equal to $n$. Thus, if the pH of the cola is about 3, then the hydrogen ion concentration is $1 \times 10^{-3}$ mol l$^{-1}$. Table 4.3 shows that this corresponds to a hydroxide concentration of $1 \times 10^{-11}$ mol l$^{-1}$.

Alternatively we could use the expression

$$[H^+] \times [OH^-] = 1.0 \times 10^{-14} \, mol^2 \, l^{-2}$$

$$1 \times 10^{-3} \, mol \, l^{-1} \times [OH^-] = 1.0 \times 10^{-14} \, mol^2 \, l^{-2}$$

Thus

$$[OH^-] = \frac{1.0 \times 10^{-14} \, mol^2 \, l^{-2}}{1 \times 10^{-3} \, mol \, l^{-1}} = 1.0 \times 10^{-11} \, mol \, l^{-1}$$

**Question 20** Making fizzy drinks involves dissolving carbon dioxide in water. If some of the carbon dioxide reacts to form hydrogen ions, then the pH of the fizzy drink will decrease.

**Question 21** Because whales stay under the water for long times, they need to retain supplies of oxygen. This is achieved by having large amounts of myoglobin in the muscle, which can store the oxygen during long dives.

**Question 22** Figure A9 shows the model with a ruler. We measured the distance between the oxygen and the hydrogen (binding sites 2 and 3) to be between 7 and 8 cm. This corresponds to an interatomic distance of 266–304 pm. Thus acesulfame K can achieve the required distance of 300 pm. The distance from the hydrogen to the CH$_3$ (sites 3 and 1) was 14–15 cm, which corresponds to 472–510 pm, again in agreement with Figure 6.8. Although not perfect, the distance from site 1 to site 2 was also reasonably close to that required.

**Figure A9**
Distances measured on the model of acesulfame K: (a) the oxygen to hydrogen distance; (b) the hydrogen to methyl distance.

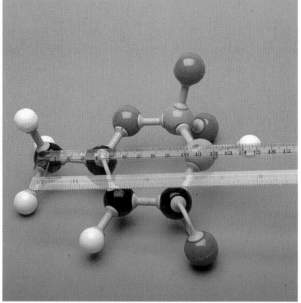

(a)

(b)

In fact, acesulfame K is the potassium compound **A5**. This no longer has the key NH group. Although it is added to food as the potassium compound, it is converted into the NH compound before it gets to the taste buds.

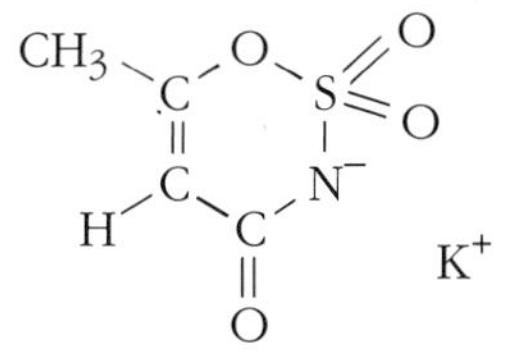

$$CH_3-C\begin{matrix}O-S\\ \| \\ C-C\\ \| \\ O\end{matrix}\begin{matrix}O\\ \diagdown \\ \diagup O\\ N^-\end{matrix}\quad K^+$$

**A5**

**Question 23** Aspartame is made from two amino acids, phenylalanine and aspartic acid, connected via an amide bond; thus hydrolysis will cleave this bond. By analogy with the general Equation A11, we can write Equation A12.

$$R^1-NH-C\diagdown_{R^2}^{O} \;+\; H_2O \;\longrightarrow\; R^1-NH_2 \;+\; HO-C\diagdown_{R^2}^{O} \tag{A11}$$

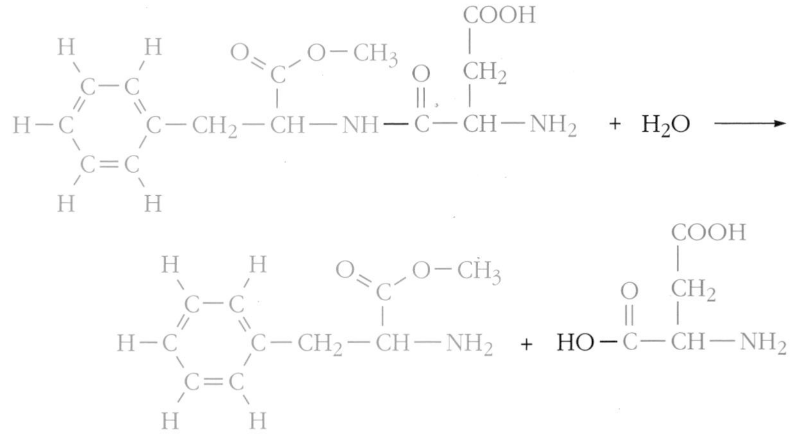

$$\tag{A12}$$

The ester bond may be hydrolysed to give phenylalanine (Equation A13).

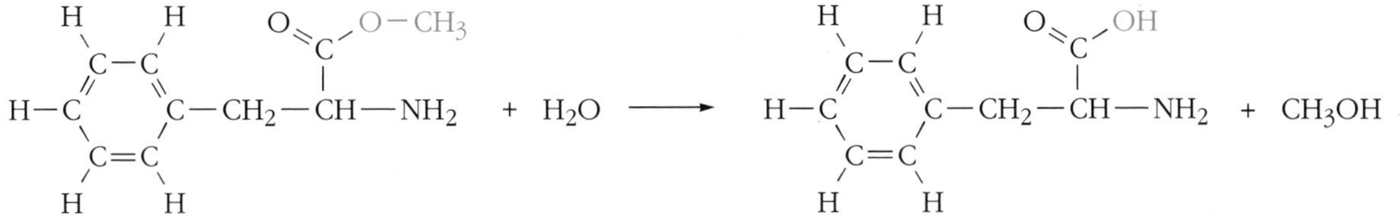

$$\tag{A13}$$

phenylalanine

The products are not sweet because they do not contain groups that correspond to the distances in Figure 6.8.

**Question 24** If we assume that the double bond in oleic acid behaves as other double bonds, which is reasonable, by analogy with the reactions in Box 6.2 we can predict the reaction with hydrogen chloride to be:

$$CH_3-(CH_2)_7-CH=CH-(CH_2)_7-COOH \ + \ HCl \ \longrightarrow \ CH_3-(CH_2)_7-\overset{\overset{\displaystyle H}{|}}{CH}-\overset{\overset{\displaystyle Cl}{|}}{CH}-(CH_2)_7-COOH$$

or

$$CH_3-(CH_2)_7-\overset{\overset{\displaystyle Cl}{|}}{CH}-\overset{\overset{\displaystyle H}{|}}{CH}-(CH_2)_7-COOH$$

Either orientation of addition is correct.

Hydrogen chloride adds hydrogen and chlorine to the double bond. Under acid catalysis, water adds H and OH to the double bond:

$$CH_3-(CH_2)_7-CH=CH-(CH_2)_7-COOH \ + \ H_2O \ \xrightarrow[\text{catalysis}]{\text{acid}} \ CH_3-(CH_2)_7-\overset{\overset{\displaystyle H}{|}}{CH}-\overset{\overset{\displaystyle OH}{|}}{CH}-(CH_2)_7-COOH$$

or

$$CH_3-(CH_2)_7-\overset{\overset{\displaystyle OH}{|}}{CH}-\overset{\overset{\displaystyle H}{|}}{CH}-(CH_2)_7-COOH$$

Again, either orientation is correct.

**Question 25** One mole of linoleic acid molecules can react with two moles of hydrogen molecules, but we have only one mole of hydrogen molecules. There is thus insufficient hydrogen for complete hydrogenation, and only partial hydrogenation will occur. Molecules of linoleic acid will react with the hydrogen until it is all used up, leaving a mixture of unchanged linoleic acid, a partially hydrogenated product (oleic acid) and a completely hydrogenated product (stearic acid). This is what happens in hydrogenation of oils. The amount of hydrogen added is deliberately insufficient to hydrogenate all the double bonds, so the fat is still unsaturated to some extent.

# Acknowledgements

Grateful acknowledgement is made to the following sources for permission to reproduce material in this part of Book 3:

## Figures

*Figure 1.1* Seven Seas Limited; *Figure 1.3* Camera Press; *Figure 1.4* reprinted by permission of the publishers from *Seven Countries: a multivariate analysis of death and coronary heart disease* by Ancel Keys, Cambridge, Mass., Harvard University Press, Copyright © 1980 by the President and Fellows of Harvard College; *Figures 1.6, 2.35, 2.36 and 3.3* B. A. Fox and A. G. Cameron (5th edition 1989) *Food Science, Nutrition and Health*, Edward Arnold, a division of Hodder & Stoughton Limited, © 1989 Brian A. Fox and Allan G. Cameron; *Figure 1.7* Ardea London; *Figure 2.32* T. P. Coultate (2nd edition 1989) *Food: the chemistry of its components*, © The Royal Society of Chemistry, 1989; *Figure 5.8* Courtesy of Milton Keynes Hospital; *Figure 5.15* Francis Leroy, Biocosmos/Science Photo Library; *Figure 5.16* Oxford Scientific Films; *Figure 6.2* Omikron/Science Photo Library; *Figure 6.10* Heather Clarke; *Figure 6.22* The Butter Council.

## Tables

*Tables 1.4 and 1.5* A. Gray (ed.) (1993), *World Health and Disease*, Open University Press; *Table 1.6* © Crown Copyright. Reproduced with the permission of the Controller of Her Majesty's Stationery Office.

# PART 2
# HEALTH

Prepared for the Course Team by Jim Iley

# Contents

# Prologue

This part of Book 3 examines how chemistry and health are inter-related. It starts with the concept of personal hygiene and keeping clean, dealing with how we minimize our exposure to micro-organisms that cause illness. It continues with a discussion of how we constantly try to eradicate disease-carrying organisms from our immediate environment so that we are less susceptible to infection. Finally, it investigates the processes by which medicines and drugs are discovered and invented to aid our recovery to good health when our bodies succumb to illness.

An underlying theme of the approach taken here is how the increasing ability to think of substances in terms of their molecular structures enables subsequent developments to take place more rapidly and in a much more specific way. There is, consequently, a rather historical 'feel' to the material, as the developments and understanding that have fed off each other, and that continue into the present day, are described. This part of Book 3 is not simply about the concepts of chemistry – though these are developed – it is also about the human endeavour and ways of thinking that flow from a molecular understanding of our environment.

# Chapter 1
# Cleanliness is next to... godliness?

In this Chapter we shall be dealing with the development of soaps and detergents, and relating their function as cleaning agents to the structure of the individual molecules from which they are made.

It has long been known that hygiene and health are inextricably linked. The ancient Hebrews devised laws to ensure that what was clean was kept very separate from what was unclean. In part this was religious ritual, but a major goal was the eradication, or at least the containment, of disease. In the Biblical book of Leviticus, which describes the period around 1100 BC, we can read the following (abbreviated) accounts of the cleansing process related to skin diseases (here given the name leprosy) that were required of the individual, and also of their garments and homes:

> *This shall be the law of the leper for the day of his cleansing. The priest shall make an examination. Then, if the leprous disease is healed, the priest shall command them to take two living clean birds and cedarwood and scarlet stuff and hyssop; and the priest shall command them to kill one of the birds. He shall take the living bird with the cedarwood and the scarlet stuff and the hyssop, and dip them in the blood of the bird that was killed; and he shall sprinkle it seven times upon him who is to be cleansed;... And he who is to be cleansed shall wash his clothes, and shave off all his hair, and bathe himself in water and he shall be clean... Then the priest shall sprinkle some oil with his finger seven times before the LORD. And some of the oil that remains the priest shall put on the tip of the right ear of him which is to be cleansed, and on the thumb of his right hand, and on the great toe of his right foot; and the rest of the oil that is in the priest's hand he shall put on the head of him who is to be cleansed. Then the priest shall make atonement for him before the LORD... and he shall be clean.*
> *(Leviticus, chapter 14, verses 2–8a, 14–18, 20b)*

> *When there is a leprous disease in a garment,... the priest shall shut up that which has the disease for seven days. If the disease has spread in the garment... the disease is a malignant leprosy; it is unclean... it shall be burned in the fire.*
> *(Leviticus, chapter 13, verses 47–52)*

> *The priest shall go in to see the house. If the disease is in the walls of the house with greenish or reddish spots, and it appears to be deeper than the surface, then the priest shall shut up the house seven days. If the disease has spread, then the priest shall command that they take out the stones in which is the disease and he shall cause the inside of the house to be scraped, and the plaster that they scrape off they shall pour into an unclean place outside the city:*
> *(Leviticus, chapter 14, verses 36–41)*

Thank goodness for the benefits of modern life! These days, cleanliness can be maintained, and disease generally kept at bay, by methods that require somewhat less monumental effort.

Although these extracts contain elements of what might appear ridiculous, we should remember that three thousand years ago there were no easily accessible cleaning agents, antiseptics, disinfectants or drugs with which to combat disease. The rigorous attention to detail, the quarantine period, and the destruction of diseased materials were almost the only means by which disease could be halted. If such attention to separation of clean and unclean had been paid by those living in bygone ages, then the plagues and disease that ravaged the population of Europe would probably have been diminished. In Victorian Britain (Figure 1.1), the average life expectancy was only 45 years, and infant mortality 150 per thousand.

**Figure 1.1**
Populations, particularly those in cities, are ravaged by epidemics when care about cleanliness is not taken seriously. Here the citizens of London panic during a cholera epidemic, while the water company gets its supply where sewage flows into the Thames. An etching by the satirical cartoonist Cruikshank, 1832. The man enthroned in the Thames, with chamberpot for crown, is 'Water-King of Southwark, Sovereign of the Scented Streams... Warden of the Sink Ports'.

▨     Read the first extract from Leviticus again. What are the substances to be used to aid the act of cleansing?

■     There appear to be three: the blood of a bird, water and oil.

Of these, only water would be generally recognized as having any major physical cleaning properties, especially given that the blood and oil were used so sparingly and in such esoteric places.

▨     From your understanding of the structure of the water molecule and your knowledge of the properties of water, what types of substance are likely to be best removed by washing with water?

■     Water is a polar substance because of the dipolar nature of water molecules; so it is probably much better at removing polar substances, such as those that are made up of ions – like salt, for example – because they are more likely to be dissolved. Compounds that are not polar, like fats, will not dissolve.

Of course, how well polar substances are removed will depend chiefly on their individual solubilities in water; those that are most soluble will be most easily removed. Chalk – calcium carbonate – is very insoluble, as we've noted elsewhere, and is more likely to be removed by being suspended in water rather than by dissolving in it.

From your own experience, you'll have noticed that greasy materials like fats and oils are poorly removed by water on its own, so today, if we want to keep clean, and particularly if we want to keep germs at bay, we would use many other cleaning substances in conjunction with water.

### Activity 1  Cleaning agents

Go round your home and make a list of the commercial cleaning products that you commonly use. Some possible examples are shown in Figure 1.2. Use the information labels to identify the types of active cleaning agent that these products contain.

**Figure 1.2**
Some domestic cleaning products, which contain a variety of different cleaning agents.

Most of the cleaning agents that you'll have identified are relatively recent additions (less than fifty years) to our armoury, others have been in use a little longer (about one hundred and fifty years), but one – soap – has been around for thousands of years. Around 600 BC, Jeremiah the prophet had this to say:

> *Though you wash yourself with lye and use much soap, the stain of your guilt is still before me, says the Lord God.*
> *(Jeremiah, chapter 2, verse 22)*

Although the people of Judah had access to better cleaning materials, and paid strict attention to cleanliness, it is clear that Jeremiah didn't think it necessarily led them to godliness! Nonetheless, the ability to make soaps was an important development in our attempts to keep clean. Apart from making ourselves look more presentable, washing removes the dirt that harbours potentially harmful micro-organisms, such as bacteria and fungi, and the grease and other material that provide their nutrients. Unfortunately, precisely how soaps came to be discovered is lost in the mists of time, although it is known that the Sumerians used soap solutions by 3000 BC. One possible sequence of events leading to their discovery has been described as follows. (In this extract two terms, alkali and alkaline, are used, which you may not have met before. They derive from an Arabic word meaning 'the ashes formed by heating to high temperature', but in chemical usage an alkali is the same as a base and alkaline means basic. Basic solutions have been commonly obtained throughout history by steeping wood ashes in water.)

> *Stone Age people used sand or ashes to scrape grease off their hands. If they rinsed away the ashes with water, they might have noted that the water felt slippery. (The ash–water mixture felt slippery because it contained alkali that dissolved the outermost layers of the skin.) At a later stage in history, the Sumerians used a slurry of ashes and water to remove grease from raw wool and from cloth so that it could be dyed. (Most dyes do not adhere to greasy cloth.) Sumerian priests and temple attendants purified themselves before sacred rites, and in the absence of soap, they too probably used ashes and water. At some point, people noticed that the more ashes there were in the water (that is, the more concentrated was the alkali solution), the more slippery water cleaned even after the ashes were no longer present, and eventually someone put two and two together and discarded the wet ashes.*
>
> *The slippery solutions clean because the alkali reacts with some of the grease on an object and converts it into soap. The soap then dissolves the rest of the dirt and grease. The more grease and oil dissolved by the alkaline solution, the more soap there is and the better the mixture cleans. People would inevitably notice this because they used the slippery solutions repeatedly until the solutions lost their potency. Thus the Sumerians, realizing that a little grease improved the performance of the alkali, proceeded to make soap solutions directly by boiling fats and oils in the alkali before using it for cleaning. Specific directions for making different kinds of soap solution have been found on cuneiform tablets. The final, almost trivial, step to solid soap was taken about 800 AD, in Gaul, perhaps in the town of Savona, when soap was separated from water by salting out, or adding salt to, the solution. (Science historian Martin Levey, however, reports that the Mesopotamians used salting out by 3000 BC.)*
>
> *(H. W. Salzberg,* From Caveman to Chemist, *American Chemical Society, Washington 1992)*

You may wish to try for yourself removing the grease from your hands using the ash from an old garden bonfire. Does the water feel slippery when you rinse them?

Soaps are some of the earliest of the chemical cleaning agents – other than water, that is – so we shall take a look at what they are, and how they work. Developing a picture of how they work at a molecular level provides a basis for understanding how some of the more recent cleaning agents work.

## 1.1 Soaps

From your general observations – possibly from cooking – you'll have noticed that oils, such as sunflower or olive oil, don't mix with water: the oil forms a separate, upper layer.

◻ Try to recall the molecular reasons for why water and oil don't mix.

◼ Water molecules are polar, and form an extensive, but ever changing, system of hydrogen bonds. The molecules making up oil are comparatively large, almost completely non-polar and interact with one another through relatively weak London forces. If the oil were to enter the water layer, the hydrogen-bonded structure of water would be disrupted as the water molecules tried to accommodate the oil. In addition, the oil molecules would lose the benefit of the London forces holding them together. This means that, if a solution of oil and water *could* exist, both the oil and water molecules would find themselves in an environment more alien than the individual separate liquids. So, oil and water don't mix to form a solution; they remain as separate liquids with the less dense on top.

You could heat a mixture of oil and water for days if you so wanted, but they still wouldn't mix together. But if you were to dissolve some washing soda – sodium carbonate ($Na_2CO_3$) – in the aqueous layer and then heat up the oil and water together, you would notice that eventually there would no longer be two layers but one. The oil and water would seem to have mixed together.

This observation was mentioned above in the extract taken from *From Caveman to Chemist*, where it was suggested that the oil and grease had dissolved in the alkaline solution. But this isn't simple dissolving. Something 'special' has happened because of the presence of the sodium carbonate, which is the substance that we've used to make a basic solution. In aqueous solutions, sodium carbonate generates hydroxide anions:

$$CO_3^{2-}(aq) + H_2O = HCO_3^{-}(aq) + OH^{-}(aq)$$

and the oil and the hydroxide anions react together to form a *new* substance, which we commonly call **soap**.

Why have they done this? The people of the ancient world were unable to formulate an answer to this question. In some ways, there is no need to be able to answer the question in order to make use of soaps. Nevertheless, by understanding the structure of fats and oils, it is possible to understand how soaps are produced and, in time, to improve them. The commonly used household detergents are a result of this knowledge.

◻ From your reading of other parts of this Course, especially Part 1 of this Book, you have several times come across compounds containing the ester functional group. We shall be making use of your knowledge of esters shortly, so now would be a good time for you to jot down all of the information you can bring to mind about esters.

(You can compare your notes with the information contained in Box 1.1. This Box also contains new information, so don't worry if you don't recall all the information given there.)

In general, there are two types of fatty substance, often called **lipids** (from the Greek word for fat, *lipos*). There are those that will break down into smaller molecules when they react react with water (this process is called **hydrolysis**), and those that won't. Vegetable oils, such as olive oil and coconut oil, and animal fats, such as lard and beef dripping, can be hydrolysed; paraffin wax and substances such as cholesterol can't be hydrolysed. Soaps are made from hydrolysable fats and oils.

The differences between these two types of lipid lie at the molecular level. Essentially, non-hydrolysable fats do not contain a functional group capable of reacting with water. A good example of this is heptacosane (hep-ta-co-zane), $C_{27}H_{56}$, a hydrocarbon found in beeswax (Figure 1.3).

**Figure 1.3**
Ball-and-stick model of heptacosane and a line diagram of the same molecule.

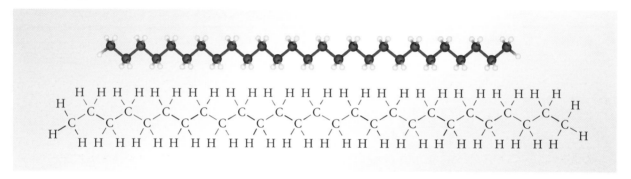

Hydrolysable fats contain the ester functional group (see Box 1.1). Although these fats don't dissolve in water (because they don't contain a sufficient number of polar groups that can form hydrogen bonds with water) they do contain an ester group that can be hydrolysed by water. For example, although beeswax or the waxy materials that form the protective coatings on fruits and berries are mixtures of compounds (Figure 1.4), one of the major components is a compound containing an ester group. One of the components of beeswax is the ester **1.1**. The long hydrocarbon chains make the compound non-polar and therefore insoluble in polar solvents such as water, but they will enable it to dissolve in non-polar liquids such as petrol. It is these hydrocarbon chains that make all fats feel 'greasy'.

$$CH_3(CH_2)_{14}-\overset{\displaystyle O}{\overset{\displaystyle \|}{C}}\underset{\displaystyle O-(CH_2)_{29}CH_3}{}$$

**1.1**

**Figure 1.4**
A variety of natural oils and waxes contain simple esters, from beeswax and the waxy coatings on fruit to the vegetable cooking oils.

## Box 1.1  More about esters

Esters are widespread in nature. Many of the structurally simple esters are pleasant smelling liquids that contribute to the fragrances and flavours of plants and fruits. Methyl butanoate (**1.2**), for example, is found in pineapples, and isopentyl acetate (**1.3**) is a constituent of banana oil.

**1.2** methyl butanoate          **1.3** isopentyl acetate

Esters are also commonly found in synthetic products. Most obvious amongst these are the polyester polymers, known generally under the names dacron, terylene and PET. Biopol, the readily biodegradable polymer, is a polyester.

These compounds contain the ester group, the general structure of which we write as:

$$R^1 - C \overset{\displaystyle O}{\underset{\displaystyle O-R^2}{<}}$$

where the $R^1$ and $R^2$ symbols are used to signify that the groups can have a variety of structures, depending on the acid and alcohol from which the ester is formed.

For example, in methyl butanoate the $R^1$ group attached to the carbon atom of the C=O part of the ester is $CH_3CH_2CH_2$ and the $R^2$ group attached to the oxygen atom of the C—O part is $CH_3$; for isopentyl acetate $R^1$ is $CH_3$ and $R^2$ is $CH_2CH_2CH(CH_3)_2$.

Esters are made by the reaction between a carboxylic acid and an alcohol, the by-product being water:

$$R^1 - C \overset{\displaystyle O}{\underset{\displaystyle O-H}{<}} \quad + \quad R^2OH \quad \longrightarrow \quad R^1 - C \overset{\displaystyle O}{\underset{\displaystyle O-R^2}{<}} \quad + \quad H_2O$$

  carboxylic acid          alcohol                    ester                  water

Both carboxylic acids and alcohols can individually dissolve in water provided that the hydrocarbon groups, $R^1$ and $R^2$, are relatively small. This is because they contain OH groups that are able to form hydrogen bonds to water molecules, and because the small hydrocarbon groups don't disrupt the water structure sufficiently to overcome this effect. However, the ester formed from these compounds contains no OH groups, and the disruptive influence of the hydrocarbon groups would be much greater if it were to dissolve. Consequently, esters generally do not dissolve in water.

The name of an ester is made up of two parts. The first part is the name of the group, $R^2$, attached to the oxygen atom. This is the part that comes from the alcohol. The second part of the name comes from the name of the carboxylic acid, $R^1COOH$, from which it is made. For example, methyl butanoate is made from methanol, $CH_3OH$, and butanoic acid, $CH_3CH_2CH_2COOH$.

One of the characteristic reactions of esters is that with water. This is usually carried out in the presence of an acid or a base because these catalyse, or speed up, the reaction. The reaction forms the parent carboxylic acid and alcohol by splitting the ester as follows:

this part forms the acid

this bond broken

this part forms the alcohol

$$R^1 - C \overset{\displaystyle O}{\underset{\displaystyle O-R^2}{<}} \quad + \quad H_2O \quad \longrightarrow \quad R^1 - C \overset{\displaystyle O}{\underset{\displaystyle O-H}{<}} \quad + \quad R^2OH$$

You may notice this process is the exact reverse of the formation of esters from alcohols and carboxylic acids. That might prompt you to ask 'which reaction occurs?' The answer is that it depends on how the reaction is carried out. If a lot of water is present then the ester is hydrolysed. If a lot of alcohol is present then the ester is formed.

Vegetable oils and animal fats have structures similar to, though slightly more complex than, those of compounds containing a single ester group, for example those found in beeswax. They are slightly more complex, because the alcohol from which they are formed contains not one OH group, like simple alcohols, but three. You may recall that the alcohol in question is called glycerol (**1.4**), known in the kitchen as the syrupy liquid glycerine.

$$CH_2 - OH$$
$$|$$
$$CH - OH$$
$$|$$
$$CH_2 - OH$$

**1.4** glycerol

- Can you recall, or work out again, how many acid groups you would expect glycerol to react with?

- Because it contains three alcohol groups, it can react with three acid groups.

The molecules that make up fats and vegetable oils therefore contain three ester groups, the general representation of which is **1.5**.

$$
\begin{array}{l}
\qquad\quad\ \ \overset{\displaystyle O}{\overset{\displaystyle \|}{\phantom{.}}} \\
CH_2 - O - C - R^1 \\
|\qquad\quad\ \ \overset{\displaystyle O}{\overset{\displaystyle \|}{\phantom{.}}} \\
CH - O - C - R^2 \\
|\qquad\quad\ \ \overset{\displaystyle O}{\overset{\displaystyle \|}{\phantom{.}}} \\
CH_2 - O - C - R^3
\end{array}
$$

**1.5**

This is the structure of *all* fats and oils that are hydrolysable. Each of the different R groups in this structure represents a long hydrocarbon chain that originates from the carboxylic acid $R^1COOH$, $R^2COOH$ or $R^3COOH$. These groups do not have to be the same because there are about forty naturally occurring acids with the general structure

$$
R - C
\begin{array}{l}
\nearrow O \\
\searrow OH
\end{array}
$$

each differing because the structure of R differs. Each animal or plant manufactures fats and oils for slightly different purposes; each oil therefore has a different composition of acid-derived groups, $R^1$, $R^2$ and $R^3$. The approximate compositions of some common fats and oils are shown in Figure 1.5. Don't forget, the fats and oils do not contain the fatty acids themselves. Lard doesn't contain 6% linoleic acid, for example, but if all the ester groups in lard were hydrolysed then the mixture of acids produced would contain 6% linoleic acid.

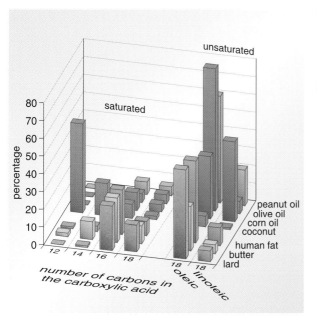

**Figure 1.5**
Approximate fatty acid compositions of some fats and oils. (You're not expected to remember the details of this Figure.)

▓ How does the information in Figure 1.5, together with your knowledge of the structure of a fat molecule, tell you that all fats and oils must be mixtures of compounds?

▓ Because each fat molecule can contain three groups derived from acids, the composition of any one fat molecule can be as follows: if all three positions are occupied by the same fatty acid group then the composition will be 100% of that fatty acid; if two positions have the same fatty acid and the third is different then the composition will be 67% and 33%; if all the positions are occupied by different fatty acids then the composition will be 33%, 33%, 33%. As none of the fats in Figure 1.5 has a composition resembling these possibilities, it must mean that they consist of a mixture of different types of compound.

Whatever the composition of the fat, when it reacts with a base, such as sodium hydroxide (NaOH), the ester groups are hydrolysed to give the constituent carboxylic acids and the alcohol, glycerol:

$$CH_2-O-\overset{\overset{O}{\|}}{C}-R^1$$
$$CH-O-\overset{\overset{O}{\|}}{C}-R^2 \xrightarrow{\text{hydrolysis}}$$
$$CH_2-O-\overset{\overset{O}{\|}}{C}-R^3$$

$$CH_2-OH$$
$$CH-OH \quad +$$
$$CH_2-OH$$

$$+ \quad \overset{O}{\underset{HO}{\overset{\|}{C}}}-R^1$$
$$+ \quad \overset{O}{\underset{HO}{\overset{\|}{C}}}-R^2$$
$$+ \quad \overset{O}{\underset{HO}{\overset{\|}{C}}}-R^3$$

The acids then react with the hydroxide ions present in the basic solution to form the corresponding ionic compounds, called carboxylates, and it is the mixture of these carboxylates that is the soap:

$$\overset{O}{\underset{HO}{\overset{\|}{C}}}-R^1$$
$$\overset{O}{\underset{HO}{\overset{\|}{C}}}-R^2 \xrightarrow{\text{NaOH}}$$
$$\overset{O}{\underset{HO}{\overset{\|}{C}}}-R^3$$

$$\overset{O}{\underset{NaO}{\overset{\|}{C}}}-R^1$$
$$\overset{O}{\underset{NaO}{\overset{\|}{C}}}-R^2$$
$$\overset{O}{\underset{NaO}{\overset{\|}{C}}}-R^3$$

**Question 1** Look back to Figure 1.5 and identify the fat or oil that will produce the 'purest' soap – that is, the one with the largest amount of only one type of acid group.

Crude soap contains glycerol and excess base. Purification can be effected by heating it in a large amount of boiling water and adding sodium chloride, which has the effect of causing pure sodium carboxylate compounds to be precipitated. The smooth soap that precipitates is dried, perfumed, and pressed into bars for household use. Dyes are added to make coloured soaps and antiseptics are added for medicated soaps.

■   Look at the general structure of the compounds that make up the soap (remember that $R^1$, $R^2$, and $R^3$ represent long-chain hydrocarbon groups) and the general structure of fats and oils. What one property would you expect soaps to have that fats and oils don't? Give an explanation for your suggestion.

■   Because soaps are ionic compounds, interactions between the dipolar water molecules and the two types of ion (sodium cations and carboxylate anions) would be expected to occur. So it is reasonable to suggest that the ionic carboxylate compounds should be more soluble in water than the oils from which they are formed.

This is why, on reacting with aqueous base, hydrolysable fats and oils appear to dissolve.

Soaps containing the sodium ion, $Na^+$, and also those containing the potassium ion, $K^+$, which are formed if potassium hydroxide (KOH) or potassium carbonate (potash, $K_2CO_3$) is substituted for sodium hydroxide or sodium carbonate in the soap-making process, are indeed soluble in water. The soaps containing potassium ions are more soluble and form the basis of the 'softer' soaps.

Why do soaps clean? It's because the two ends of the soap molecule are so different. We can think of soap molecules as being made up from an ionic 'head' – the carboxylate group – and an hydrocarbon 'tail' (Figure 1.6). The negatively charged carboxylate head is polar and so interacts favourably with water. The long-chain hydrocarbon tail is non-polar and so interacts favourably with non-polar substances, such as grease, but not with water. The net effect of these two opposite tendencies is that soaps interact favourably with both grease and water.

hydrocarbon tail

ionic head

**Figure 1.6**
Schematic representation of a soap molecule.

Dirt is usually a mixture of fatty material and solid particulate material. The fatty material on soiled fabrics is mainly a mixture of natural substances that exude from skin. This is known as sebum, and is composed of roughly one-third fatty acids, one-third glycerol esters and one-third simple fatty esters (like the beeswax ester mentioned earlier). There may also be a small quantity of hydrocarbons.

**Figure 1.7**
A schematic picture of (a) a micelle formed by a soap and (b) a soap micelle dissolving the molecules of a fat. Micelles are dynamic entities: the hydrocarbon tails are constantly 'waggling' about, and molecules of soap are continually entering and leaving the micelles.

When soaps are dispersed in water, the long hydrocarbon tails cluster together to form a sphere, the interior of which contains the hydrocarbon tails, while the ionic heads lie on the surface of the cluster and are exposed to the water (Figure 1.7a). As we saw in Part 1, this is exactly how emulsifiers behave. This kind of organization of the molecules maximizes the attractive London forces between the hydrocarbon tails, as well as the ion–dipole interactions between the charged carboxylate groups and water molecules. At the same time, it minimizes the disruption caused to the hydrogen bonding between the water molecules of the liquid. These spherical clusters of soap molecules are called **micelles**.

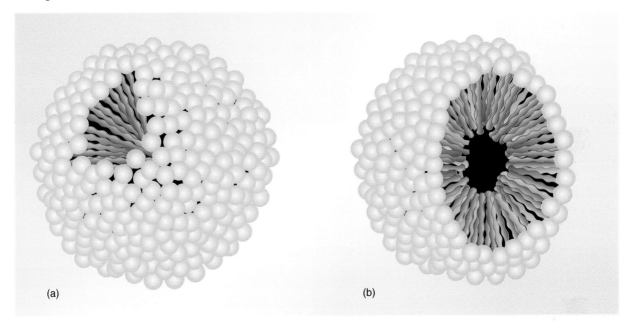

(a)  (b)

■ How would you expect these soap micelles to dissolve grease and fat?

■ The hydrocarbon tails in the interior of the micelles form a non-polar environment. Grease and fat can dissolve in this non-polar environment because of the attractive London forces between the grease molecules and the hydrocarbon tails of the soap molecules (Figure 1.7b).

So, the fats are dissolved in the centre of the micelle which, because it has an ionic surface of $-CO_2^-$ groups, is soluble in water. The grease-containing micelle can be simply washed away.

Soaps derived from animal and vegetable fats are adequate for most personal hygiene purposes. Moreover, they are 'environmentally friendly' because they are readily biodegradable. Bacteria are able to use them as an energy source, which means that they are easily broken down – ultimately to carbon dioxide and water. In hard water areas, however, soaps have a major drawback.

■   Hard waters contain significant concentrations of magnesium and calcium cations. Take a look at Table 1.1, which lists the solubilities in water of some carboxylate compounds that are derived from fats and oils. What do you notice about those that involve magnesium and calcium cations?

**Table 1.1** Solubilities in water of soaps with different cations.

| Carboxylate anion | Solubility/g kg$^{-1}$ | | | |
| --- | --- | --- | --- | --- |
| | Sodium soap | Potassium soap | Magnesium soap | Calcium soap |
| oleate | 100 | 250 | 0.24 | 0.4 |
| stearate | soluble | soluble | 0.03 | 0.04 |

■   Compared with the sodium and potassium soaps, the magnesium and calcium soaps are not very soluble.

The consequence of this is that, in hard water, when the magnesium or calcium ions in the water encounter the carboxylate ions in the soap, they combine and precipitate from solution. This can be written as:

two carboxylate ions are required for each calcium because each calcium ion has two charges whereas each carboxylate ion has only one

$$Ca^{2+}(aq) \quad + \quad 2RCO_2^{-}(aq) \longrightarrow Ca(RCO_2)_2(s)$$

general formula of the carboxylate ion            formula of the calcium salt

These solid precipitates are better known as the scum that is formed after a particularly soapy bath!

■   As an exercise before reading the next Section, try to think how you might try to develop a cleaning material with similar properties to soap but which would be more soluble and so wouldn't form scums. It might help you to list the properties of soap and the features that give rise to these properties, and to identify the source of the problem and the kind of information you'd need before you could proceed.

■   You can compare your ideas with those we've come up with at the beginning of the next Section.

## 1.2 Detergents...anionic surfactants of a different kind

Soaps work because they generally dissolve in water, and are themselves able to dissolve other fats and oils. They dissolve in water because they have an ionic end, in this case the negatively charged carboxylate group, which can form attractive interactions with water molecules. They will dissolve grease because the interior of the soap micelles contains long-chain non-polar hydrocarbon tails allowing it to behave like a hydrocarbon solvent. The problem with soaps is that the calcium and magnesium compounds tend to be insoluble. So the problem resides in the negatively charged carboxylate group.

How then can we devise a soap with better solubility? Clearly, we need a molecule that contains both an ionic end and a hydrocarbon end. Because it is the ionic end in soaps that gives the problems, perhaps we could change the carboxylate ionic end for some other negatively charged group that will produce soluble calcium and magnesium compounds. This means that we need some more information. If we want to introduce a different negatively charged group into the soap then we need to know which one to choose. To do that we need to know the solubilities of some simple compounds.

■ Table 1.2 contains solubility data for various compounds involving the negatively charged phosphate, sulfate and carbonate ions. Use these data to suggest a negatively charged ion that might provide a suitable starting point for a more soluble soap.

**Table 1.2** Solubilities in water of some phosphate, sulfate and carbonate compounds

| Anion | | Solubility/g kg$^{-1}$ | | | |
|---|---|---|---|---|---|
| | | $Na^+$ | $K^+$ | $Mg^{2+}$ | $Ca^{2+}$ |
| $^-O-\overset{\overset{O}{\|\|}}{\underset{\underset{O^-}{\|}}{P}}-O^-$ | (phosphate, $PO_4^{3-}$) | 1040 | 1670 | 0.2 | 0.02 |
| $^-O-\overset{\overset{O}{\|\|}}{\underset{\underset{O}{\|\|}}{S}}-O^-$ | (sulfate, $SO_4^{2-}$) | 195 | 120 | 710 | 3.0 |
| $^-O\overset{\overset{O}{\|\|}}{\diagup}\overset{C}{\diagdown}O^-$ | (carbonate, $CO_3^{2-}$) | 215 | 1469 | 0.1 | 0.01 |

■ Although the sodium and potassium compounds of all three anions are very soluble, in particular the phosphates, the solubilities of the magnesium and calcium compounds of phosphate and carbonate are very low. The sulfates of magnesium and calcium are at least 100 times more soluble than the other two types. So, it would seem that the sulfate ion is a good candidate.

This is a sensible deduction. If we look at the structural relationship between the carboxylate anion of soap and the carbonate anion:

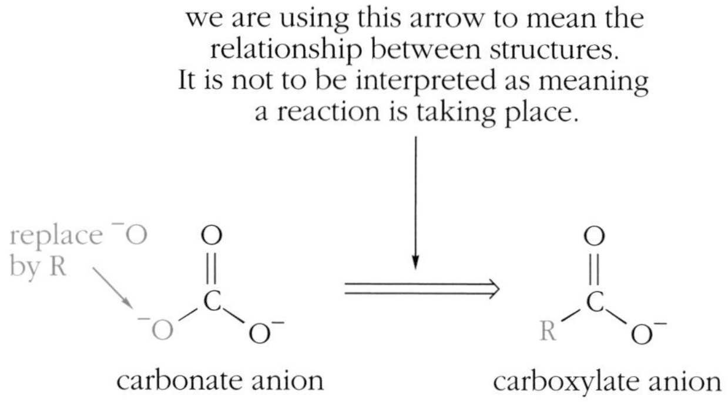

we are using this arrow to mean the
relationship between structures.
It is not to be interpreted as meaning
a reaction is taking place.

replace $^-$O
by R

carbonate anion                              carboxylate anion

then you can see that, by choosing sulfate as the model anion, the type of cleaning agent we want is a sulfonate:

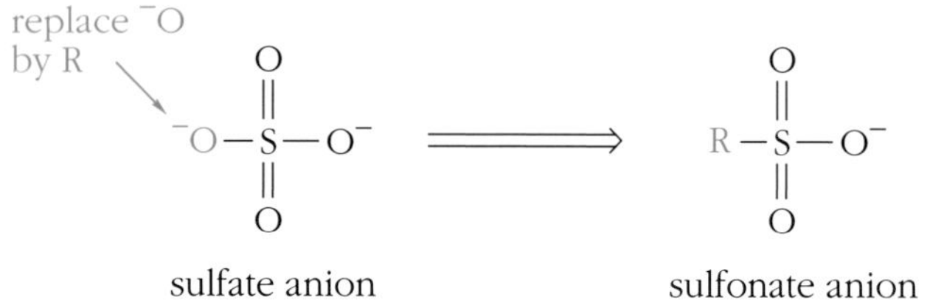

replace $^-$O
by R

sulfate anion                                sulfonate anion

What we've done here is mentally to take two anions, carbonate and sulfate, each of which contains two negatively charged $O^-$ groups, and replace one of the $O^-$ groups by a long-chain hydrocarbon. Notice that we haven't even attempted to describe how we might actually carry out such interconversions, using chemical reactions, which could be quite a challenging task. This is simple 'Lego-brick' chemistry. I mean by this that we are thinking about molecules as if they are structures that are made up of molecular 'bricks'. These bricks can be removed, replaced or interchanged to adapt a structure in much the same way as we might remove, replace or interchange Lego bricks to modify a toy house that we are building. The analogy goes further, because we can even talk of 'playing around with molecular structure' without worrying about how we might do so. We are simply using our knowledge to design new molecules with potentially useful properties.

Because the starting anions, carbonate and sulfate, have two negative charges, the two anions that are the outcome of our reasoning, carboxylate and sulfonate, have one negative charge, which is the minimum required to form the ionic 'head' of a detergent molecule.

Sulfonates were the first synthetic cleaning agents to be made and began to appear in the mid-1930s. Such synthetics are generally called **detergents** to identify them as being different from soap. On product packaging they can be identified by the term **anionic surfactant**, although soaps, too, are anionic surfactants. This term is used because the molecules of both soaps and sulfonate detergents have an anionic end. Surfactant is a contraction of *surface-active agent*, the term used to describe a detergent's ability to change the properties of the surfaces formed between water and other liquids and solids (such as oils and greases).

**Question 2** Extend the reasoning we've just developed to design two different types of detergent based on the phosphate group. Use the data in Table 1.2 to predict the properties that such detergents might have.

**Question 3** Which of the following anions would you assess to have the potential to be developed into anionic surfactants?

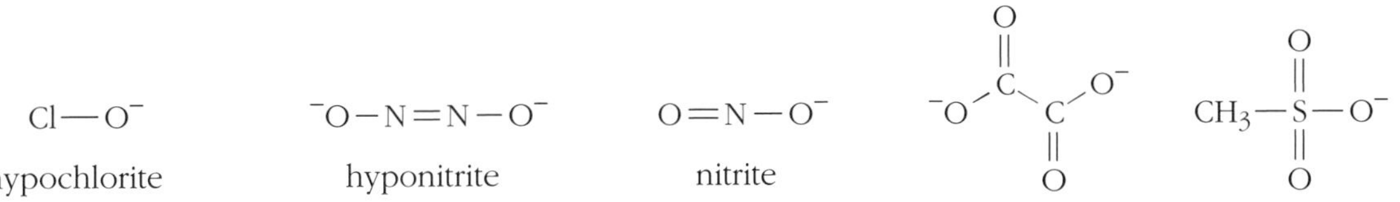

$$Cl-O^-$$

hypochlorite

$$^-O-N=N-O^-$$

hyponitrite

$$O=N-O^-$$

nitrite

oxalate

methanesulfonate

**Question 4** Use the solubility information in Table 1.3 to design a potential detergent with the highest solubility.

**Table 1.3** Solubilites in water of some ionic compounds.

| Anion | | Solubility/g kg$^{-1}$ | | | |
|---|---|---|---|---|---|
| | | Na$^+$ | K$^+$ | Mg$^{2+}$ | Ca$^{2+}$ |
| 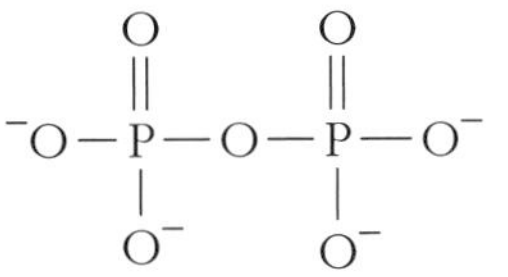 (pyrophosphate, $P_2O_7^{4-}$) | | 54 | soluble | insoluble | insoluble |
| 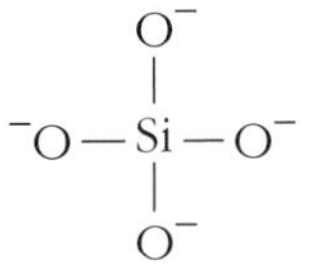 (orthosilicate, $SiO_4^{4-}$) | | soluble | not known | insoluble | insoluble |
| 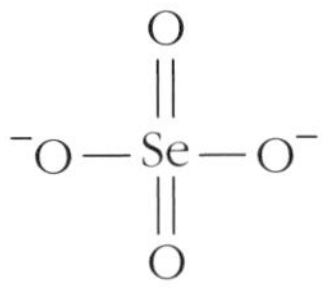 (selenate, $SeO_4^{2-}$) | | 840 | 1105 | very soluble | 79 |

Sulfonate detergents were originally developed because there was a need for cleaning agents with improved solubility in the textile dyeing industry, where it is essential to remove all traces of grease and other materials adhering to the fabric before it can be printed and finished. Detergents, such as washing powders and liquids, are now also commonly used around the home for most cleaning purposes.

Apart from taurocholate, a compound found in bile, sulfonate detergents are not known to exist in nature. They are synthetic materials made from products of the petrochemical industry, and are usually alkylbenzene sulfonates (ABS). They are ionic compounds, in which the cation is usually sodium and the anion has the general structure shown in **1.6**.

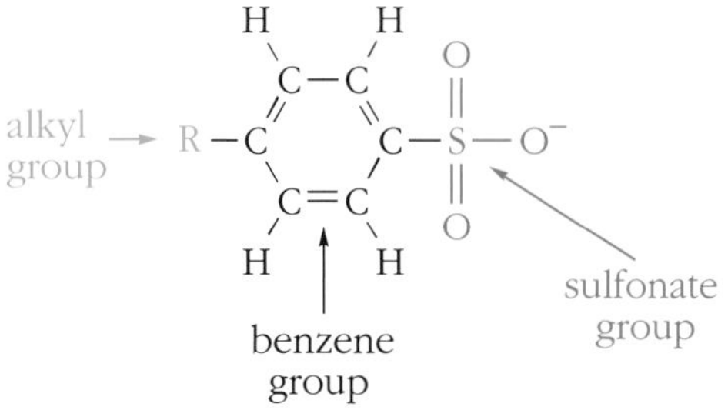

**1.6**

We met benzene in Book 2, Part 1, Chapter 5, and we shall be examining the structure of benzene systems in more detail shortly.

The sulfonate group is the polar end of the molecule that enables the detergent to dissolve in water. The alkyl and benzene groups form the hydrocarbon end that enables the detergent to dissolve fats and oils. Soaps, because they are synthesized from naturally occurring fats and oils, have only a limited range of structures as the range of carboxylic acids used to make fats is limited. Synthetic detergents, however, can be tailor-made to fit a specific cleaning task by varying the alkyl group R in the general structure. Initially, the R group used in most detergents had the following structure:

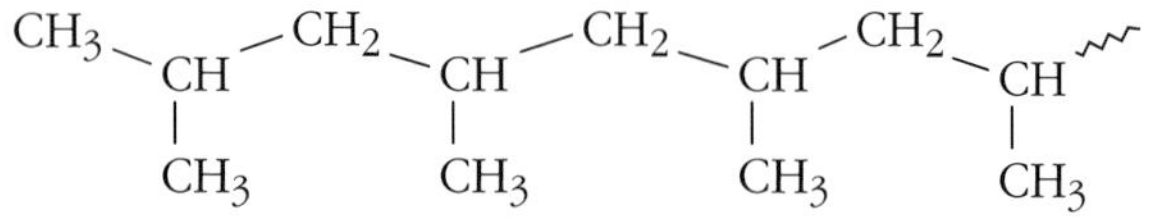

The reason for this choice was simple. Propene (**1.7**) (which used to be called propylene, and is used to make the polypropylene plastics found around the home) was – and still is – a major product of the petroleum industry.

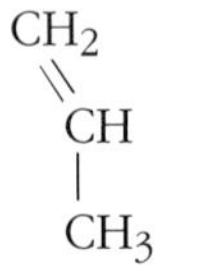

**1.7** propene 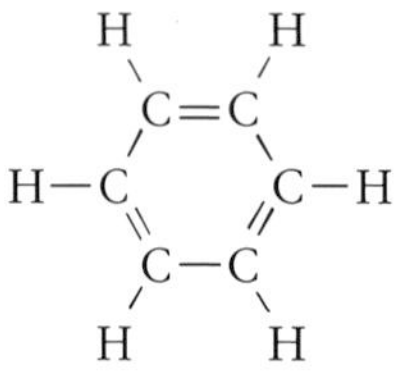                          **1.8**

Four molecules of propene are easily linked together to form what is called a tetramer (from the Greek *tetra* meaning four), and this is then joined to benzene (**1.8**) to form the alkylbenzene part of the detergent. This process can be represented as follows:

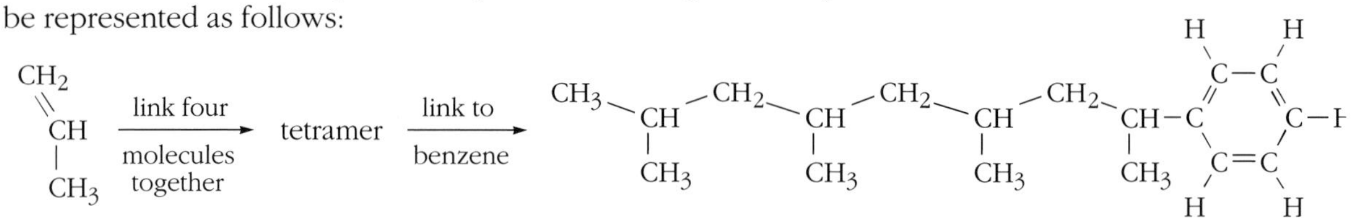

Notice that here we have used the arrow notation to show a process of chemical change, but that we have also included some description of what that change involves. We shall continue to use this shorthand way of describing reactions, and in some circumstances we may even write the chemicals that bring about the change over the arrows too. We do this because we are more interested in the change that has taken place rather than the chemistry involved in bringing it about.

■ Take a look at the molecular structure of the alkylbenzene formed from propene, and compare it with that of propene. Try to identify the four propene units in the alkyl group. (You'll notice that one of the propene units contains an extra hydrogen. Don't worry about this – it's a consequence of the chemistry involved in making the alkyl group.)

■ The propene units are as shown on the following structure:

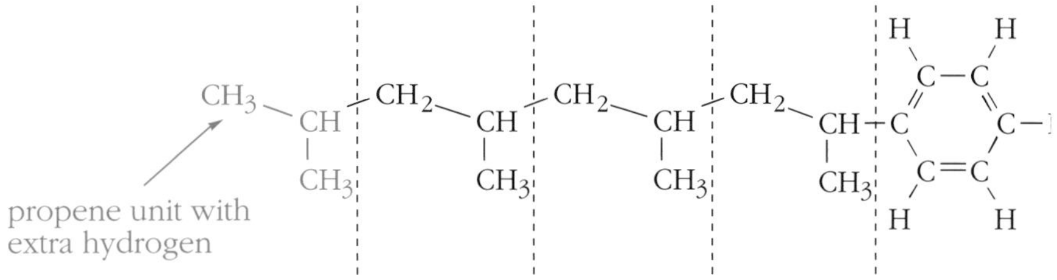

propene unit with extra hydrogen

The next step in the process is for the benzene end of the alkylbenzene to react with sulfur trioxide gas, which has the formula $SO_3$ (**1.9**),

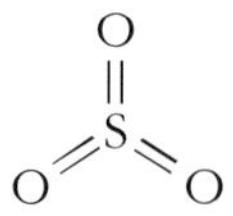

**1.9**

to form a sulfonic acid, which is then neutralized by the addition of base (NaOH) to form the sulfonate detergent:

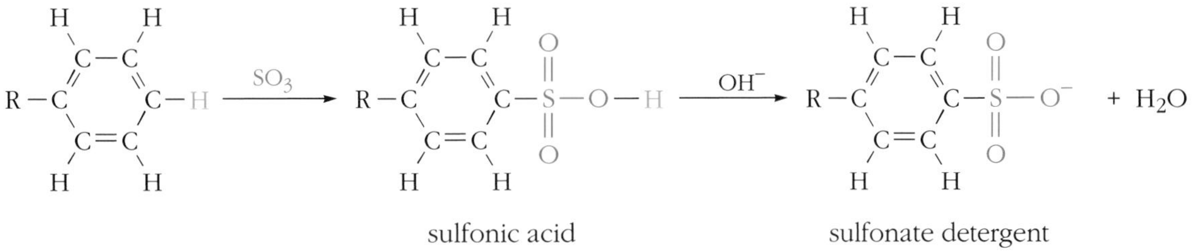

sulfonic acid            sulfonate detergent

You might be wondering 'why not link the propene tetramer directly to sulfur trioxide?'. That is a good question. Suffice it to say that benzene systems react easily with $SO_3$ whereas alkyl systems don't. It makes sense, then, to incorporate a benzene group so that the sulfonate head can be made easily.

## Activity 2  A molecular model of benzene

At this stage, it seems appropriate that you should use the model kit to make a molecular model of benzene so that you can get a 'feel' for its structure. You will find that this will prove particularly useful when we deal with drug development in Chapter 6.

To make the model you will need six black centres to represent the carbon atoms and six white centres to represent the hydrogen atoms. You will also need nine short, inflexible bonds and six long flexible ones.

First, to each C centre attach one short and one long bond. To the short bond attach a white H centre. You should now have six —C—H units like that in Figure 1.8.

**Figure 1.8**
Model of a —C—H unit made with the model kit.

Now, using two of the flexible bonds, join two of these units together to make a —CH=CH— unit like that in Figure 1.9. *Make sure that the H centres are both on the same side of the double bond*. Make three of these —CH=CH— units. Joining two C centres by using two flexible bonds is the way of representing a carbon–

**Figure 1.9**
Model of a —CH=CH— unit made with the model kit.

carbon double bond. All that is left to do is to join these three units together using the three remaining short bonds. When you have done that, you should have a model of the benzene molecule that looks like Figure 1.10.

**Figure 1.10**
Model of benzene made with the model kit.

Note that each carbon atom in benzene forms four bonds to other atoms, so its valency is satisfied.

A real molecule of benzene is a perfect hexagon. Your model probably doesn't resemble a *perfect* hexagon, but this is purely a result of the nature of the short inflexible and long flexible bonds supplied with the kit. You will have to imagine your model to be a perfect hexagon.

▪ What is the molecular formula of benzene?

■ The molecular formula is $C_6H_6$.

Because it is composed of only carbon and hydrogen, benzene is classed as a hydrocarbon. In the 19th century, chemists struggled to work out what kind of structure a compound with molecular formula $C_6H_6$ would have. This was an intriguing problem given that each carbon atom needed to form four bonds. Eventually, in 1865, the German August Kekulé guessed that it must have a cyclic structure with each carbon atom involved in double bond formation, as in the model you have made.

One of the most striking features of the model is that it is flat; that is, all the atoms lie in the same plane. This is entirely a consequence of the double bond system used to make the ring. Pick up your model and hold it so that you can see all the atoms in the same plane. We say that the benzene ring is *planar*, and *the benzene ring system* – which is found in many types of compound, such as the alkylbenzene sulfonate detergents – *is always flat*.

Now hold your model so that it resembles the ball-and-stick picture in Figure 1.10. The plane of the ring should be parallel with the plane of the paper. It would be very tiresome if every time we wanted to represent benzene we used this ball-and-stick fashion, so we use abbreviated structures. We shall

initially use an abbreviated structure that includes letters for the atoms:

$$
\begin{array}{c}
\text{H} \\
| \\
\text{C} \\
\text{H}-\text{C} \quad \quad \text{C}-\text{H} \\
\quad \parallel \quad \\
\text{H}-\text{C} \quad \quad \text{C}-\text{H} \\
\text{C} \\
| \\
\text{H}
\end{array}
$$

but shall gradually move over to using

$$
\begin{array}{c}
\text{H} \\
\text{H} \quad \quad \quad \text{H} \\
\\
\text{H} \quad \quad \quad \text{H} \\
\text{H}
\end{array}
$$

where the carbon atoms have been omitted (but not forgotten!).

In this type of structure, whenever there is a junction between bonds it is assumed that a carbon atom is present. It's just that for clarity we leave it out. In fact, this representation can be simplified further:

In this last representation the hydrogen atoms, and even the bonds to them, have been omitted. They haven't been 'lost', it is just that to simplify the drawings for clarity they are not included, but we should always assume them to be there. These three types of diagram are all equivalent representations of the model of the benzene molecule you have made.

Now, rotate your model through half a turn (clockwise or anticlockwise, it doesn't matter) so that the plane of the ring is again parallel with the plane of the paper.

▨ Draw an abbreviated structure for this way of looking at benzene.

▪ Any one of the following three structures is correct:

These look identical with the previous structures except that each of the

double bonds appears to have moved one position further round the ring. But, we didn't change our model – we simply turned it over – so the benzene molecule hasn't been changed. This leads us to the conclusion that the following two drawings are equivalent representations of the benzene molecule:

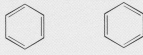

You will find that we shall use either.

There is a whole host of compounds that contain ring systems similar to that in benzene. Let's use our model of benzene, together with our Lego-brick approach, to make a model of a simple derivative of benzene – toluene (tol-you-een). Toluene is methylbenzene; that is, benzene plus a methyl, $CH_3$, group. So you'll need another black C centre to which you should attach three white H centres using the short bonds (Figure 1.11).

**Figure 1.11**
Model of a methyl group made with the model kit.

This is the methyl group that we need to attach to benzene.

Pick up the benzene molecule in one hand and the methyl group in the other, and try to attach them together. You should find that you can't because there are no 'spare' bonds to use. How can we do it? Well, remove one of the hydrogen centres, but not the bond, from the benzene molecule. This gives us a 'spare' bonding position to which we can attach the $CH_3$ group – so do that now. The model you've got is that of toluene.

▨ Write down an abbreviated structure for toluene.

▪ Any of the following structures, which chemically are all the same, is correct:

Whereas benzene contains six hydrogens bonded to the ring carbon atoms, in the **benzene ring system** of toluene only five of the carbon atoms are bonded to hydrogen – the sixth is bonded to the carbon atom of the $CH_3$ group. This process of replacing an H atom by a $CH_3$ groups is analogous to adding the propene tetramer to benzene to form an alkylbenzene sulfonate detergent.

In our Lego-brick approach to molecular structure, we have obtained toluene from benzene by removing one of the hydrogen atoms in benzene and replacing it with the $CH_3$ group. That has actually involved *breaking a C—H bond and forming a new C—C bond*. If we were really to make toluene from benzene we would have to use chemical reactions that do precisely those operations. We shall not be discussing those here, however, since they are outside the scope of this Course.

**Figure 1.12**
A scene showing how suds from synthetic sulfonate detergents can foul the environment, here Montgomery County, Pennsylvania, USA. Molecular modification of sulfonate detergents has enabled such scenes to be a thing of the past.

Despite their suitability as good cleaning agents, the sulfonate detergents based on the propene tetramer have an undesirable environmental effect – they are not biodegradable. The bacteria in the environment that can break down soaps can't break down this type of detergent. In the 1960s this resulted in the fouling of rivers with enormous quantities of suds (Figure 1.12).

■ Take a look at the molecular structures of a typical soap and the propene-based sulfonate detergent. List some differences between the two structures that might have a bearing on the difference in biodegradability.

soap

ABS detergent

■ There are three major differences between the two types of surfactant:

| *Soap* | *Detergent* |
|---|---|
| anionic end is a carboxylate | anionic end is a sulfonate |
| hydrocarbon chain contains only $CH_2$ groups | hydrocarbon chain contains a benzene ring |
| hydrocarbon chain is linear | hydrocarbon chain has $CH_3$ groups branching out from it |

Before continuing, take some time to think how you might go about finding out which of these molecular differences is responsible for the biodegradability. Jot down your ideas then compare them with those described below.

I think if I were to examine the problem, I'd set about it in the following way. First, I'd establish that I wouldn't vary the sulfonate group. We've already decided we want to use that group because its compounds have the best solubility in water. That means we only have two choices to make: we can make a sulfonate that either doesn't contain the benzene ring or contains an alkyl chain that doesn't have any groups branching out from it. There is always the third option, of course, which is to make both of these modifications at the same time, but in science it is always better to vary one thing at a time.

We need to find out which of these is responsible for the environmental problem. The simplest option, from a synthetic point of view, is to make a sulfonate with a linear hydrocarbon chain rather than the branched one that we get from propene. How can we do this? Well, the branching occurs because propene contains a $CH_3$ group:

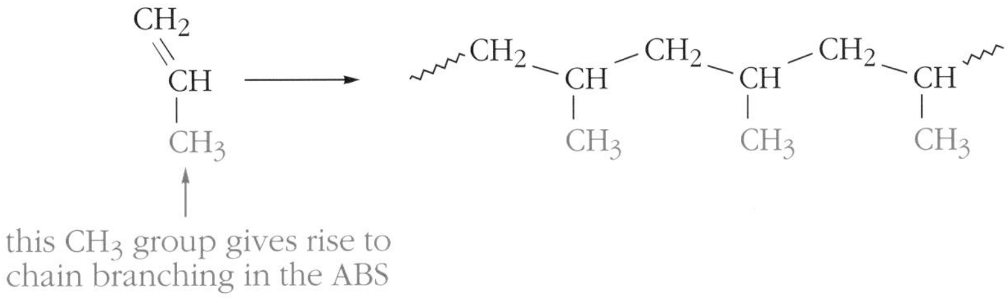

this $CH_3$ group gives rise to chain branching in the ABS

Perhaps, if we use a different starting material, one that is similar to propene but without the $CH_3$ group, we might be able to make a linear sulfonate detergent. The starting material for this strategy is ethene (formerly known as ethylene), a major petrochemical used to make all the polyethene products that we use every day. Molecules of ethene can be linked together in the same way as those of propene, to form a linear alkyl group, which can then be linked to benzene to form a linear alkylbenzene:

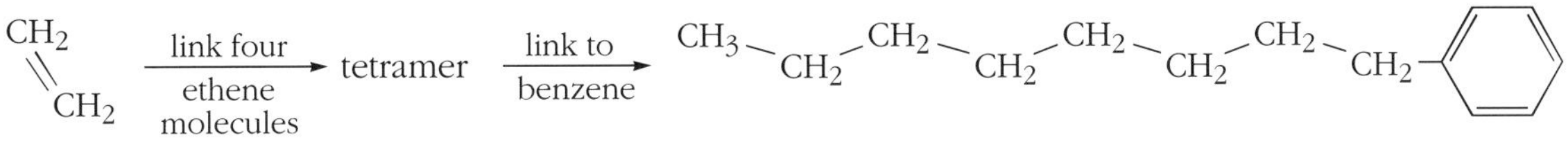

ethene

linear alkylbenzene

Not surprisingly, the detergents made from ethene are called **linear alkylbenzene sulfonates**.

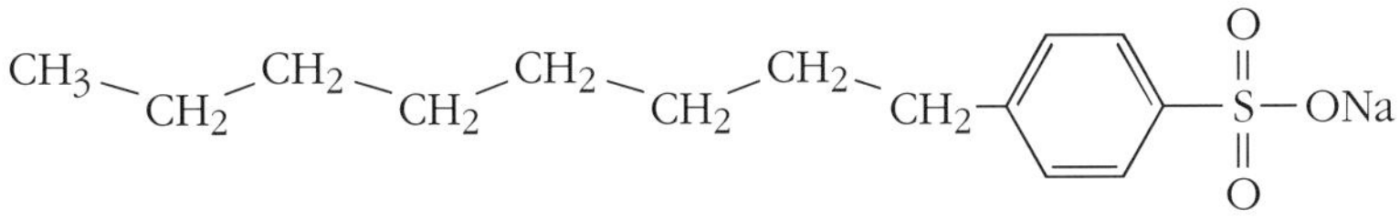

linear alkylbenzene sulfonate detergent

Thankfully, these are biodegradable, so the problem associated with propene-based detergents is related to chain branching. The bacteria seem to prefer to degrade linear alkyl chains.

A different approach to the problems surrounding the biodegradability of detergents is obtained by linking the long-chain hydrocarbon tail to the ionic head group in an alternative fashion. Instead of replacing the $O^-$ group in the sulfate ion, $SO_4^{2-}$, by a long-chain hydrocarbon chain, R, as we did to design the sulfonate detergents:

$$\underset{\text{by R}}{\text{replace}} \longrightarrow {}^-O - \overset{\overset{\displaystyle O}{\|}}{\underset{\underset{\displaystyle O}{\|}}{S}} - O^- \Longrightarrow R - \overset{\overset{\displaystyle O}{\|}}{\underset{\underset{\displaystyle O}{\|}}{S}} - O^-$$

$$\text{sulfate anion} \qquad\qquad \text{sulfonate anion}$$

it is possible to replace an $O^-$ group by linking the alkyl group through an oxygen atom:

$$\underset{\text{by RO}}{\text{replace}} \longrightarrow {}^-O - \overset{\overset{\displaystyle O}{\|}}{\underset{\underset{\displaystyle O}{\|}}{S}} - O^- \Longrightarrow R - O - \overset{\overset{\displaystyle O}{\|}}{\underset{\underset{\displaystyle O}{\|}}{S}} - O^-$$

$$\text{sulfate anion} \qquad\qquad \text{alkyl sulfate ester}$$

This gives rise to an alkyl sulfate ester. At the molecular level, the difference between alkyl sulfate esters and sulfonates is that in sulfonates the hydrocarbon tail is bonded directly to the sulfur atom by a carbon–sulfur bond, whereas in sulfate esters the hydrocarbon tail is bonded to an oxygen atom by a carbon–oxygen bond and it is this oxygen atom that is bonded to the sulfur through an oxygen–sulfur bond.

▨   Why do you think sulfate esters can act as detergents?

◼   The sulfate ester group is ionic and, given the solubility of compounds containing the sulfate ion $SO_4^{2-}$ (Table 1.2), is likely to be soluble in water. The long-chain hydrocarbon tail, R, provides the ability to dissolve non-polar substances like fats and oils.

▨   What kinds of compound have you come across that are likely to be the source of these RO groups?

◼   The RO group forms the basis of the alcohols, ROH. If we can replace the H atom in alcohols by the sulfate group, then alcohols will provide the source of RO.

This is indeed the case. Long-chain alcohols, either from natural sources or made synthetically as by-products of the petrochemical industry, can react directly with sulfur trioxide, $SO_3$, in the presence of sodium hydroxide to form the sulfate esters:

$$R - O - H \; + \; \overset{\displaystyle O}{\underset{\displaystyle O}{\overset{\|}{S}}}\!\!\diagdown_O \longrightarrow R - O - \overset{\overset{\displaystyle O}{\|}}{\underset{\underset{\displaystyle O}{\|}}{S}} - O - H \xrightarrow{\text{NaOH}} R - O - \overset{\overset{\displaystyle O}{\|}}{\underset{\underset{\displaystyle O}{\|}}{S}} - ONa \; + \; H_2O$$

■ Knowing what you do about the sulfonate detergents, what would you do to ensure that the sulfate esters are biodegradable?

■ Biodegradable sulfonate detergents required linear long-chain hydrocarbon tails, so it would seem sensible to ensure that the hydrocarbon chains of sulfate esters are linear too.

These linear **sodium alkyl sulfate** detergents are readily biodegradable (Figure 1.13), rivalling soaps for their speed of degradation. This is because the sulfur–oxygen bond in the sulfate esters is susceptible to hydrolysis, just like the carbon–oxygen bond in esters:

this bond
is broken

forms the
alcohol

$$R-O-\overset{\overset{\textstyle O}{\|}}{\underset{\underset{\textstyle O}{\|}}{S}}-O^{-} \ + \ H_2O \ \longrightarrow \ R-O-H \ + \ H-O-\overset{\overset{\textstyle O}{\|}}{\underset{\underset{\textstyle O}{\|}}{S}}-O^{-}$$

forms
sulfate

this bond
is broken

forms the
alcohol

$$R^2-O-\overset{\overset{\textstyle O}{\|\!\!\!\backslash}}{C}\diagdown_{R^1} \ + \ H_2O \ \longrightarrow \ R^2-O-H \ + \ H-O-\overset{\overset{\textstyle O}{\|\!\!\!\backslash}}{C}\diagdown_{R^1}$$

forms
carboxylic
acid

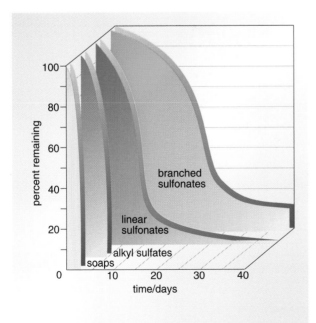

**Figure 1.13**
Rates of biodegradation of different types of detergent. The vertical axis represents the amount remaining in the environment.

This hydrolysis forms the sulfate ion, which is a commonly encountered natural mineral, and the long-chain alcohol. These long-chain alcohols are used as energy sources by micro-organisms in the environment and degrade rapidly. Many of the household cleaning agents that you listed at the beginning of this chapter contain these sulfate detergents.

**Question 5** Suppose you wanted to formulate a cleaning agent that you were confident would biodegrade within a week. Use the data in Figure 1.13, together with knowledge already gained from your study of this Book, to suggest a suitable surfactant for your formulation.

Before moving on, let's review what we've discovered about the process by which synthetic detergents have developed from an understanding of soaps, because the sequence of events reveals a great deal about the method of chemistry.

First, it was noted that soaps, formed from a naturally available material, were good cleaning agents that have certain drawbacks related to solubility. The obvious question arises 'Can we improve on the cleaning ability of soap?', which immediately raises the question 'What are the essential features of soap molecules that give soap its properties?'. After these are identified, a choice has to be made as to which feature needs to be modified to improve the performance of the material. This is followed by making the new materials containing the modified features and testing them. After obtaining the results, the changes are refined, and new materials are made and tested.

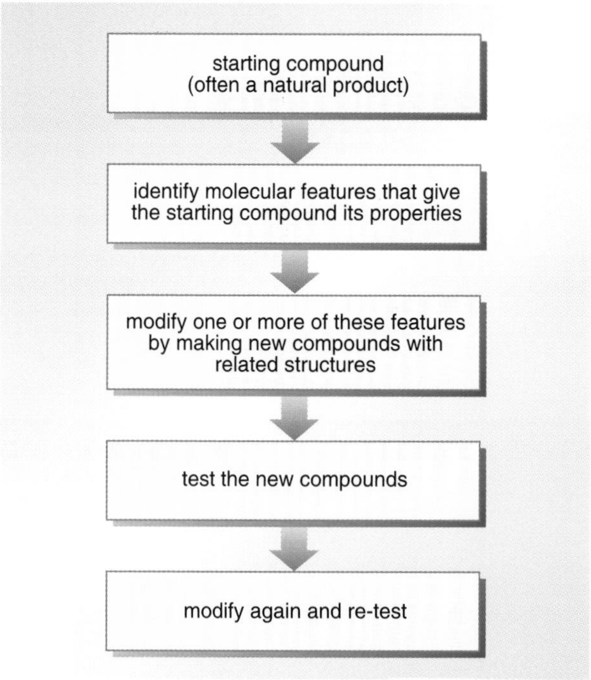

**Figure 1.14**
Flow diagram to show the process of developing a new material from a starting compound.

This process is shown schematically in Figure 1.14. You'll discover later that this is how new drugs are developed, and you could also apply it to the discovery of new materials that you studied earlier in the Course.

> **Question 6** Follow the flow diagram in Figure 1.14 and, for each box, identify a specific stage in the development of synthetic detergents from soaps. Put your answer in the form of a flow diagram similar to Figure 1.14.

## 1.3 Summary of Chapter 1

In Chapter 1 you have found out how:

Soaps are formed by the hydrolysis of fats and oils using a solution of a base.

The cleaning properties of soap are a result of its molecular structure: an ionic sodium compound of a carboxylic acid that forms a water-soluble head group, and a long-chain hydrocarbon group that forms a non-polar tail.

Soaps form micelles in water, with the ionic head groups at the surface and the hydrocarbon tails forming a non-polar interior in which fatty substances can dissolve.

Magnesium and calcium compounds of soaps are not very soluble, which means that soaps are poor cleaning agents in hard water areas.

By applying a Lego-brick approach to molecular structure, sulfonate detergents that have improved solubility characteristics over soaps can be designed from a knowledge of ion solubility.

Branched sulfonate detergents are only poorly biodegradable whereas linear sulfonate detergents are more readily biodegradable.

Alkyl sulfate detergents are formed by linking long-chain alcohols to sulfur trioxide; this type of detergent rivals soap for its biodegradability.

You have also seen that:

The benzene ring is a flat, planar system and that derivatives of benzene can be formed by removing a hydrogen atom and replacing it with some other group.

Esters are readily hydrolysed to form a carboxylic acid and an alcohol.

# Chapter 2
# From detergents to antibacterials

In Chapter 2 we shall continue to develop the idea of detergency, but will discover that other types of substance can also act as detergents. This will lead us to substances that have an antibacterial effect, as well as a detergent action. So our story will have progressed from simply keeping clean by washing, to the concept of destroying potentially harmful organisms.

## 2.1 Non-ionic surfactants

From what we've discovered about anionic surfactants, the major features of a cleaning agent are that (i) it will dissolve in water, and (ii) it will dissolve fats and oils. In order to dissolve greasy materials the detergent needs to have a hydrocarbon part to its molecular structure. To dissolve in water it must contain a polar feature that can interact with water molecules; in soaps this is the carboxylate anion, in detergents it is the sulfonate or sulfate anion. But ions are not the only substances that can dissolve in water. For example, alcohol (ethanol) and sugar are two commonly encountered substances that are neutral and non-ionic yet dissolve readily in water.

> ethyl          alcohol
> group          group
>
> $CH_3 — CH_2 — OH$
>
> **2.1** ethanol

Ethanol (**2.1**) contains an OH group like the one in water. This OH group can form hydrogen bonds to the OH groups in water and, because the hydrocarbon part of the molecules is small and contains only two carbon atoms, the ethanol dissolves because there is little overall disruption to the water structure. Other alcohols, in which the ethyl group is replaced by longer chain hydrocarbon groups, tend to dissolve in water only slightly because the disruption to water structure caused by the hydrocarbon end outweighs the water-soluble effect of the OH group. Nevertheless, such alcohols with longer hydrocarbon chains have grown into common use, as your list for Activity 1 may intimate. These compounds act as surfactants because the hydrocarbon chain interacts with fats and oils, the alcohol group with water. Because they don't have any charged groups they're called **non-ionic surfactants**. These are waxy materials and are seldom, if ever, used on their own, but are often encountered in a soap or detergent, because together the two have enhanced cleaning action. They are often added to liquid soaps, for example, because they impart a quality to the product that is advertised as 'rich', 'creamy', 'smooth' or 'silky'.

Probably the most common type of non-ionic surfactant encountered is the ethanolamides. These are formed when a fatty acid reacts with an ethanolamine. For example, coconut ethanolamide is made from the major fatty acid of coconut oil, lauric acid:

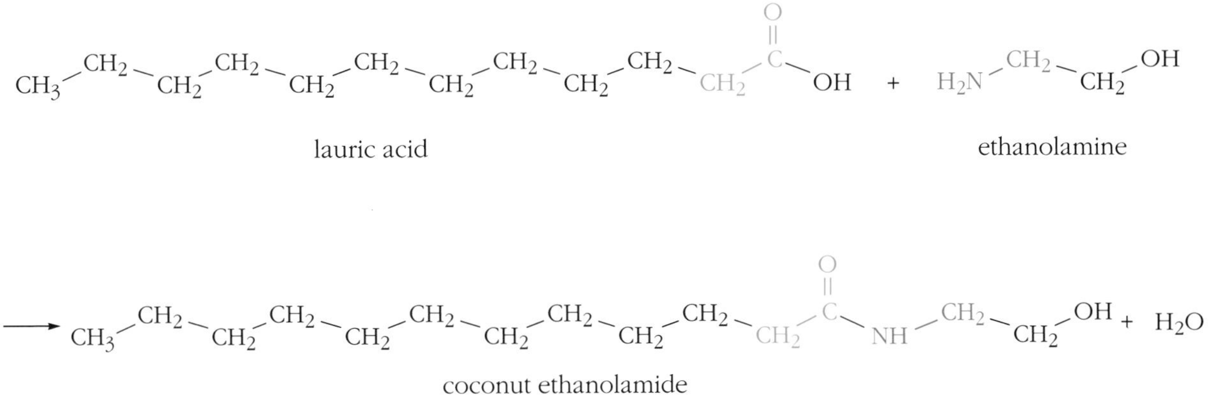

lauric acid                                                                    ethanolamine

coconut ethanolamide

---

### Box 2.1  Amines

Amines are another of the functional groups of organic chemistry. The characteristic feature of amines is a nitrogen atom bonded to three other atoms, at least one of which is a carbon atom:

Amines are therefore derivatives of ammonia, $NH_3$. There are three types of amine, each the result of successively replacing one of the hydrogen atoms in ammonia with an alkyl group. **Primary amines** have only one of the hydrogen atoms replaced, **secondary amines** have two, and **tertiary amines** have three:

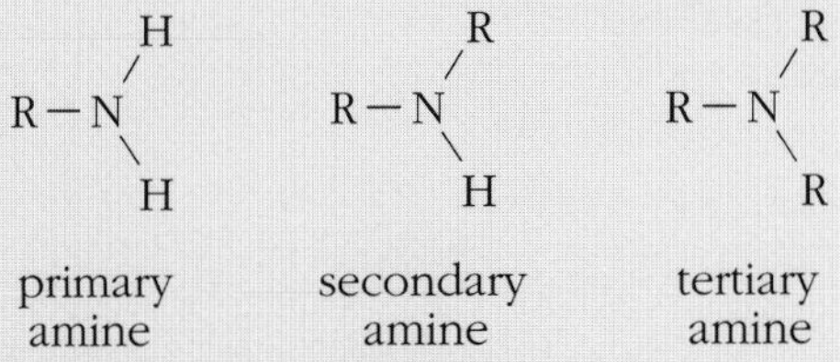

primary          secondary          tertiary
amine            amine              amine

The most characteristic property of all three types of amine is that they are bases: in water they produce basic solutions. This is because they can react with water to form a positively charged ammonium cation and a hydroxide anion, as shown in the following example for primary amines, $RNH_2$:

$$RNH_2(aq) + H_2O(l) = RNH_3^+(aq) + OH^-(aq)$$

It is the presence of the hydroxide ions that results in basic solutions.

Another important property of amines is their reaction with acids to form an ammonium cation:

$$RNH_2(aq) + H^+(aq) = RNH_3^+(aq)$$

In the same way that tertiary amines are related to ammonia by replacing all of the hydrogen atoms with alkyl groups, quaternary ammonium cations are formed when all of the hydrogen atoms in the ammonium cation are replaced by alkyl groups:

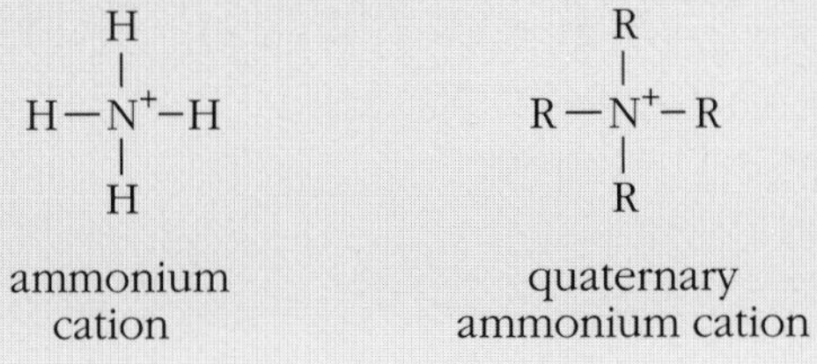

ammonium                quaternary
cation                  ammonium cation                                      (continued overleaf)

By convention, we write the positive charge in these cations as being associated with the nitrogen atom, though this is not strictly correct. Quaternary ammonium compounds are electrically neutral, being made up from the ammonium cation and an anion, for example $Cl^-$:

$$R-\overset{\overset{\displaystyle R}{|}}{\underset{\underset{\displaystyle R}{|}}{N^+}}-R \qquad Cl^-$$

general structure for a
tetraalkylammonium chloride

As you found out in Part 1, when studying the chemistry of proteins, amines react with carboxylic acids to form amides:

$$R^1{-}\overset{\overset{\displaystyle O}{||}}{C}{-}OH \quad + \quad R^2{-}NH_2 \quad \longrightarrow \quad R^1{-}\overset{\overset{\displaystyle O}{||}}{C}{-}NH{-}R^2 \quad + \quad H_2O$$

amide

Amines often, but not always, have pungent, unpleasant smells: for example, the evocatively named putrescine (**2.2**) and cadaverine (**2.3**) are two amines responsible for the smell of decaying flesh. Spermine (**2.4**) can be isolated from human sperm. Putrescine and cadaverine both contain two primary amine groups, whereas spermine contains two primary and two secondary amine groups.

$$H_2N{-}CH_2{-}CH_2{-}CH_2{-}CH_2{-}NH_2 \qquad\qquad H_2N{-}CH_2{-}CH_2{-}CH_2{-}CH_2{-}CH_2{-}NH_2$$

**2.2** putrescine                                              **2.3** cadaverine

$$H_2N{-}CH_2{-}CH_2{-}CH_2{-}NH{-}CH_2{-}CH_2{-}CH_2{-}NH{-}CH_2{-}CH_2{-}NH_2$$

**2.4** spermine

The surfactant produced is an amide of lauric acid, which can be identified on product labelling under the various guises of lauryl ethanolamide, coconut ethanolamide or vegetable ethanolamide. A variant of this is a diethanolamide, which is made from lauric acid and diethanolamine (**2.5**):

$$CH_3{-}CH_2{-}CH_2{-}CH_2{-}CH_2{-}CH_2{-}CH_2{-}CH_2{-}\overset{\overset{\displaystyle O}{||}}{C}{-}N\overset{\displaystyle CH_2{-}CH_2{-}OH}{\underset{\displaystyle CH_2{-}CH_2{-}OH}{|}}$$

lauryl diethanolamide

$$H{-}N\overset{\displaystyle CH_2{-}CH_2{-}OH}{\underset{\displaystyle CH_2{-}CH_2{-}OH}{}}$$

**2.5** diethanolamine

You will find this identified as cocamide DEA on product labels.

Both types of ethanolamide function as surfactants because of the presence of both the hydrocarbon tail and the OH groups in the head, which can form hydrogen bonds to water.

These non-ionic surfactants can be described as **semi-synthetic detergents**: in part, they are derived from naturally occurring fatty acids, but are formed by combining these with ethanolamines by synthesis. 'Environmentally friendly' cleaning agents often contain these non-ionic surfactants, and they are promoted as 'derived from natural sources' and 'biodegradable'. They are, of course, not known in nature but are the result of chemical ingenuity.

- Why might you expect these ethanolamide surfactants derived from coconut oil to be biodegradable?

- The fatty acid from which they are derived is naturally occurring and is a straight-chain fatty acid. Straight-chain fatty acids are used readily by micro-organisms as energy sources.

Long-chain 'fatty' alcohols themselves are not particularly soluble in water because hydrogen bonding of the single OH group to water molecules is not able to overcome the incompatibility of the hydrocarbon chain with water. An example of this type of alcohol is lauryl alcohol (**2.6**), which is a 12-carbon alcohol:

**2.6** lauryl alcohol

It gets tedious and cumbersome to write out large structures in this fashion all the time, so from now on we shall use abbreviated structures in which the carbon and hydrogen atoms are not explicitly identified. So lauryl alcohol would be written as **2.7**:

**2.7** an abbreviated structure of lauryl alcohol

Don't forget, at each junction of two bonds there is a carbon atom, and if nothing else is indicated then each carbon atom has the appropriate number of hydrogen atoms to satisfy its valency of 4.

One approach that has been taken to improve the water solubility of surfactant compounds such as these is the addition of further oxygen atoms at the alcohol head. This is achieved through the reaction between the fatty alcohol and ethylene oxide (another product of the petrochemical industry):

ethylene oxide

from lauryl alcohol                                   from ethylene oxide

The alcohol OH group reacts with ethylene oxide, which 'opens up' to form a new alcohol head. However, the original oxygen atom of the fatty alcohol is still present in the head and is itself capable of forming hydrogen bonds to water:

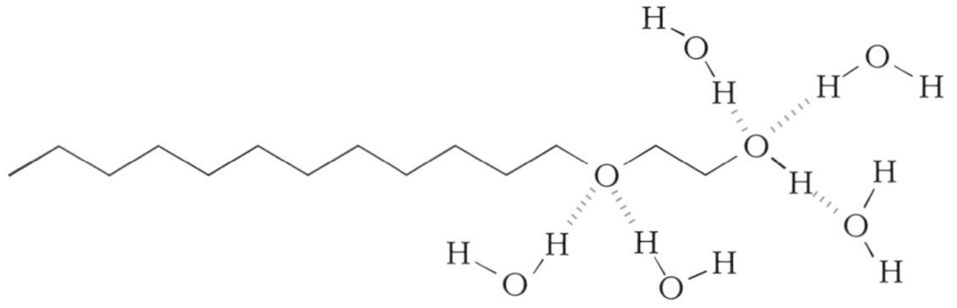

These extra hydrogen bonds to water, which the fatty alcohol doesn't contain, increase the water solubility of the surfactant.

Of course, the OH group in this new molecule can also react with ethylene oxide, just as did the original OH of the fatty alcohol. The outcome will be a new compound, **2.8**, whose molecular structure contains an extra unit from ethylene oxide.

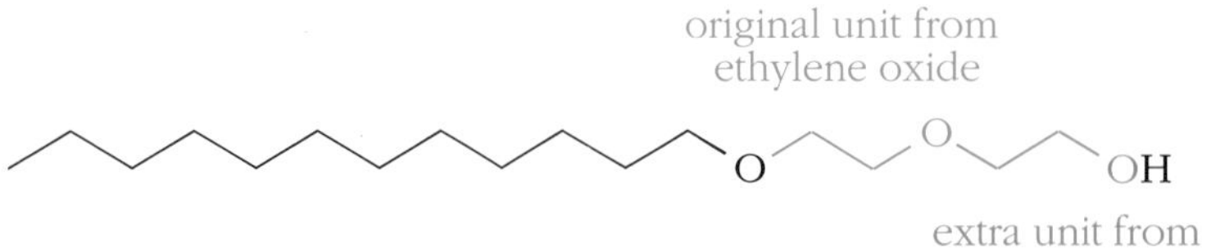

original unit from
ethylene oxide

**2.8**

extra unit from
ethylene oxide

This new molecule contains another oxygen atom in the head, so more hydrogen bonds can be formed, making it even more soluble in water.

Every time ethylene oxide reacts with the alcohol OH group a new alcohol is formed. So, it might have crossed your mind to ask 'How is it possible to control the reaction so that the reaction produces the alcohol we want?'. The answer is that it is quite difficult. The most common outcome of such a reaction is a mixture of products, each the result of a reaction with a different number of ethylene oxide molecules:

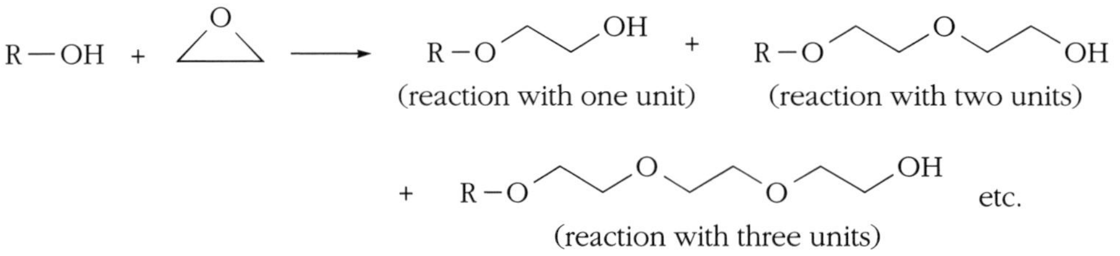

R—OH  +  (reaction with one unit)        R—O  OH        +        R—O  O  OH
                     (reaction with one unit)                        (reaction with two units)

+    R—O  O  O  OH    etc.
                 (reaction with three units)

These surfactants based on ethylene oxide can be recognized in commercial products as either **polyethylene glycols** (PEGs for short) or **fatty alcohol ethoxylates**. The name polyethylene glycol comes from the fact that ethylene glycol (which is the antifreeze used in car radiators) has the structure **2.9**, and the water-soluble end of these surfactant molecules

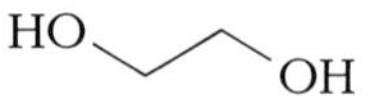

HO  OH

**2.9** ethylene glycol

resembles a polymer of ethylene glycol. The general structure of PEG surfactants based on fatty alcohols can be simplified to $R(OCH_2CH_2)_nOH$, where the R group comes from the fatty alcohol and $n$ is the number of repeating units derived from ethylene oxide.

**Question 7** PEG 75 lanolin is a surfactant found in modern soap formulations. From its name, what might you deduce about the source of the alcohol and the number of ethylene oxide repeating units in this PEG?

**Question 8** Coconut ethanolamide is a non-ionic surfactant derived from lauric acid. Starting from coconut ethanolamide, suggest a new non-ionic surfactant that also incorporates PEG technology.

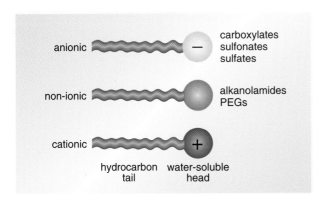

**Figure 2.1**
Schematic representation of the three types of surfactant. (The names of the types of compound that form cationic surfactants have been deliberately left out so that you can fill them in later.)

## 2.2 Cationic surfactants

So far we've seen that molecules that contain long-chain alkyl groups at one end and either an anion or a water-soluble neutral group – such as an alcohol – at the other behave as detergents. It seems reasonable to suppose, then, that a long-chain alkyl group attached to a positively charged water-soluble group might also be a detergent. Indeed, such substances are detergents, so we have three general types of surfactant as depicted in Figure 2.1.

What kinds of compound are these cationic surfactants? What's required is some kind of group that readily forms a positive charge and to which the long-chain alkyl group can be attached. An obvious choice involves derivatives of the household agent ammonia, $NH_3$, which is commonly encountered in the aqueous solutions used as oven cleaners.

As we mentioned earlier, ammonia is a base, and it readily forms ammonium cations on reaction with acids:

$$NH_3(aq) + H^+(aq) = NH_4^+(aq)$$

Now, for a surfactant we need an ammonium compound that contains a long-chain alkyl group. Perhaps you can see by looking at the above reaction that, to get such an alkylammonium compound, we need to use an alkylamine, $RNH_2$, which would react to form an alkylammonium cation:

$$RNH_2 + H^+(aq) = RNH_3^+(aq)$$

Unfortunately, in the presence of bases this reaction is reversed:

$$RNH_3^+(aq) + OH^-(aq) = RNH_2(aq) + H_2O(l)$$

and the surfactant properties would be too easily lost. How can we overcome this problem? It turns out that it's not too difficult, especially if we take a leaf out of nature's book.

Among the many compounds occurring in nature is choline (pronounced co-lean), which is an ionic compound consisting of the cation **2.10** and the Cl⁻ anion. Choline is a compound essential for the formation of cell membranes.

from ethanolamine

$$CH_3 \underset{CH_3}{\overset{CH_3}{\underset{|}{N^+}}} \underset{CH_2}{\overset{CH_2}{\diagup}} OH \qquad H_2N \underset{CH_2}{\overset{CH_2}{\diagup}} OH$$

**2.10** choline

ethanolamine

You might be able to recognize that choline is a derivative of ethanolamine, but the most distinctive feature of choline is that it is an ammonium compound formed by surrounding the nitrogen atom with four alkyl groups (three of them being $CH_3$ groups). Unlike the H atoms of simple ammonium compounds, which are readily removed by base, the alkyl groups in these **tetraalkylammonium** compounds are not easily removed.

So, the kinds of ammonium compound that form cationic surfactants are ones that have four alkyl groups around the nitrogen atom, of which one is a long-chain hydrocarbon group:

$$\text{long chain hydrocarbon group} \diagdown \underset{R^3}{\overset{R^1}{\underset{|}{\overset{|}{N^+}}}} - R^2$$

general structure of a cationic surfactant

You should add the name of ammonium compounds to the various types of surfactants in Figure 2.1.

If you look back to your list of the contents of cleaning agents that you made at the beginning of Chapter 1, you might notice that cationic surfactants are not generally used as cleaning agents, but they do have some specific uses as fabric conditioners and disinfectants/antiseptics. Their ability to act as antiseptics was discovered in the mid-1930s, when they were found to be highly effective **germicides** against common infectious bacteria (see Box 2.2).

**Figure 2.2**
The throat lozenges Merocaine® and Dequadin® contain alkylammonium compounds, which exert antibacterial activity through their cationic surfactant properties.

Cationic surfactants cannot be used for general microbial infections because, in the same way that they destroy bacteria, they destroy red blood cells. However, they can be used as **disinfectants** (that is, they kill bacteria on inanimate objects like sinks, baths and floors) and **antiseptics** (that is, they kill bacteria on living tissues). They can be used as antiseptics for those internal surfaces – such as the mucous membranes of the throat and vagina – from which they won't enter the bloodstream. Two common throat lozenges containing cationic antibacterial agents are shown in Figure 2.2. Box 2.3 shows the molecular structures of some of these agents.

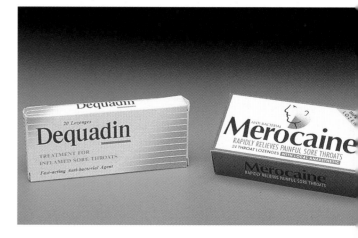

## Box 2.2 How cationic surfactants work as antiseptics

Cationic surfactant antiseptics work by disrupting the cell membranes of bacteria. These membranes are made up of **phospholipid** molecules (**2.11**), which resemble the oils that are used to make soaps. In phospholipids, two of the three oxygen atoms of glycerol are linked to long-chain fatty acids, and the third is linked to a choline molecule through a phosphate group (the structure of a phospholipid is complicated and you are not expected to remember it – just notice the various bits from which it is made):

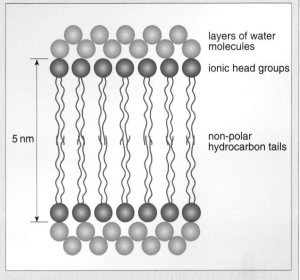

**Figure 2.3**
A representation of a phospholipid double layer. The phospholipid molecules line themselves up so that two layers are formed. The ionic groups face the outside and interact with water molecules (red spheres), and the hydrocarbon groups form a non-polar interior.

glycerol part

**2.11** a phospholipid

Each molecule therefore contains two hydrocarbon tails. In cell membranes, these molecules organize themselves into two layers that sit 'back-to-back'. The long-chain hydrocarbon groups point into the middle of the layer, and the ionic groups are at the surface where they can interact with water (Figure 2.3).

The ammonium and long-chain hydrocarbon groups of cationic detergents resemble quite closely the positively charged choline head group and fatty

acid hydrocarbon of a phospholipid. This means that molecules of the cationic detergent can take the place of phospholipid molecules in the cell membrane. If enough detergent molecules enter the membrane, the membrane structure is lost and the cell dies, usually because it bursts open.

## Box 2.3 Common antibacterial agents

Some of the common cationic antibacterials in general use are benzalkonium chloride (**2.12**), cetrimide (**2.13**) and cetylpyridinium chloride (**2.14**). Although each of these is somewhat different in structure, the most

important feature is the positively charged nitrogen atom of the ammonium group, which forms an ionic head at the end of a non-polar hydrocarbon chain. The anion in each case is chloride, $Cl^-$.

$R = C_{12}H_{25}$ and $C_{14}H_{29}$

**2.12** benzalkonium chloride

**2.13** cetrimide

**2.14** cetylpyridinium chloride

Like anionic surfactants, cationic surfactants when formulated as detergents are often combined with non-ionic detergents. However, they are incompatible with anionic surfactants. This is because, on mixing, anionic and cationic surfactants give a scum; the anionic group of one surfactant is attracted to the cationic group of the other to form a compound in which the charged groups are buried in the interior of a hydrocarbon coating, which would be insoluble in water (Figure 2.4).

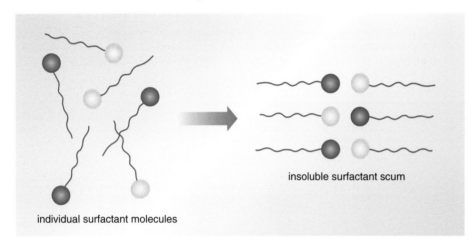

**Figure 2.4**
Formation of a surfactant scum on mixing cationic and anionic detergents.

This property of cationic detergents to be attracted to negatively charged materials has been put to good use in their role as fabric conditioners. Many fabrics have negatively charged surfaces because of the functional groups that the fibres contain within their structure. Once dirt and unwanted grease have been removed from the surface using anionic surfactants, the addition of a fabric conditioner results in the surfactant molecules being attracted to the fabric surface and adhering to it. Because the cationic head of the surfactant interacts with the fabric surface, it is the hydrocarbon tail that sticks out from the surface (Figure 2.5). These hydrocarbon groups lubricate the surface, reducing friction and static, and give the fabric a 'soft' feel.

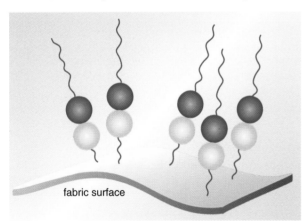

**Figure 2.5**
The surfaces of fabrics contain negatively charged carboxylate, $CO_2^-$, groups (yellow) to which cationic surfactants (blue) are attracted by ionic interactions. The presence of long-chain hydrocarbon groups gives the surface a soft smooth feel.

**Question 9** Would you expect the following sulfonium chloride to have surfactant properties? Explain your answer.

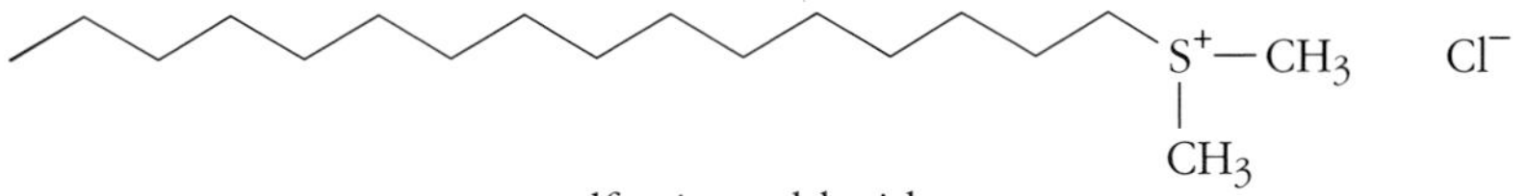

$$\text{S}^+\!-\!\text{CH}_3 \quad \text{Cl}^-$$
$$|$$
$$\text{CH}_3$$

a sulfonium chloride

**Question 10** Glass tends to have a negatively charged surface, whereas plastics tend to have positively charged surfaces. Which type or types of surfactant – cationic, non-ionic or anionic – would you choose to clean articles made from these materials? Which types would be unsatisfactory?

Cationic surfactants, because they have a dual action, form a link between materials that simply clean, such as soaps and detergents, and those that act as antiseptics and disinfectants by killing bacteria and other microbes. The idea that disease can be caused by microbes goes back over a century to the mid-1800s, and some of the antiseptics and disinfectants that we use today were developed from that period, and sometimes earlier. You will encounter the chemistry that underpins these in the next Chapter.

## 2.3 Summary of Chapter 2

In Chapter 2 you have found out that:

Molecules with surfactant properties are not restricted to the cationic soaps and detergents – both non-ionic and cationic surfactants exist.

Molecules that contain a long-chain hydrocarbon group attached to an alcohol group can act as non-ionic surfactants.

Non-ionic surfactants fall into two groups, the ethanolamides and the polyethylene glycols.

Ethanolamide surfactants are formed semi-synthetically from naturally occurring carboxylic acids and either ethanolamine or diethanolamine.

Polyethylene glycols are formed from fatty alcohols and ethylene oxide.

Molecules that contain a long-chain hydrocarbon group attached to a positively charged ammonium group can act as cationic surfactants.

Cationic surfactants can be used as fabric conditioners or as disinfectants and antiseptics.

Antiseptic cationic surfactants work by disrupting the phospholipid membranes of cells.

The cationic head groups of the cationic surfactants in fabric conditioners are attracted to the negatively charged groups on the surface of the fabric, leaving the hydrocarbon groups to give the fabric a soft texture to the surface.

You have also seen that:

Amines are derivatives of ammonia that produce basic aqueous solutions, and which form ammonium cations.

# Chapter 3
# Some common antiseptics and disinfectants

In Chapter 3 we advance our story by examining some further examples of substances that can act as antiseptics and disinfectants. The relationship between mode of action and molecular structure, in particular, will be a focus of attention.

## 3.1  Coal tar, carbolic acid and phenols

One of the more vivid memories of my childhood is the pervasive smell in my grandmother's house of coal-tar soap. It's an odour seldom encountered these days, but there can be hardly a household in the country that does not contain a product that owes its existence to compounds developed from those present in coal tar. The liquid antiseptics, such as Dettol, are one such product.

In this country, the person most closely associated with exploiting the antiseptic properties of coal tar is Joseph Lister (Figure 3.1), but he was not the first person to observe its germicidal activity. In France, coal tar adsorbed onto a clay powder was recommended as a disinfectant for manure-based fertilizer as early as 1844. Fifteen years later a similar powder was tested as a plaster to disinfect wounds. Unfortunately, its value was lost by the tendency of the plaster to turn solid, but by the end of 1859 two French pharmacists – Ferdinand LeBeuf and Jules Lemaire – introduced an emulsified coal tar solution. To emulsify the coal tar they added water and tincture of quillaia, which is rich in natural detergents called saponins. Lemaire was also a physician, and such was the success he achieved in treating septic wounds with the coal tar solution, that by 1862 all the civil hospitals in Paris had authorized its use.

Knowing that coal tar emulsions have antiseptic properties, it seems reasonable to pose the question 'Why?' This was a question that Lemaire, too, wanted to answer.

■   Coal tar is a mixture of a whole variety of compounds. Knowing this, what might you try to do to find out what gives coal tar its antiseptic properties?

■   It would seem sensible to try to separate the various compounds in coal tar and test them individually.

Coal tar can be separated into a variety of components simply by heating, in a way similar to the fractional distillation of crude oil (Book 2, Part 2, Figure 6.15). The compounds that boil at lower temperatures distill off first, and the higher boiling compounds later. Taking fractions that distil in different temperature ranges enables a crude separation of the compounds in coal tar to be made, as indicated in Figure 3.2. This doesn't separate coal tar into individual compounds however. Coal tar contains so many compounds that a continuous range of compounds is distilled, each fraction containing a mixture of compounds. Of course, the mixture in each fraction is simpler than the mixture in coal tar.

**Figure 3.1**
Joseph Lister (1827–1912). In 1965, Britain celebrated the centenary of Lister's contribution to the development of antiseptic surgery by issuing two stamps. The one shilling stamp is overprinted with the molecular structure of the major compound responsible for antiseptic activity – phenol.

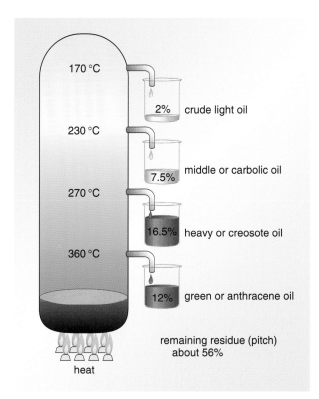

**Figure 3.2**
Fractions obtained from the distillation of coal tar.

Each of these fractions can then be treated in other ways to obtain the individual compounds contained in them. For example, the light oil can be washed with aqueous sodium hydroxide solution. Vigorously mixing the oil and aqueous layers together allows the hydroxide anions to react with any acids in the oil to form water-soluble ionic compounds. As these are formed, they pass out of the oil and into the aqueous solution. Then, when the oil and water layers are allowed to separate, the aqueous layer can be removed to leave the oil, which now contains no acidic materials

The crude light oil is then washed with an aqueous acid solution. When the oil and water layers mix, any bases in the oil react with the acid to form water-soluble ionic compounds, which dissolve in the aqueous phase.

The two phases are allowed to separate, and the aqueous layer is removed. This leaves the crude light oil, but now it has been depleted in both acidic and basic compounds. What remains is essentially a mixture of neutral organic compounds – that is, those compounds that have neither acidic nor basic characteristics (Figure 3.3).

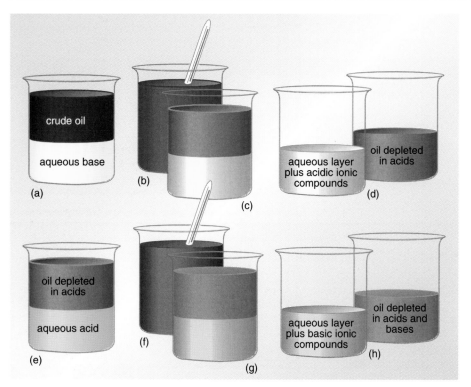

**Figure 3.3**
Washing procedure for crude light oil from coal tar. First, aqueous sodium hydroxide
solution is added to the oil (a) and the two layers are vigorously mixed (b). Acids in the oil
react with the basic solution to form water-soluble compounds, which dissolve in the
aqueous layer. The layers are allowed to separate (c) and the aqueous layer is removed
(d). The oil is now depleted in acidic compounds. Aqueous acid is then added to the oil (e)
and the two layers are again mixed vigorously (f). Any bases in the oil react with the acid to
form water-soluble ionic compounds, which dissolve in the aqueous layer. The layers are
allowed to separate (g) and the aqueous layer is removed (h). The oil is now depleted in
both acidic and basic compounds and contains essentially neutral organic compounds.

The washed oil is then distilled again, and, if fractions are taken carefully
enough, pure compounds can be obtained. For example, benzene (boiling
temperature 80 °C) and toluene (boiling temperature 111 °C), two
compounds we met earlier, are obtained from crude light oil in this way.

Lemaire was pointed towards a compound that can be obtained from carbolic
oil, and which, at that time, was generally known as carbolic acid (see Box
3.1).

The Manchester industrial chemist F. C. Calvert was interested in carbolic acid
because it was needed in the manufacture of the new synthetic dyestuffs for
the textile industry. Calvert sold most of his carbolic acid to a French firm and,
probably because of these business connections, it was he who suggested to
the French Academy of Sciences that carbolic acid was the disinfectant
substance in coal tar. Lemaire quickly established that this was so.

After reading an account of how infectious diseases were caused by bacteria,
Lister set about finding a substance that would destroy such microbes and so

## Box 3.1 Carbolic acid from coal tar

Carbolic acid can be isolated from coal tar by first distilling the coal tar to give an oil called carbolic oil, which has a pungent odour like coal-tar soap. Carbolic oil is then distilled a second time by passing steam through it. This second oil contains carbolic acid. Washing the oil with calcium hydroxide solution (slaked lime), converts the acid into a water-soluble ionic compound that dissolves in the water layer. The aqueous basic layer containing this compound is then separated from the remainder of the oil. Carbolic acid is then liberated from the basic solution by adding acid to it. This neutralizes the base, and converts the calcium compound of carbolic acid back into carbolic acid. The crude carbolic acid obtained from the aqueous layer

can be further purified by distillation (it has a boiling temperature of 182 °C). The name we give carbolic acid today is phenol, a name first proposed in 1842.

You can make a molecular model of phenol using your model kit quite simply. You will need the model of benzene you constructed earlier, as well as an extra short stiff bond and a red oxygen centre. Assemble these so that you have a model like that in Figure 3.4. This is a model of phenol.

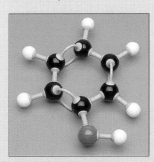

**Figure 3.4**
A ball-and-stick model of phenol.

■ Draw an abbreviated structure for phenol.

■ Any of the following is a suitable abbreviated structure:

The molecular formula of phenol is $C_6H_6O$, but more usually we write it as $C_6H_5OH$ to show that it contains a benzene ring and the OH functional group. The molecular and structural formulas reveal

that phenol is a derivative of benzene, which is obvious from the way we made our model starting from benzene.

**Question 11** Look at the structure of phenol depicted on the Lister stamp (Figure 3.1). It is obviously intended to give an impression of the structure. What is needed to make it a correct structure?

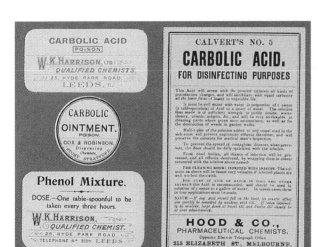

**Figure 3.5**
Labels from products containing carbolic acid used in the early 1900s.

prevent infection. His choice of carbolic acid arose because he came across a newspaper account of its use to treat sewage in Carlisle. Success at first was sporadic but, with improved techniques of use, the benefits of using carbolic acid as an antiseptic eventually became apparent and Lister became famous as the first person to use antiseptic surgery intentionally. Carbolic acid itself became a widely used disinfectant and antiseptic (Figure 3.5).

How does it work? There seem to be two ways. First, it denatures proteins. That is, it forms hydrogen bonds to the proteins that are needed both for cell structure and for catalysing the chemical reactions that go on inside cells. This alters the structure of these proteins and destroys their biological function.

The second way you may be able to work out for yourself (admittedly with a little help!).

▦   Look at the structure of phenol. Identify the part of the molecule that is likely to interact favourably with water molecules and that which is likely to have unfavourable interactions with water.

■   The OH group in phenol, like that in water itself, should be able to form hydrogen bonds to water molecules. The ring fragment is composed of only carbon and hydrogen atoms, and so is likely to have a disruptive effect on water structure.

▦   What property does a substance have if its molecular structure contains a hydrocarbon fragment at one end and a water-soluble fragment at the other?

■   Such substances act as detergents.

Indeed, phenol damages bacterial membranes partly by acting as a detergent and solubilizing the materials that make up the phospholipid cell membrane.

▦   Which type of detergent does phenol resemble?

■   It resembles a non-ionic detergent.

Unfortunately, phenol itself is a rather caustic substance, causing general corrosion or irritation of tissues depending on the concentration that is used. In the UK, proprietary preparations can contain no more than 1% of phenol; at such levels it acts as a **bacteriostat** (the bacteria aren't killed, but the colony ceases to grow in number) rather than a **bacteriocide** (the bacteria are killed).

▦   If you assume that increased bacteriocidal activity is related to its ability to act as a detergent, in general terms how might you alter the molecular structure of phenol to generate a new compound that is likely to be a better antiseptic? (Hint: think about the structures of the soaps and detergents.)

■   Both soaps and detergents have long-chain hydrocarbon groups. So, one possibility might be to add hydrocarbon groups to the hydrocarbon ring.

The cresols (**3.1**)–(**3.3**), which are also obtained from the carbolic oil fraction of coal tar, have similar antiseptic activity to phenol, but have less general toxicity and so are safer to use. As well as containing an OH group, these compounds have a $CH_3$ group attached in various positions to the benzene ring. Soap solutions of cresol are marketed as the antiseptic detergent Lysol.

**3.1**
boiling temperature 191°C

**3.2**
boiling temperature 203°C

**3.3**
boiling temperature 202°C

If a longer hydrocarbon chain is attached to the ring, the activity may be increased considerably. This is because the hydrocarbon chains enable these molecules to cause greater disruption to the phospholipid cell membrane. One such compound is *n*-hexylresorcinol **3.4** (the hexyl term comes from the Greek word for six, and there are six carbon atoms in the hydrocarbon chain), which also contains an extra OH group attached to the ring.

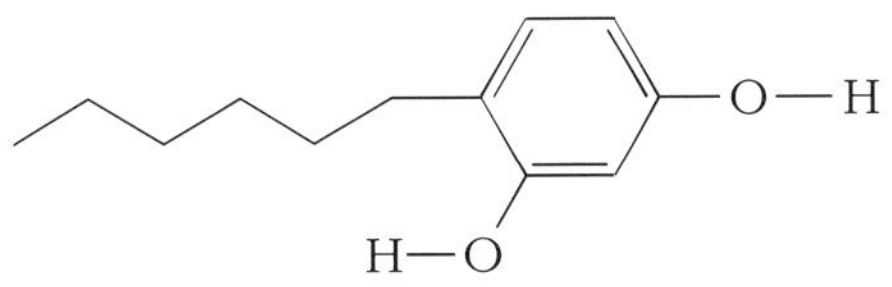

**3.4** *n*-hexylresorcinol

▨  Why might a compound like *n*-hexylresorcinol require an extra OH group in the benzene ring?

▨  The presence of the hydrocarbon chain will reduce the solubility of the molecule in water. The presence of the second OH group probably ensures that the compound remains water soluble.

The similar, naturally occurring, compound thymol (**3.5**), which is present in the essential oil derived from thyme, is also a much more powerful antiseptic than phenol, and is used chiefly in mouth-washes and gargles.

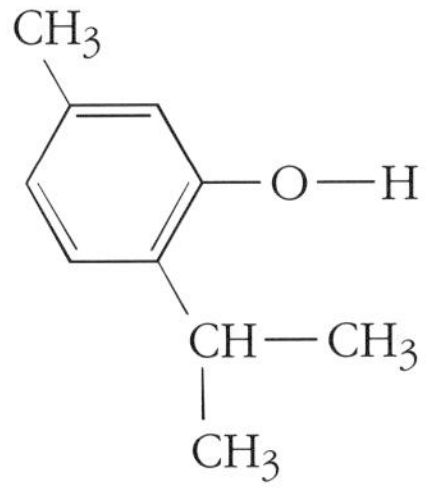

**3.5** thymol

▨  Compare the features of the molecular structures of thymol, phenol and cresol. What physical limitation might there be to the use of thymol rather than phenol and cresol?

▨  Thymol contains a three-carbon hydrocarbon chain that is absent from both phenol and cresol. So thymol is likely to be much less water soluble than phenol or cresol.

This is indeed the case; whereas one litre of water at 25 °C will dissolve 83 g of phenol or 20 g of cresol, it will dissolve only about 1 g of thymol.

It is often found that the introduction of a chlorine atom into a molecule has a similar effect to introducing long-chain hydrocarbon groups; both tend to increase antiseptic activity and decrease water solubility. For example, less than 10 g of chlorocresol will dissolve in a litre of water at 25 °C compared with 20 g of cresol. Some commonly used antiseptics that make use of this principle are hexachlorophane (pronounced heksa-klor-owe-fane) (**3.6**), chloroxylenol (pronounced kloro-zile-en-ol) (**3.7**), and trichlorophenol (try-kloro-pheenol) (**3.8**). Hexachlorophane is used as a disinfectant in medicated soaps, chloroxylenol is used in Dettol (Figure 3.6), and trichlorophenol is the material that gives rise to the name of the antiseptic TCP.

**3.6** hexachlorophane          **3.7** chloroxylenol          **3.8** trichlorophenol

**Figure 3.6**
Some products containing antiseptic phenol derivatives.

**Question 12** Eugenol (**3.9**) is a compound that can be isolated as the major constituent of oil of cloves. Decide whether or not you might use eugenol as an antiseptic and give your reasons.

**3.9** eugenol

## 3.2 Bleach

*Gas! Gas! Quick, boys! – An ecstasy of fumbling,*
*Fitting the clumsy helmets just in time;*
*But someone still was yelling out and stumbling*
*And flound'ring like a man in fire or lime…*
*Dim, through the misty panes and thick green light,*
*As under a green sea, I saw him drowning.*
*In all my dreams, before my helpless sight,*
*He plunges at me, guttering, choking, drowning.*

*If in some smothering dreams you too could pace*
*Behind the wagon that we flung him in,*
*And watch the white eyes writhing in his face,*
*His hanging face, like a devil's sick of sin;*
*If you could hear, at every jolt, the blood*
*Come gargling from the froth-corrupted lungs,*
*Obscene as cancer, bitter as the cud*
*Of vile, incurable sores on innocent tongues, –*
*My friend, you would not tell with such high zest*
*To children ardent for some desperate glory,*
*The old Lie: Dulce et decorum est*

*Pro patria mori.*

*(Wilfrid Owen, Dulce et decorum est, 1917)*

As Owen so vividly describes, chlorine is a thoroughly nasty substance. It is a yellow-green – hence its name, *chloros* is Greek for yellow green – dense, choking gas. It attacks the mucous membranes of the eyes, nose, throat and lungs, and causes the lungs to fill with fluid so that the person exposed to it drowns internally. Chlorine was one of the first chemical warfare agents.

**Figure 3.7**
Soldiers of the First World War following an attack by chlorine gas.

It is an indictment on humankind that, given the uniquely creative activity of chemistry, chemical knowledge can be used deliberately for destruction.

Chlorine was discovered in 1774 by C. W. Scheele in Sweden, and it exists as molecules that contain two chlorine atoms: Cl—Cl or $Cl_2$. By 1785, the bleaching properties of a solution of chlorine in water had been noted, and by 1788 such aqueous solutions had been recommended as disinfectants after they had been observed to prevent the obnoxious smells caused by decaying organic matter. Clearly, then, dissolving chlorine in water reduces the acute toxic effects of the gas but still provides a solution that will act as a disinfectant. And it is certainly easier to handle a liquid than it is to handle a gas!

Actually, when chlorine dissolves in water it doesn't simply form a solution as, say, sodium chloride does. Chlorine and water react together to form a new substance – hypochlorous acid, HOCl. We can write this as follows:

$$Cl_2(aq) + H_2O(l) = HOCl(aq) + H^+(aq) + Cl^-(aq)$$

It is the hypochlorous acid, HOCl, that exhibits the disinfecting properties. Unfortunately, solutions of chlorine in water are unstable, losing their disinfecting properties through gradual loss of chlorine, as well as because hypochlorous acid is destroyed by ultraviolet radiation. However, if chlorine is dissolved in basic solutions of sodium or potassium hydroxide, the resulting **bleach** solutions are much more stable. This is because in basic solution the hypochlorite ion, $OCl^-$, is formed:

$$Cl_2(aq) + 2OH^-(aq) = OCl^-(aq) + Cl^-(aq) + H_2O(l)$$

and this is much more stable than hypochlorous acid. This has been known for a very long time. Eau-de-Javelle, first marketed in 1825, is a potassium hypochlorite solution; Eau-de-Labarraque, named after a Parisian apothecary, is an alkaline solution of sodium hypochlorite and sodium chloride. Even today, the bleach solutions we buy in the supermarket, such as Domestos and Parozone, are essentially aqueous hypochlorite solutions.

A trade-off has to be reached in formulating effective chlorine-based disinfectants: stable solutions are formed in basic conditions, but in such solutions the 'active' chlorine is present as the hypochlorite anion, which is not a very good disinfectant; in more acidic solutions (pH 4 to pH 7), the active chlorine is present as hypochlorous acid, which is a very effective disinfectant (see Box 3.2) but is much less stable:

$$H^+(aq) + OCl^-(aq) = HOCl(aq)$$

A balance between these two extremes is formed by controlling the pH of the solution – that is, by controlling the amount of acid or base present.

A bottle of bleach always carries a warning about not mixing it with acidic substances. This is because in very acidic solutions the hypochlorous acid and sodium chloride in the bleach can react together to generate chlorine:

$$H^+(aq) + HOCl(aq) + Cl^-(aq) = Cl_2(aq) + H_2O(l)$$

Chlorine gas is not particularly soluble in acid solutions, and the gas is liberated from solution. I, for one, wouldn't want small-scale chemical warfare in my kitchen or bathroom!

## Experiment 3.3  The pH of bleach, soap and detergent solutions

Take a look at the equation that represents how chlorine forms from acidic bleach solutions. Now compare it with the equation that describes what happens when chlorine dissolves in water. Can you see how they are related? They are the *same* equation except they are written in the opposite directions. This means that we have established that the reaction can go in *both* directions. We can read the equations as meaning that hypochlorous and hydrochloric acids react together to form chlorine and water, or, alternatively, that chlorine reacts with water to form hypochlorous and hydrochloric acids. Reactions like this, which go in either direction, are said to be **reversible**. How much of each substance is present depends on several factors: the amounts of material used to carry out the reaction, the molecular structures of the compounds involved, and the conditions under which the reaction is carried out, for example the temperature or solvent used. In this case, when the reaction is acidic, chlorine and water are the major products, but when the reaction is basic, hypochlorite and chloride are the major products.

### Box 3.2  Bleach as a disinfectant

Bleach disinfects because the hypochlorous acid reacts with cell proteins that are responsible for cell structure, as well as with the enzymes that are vital to the chemical reactions that take place in the cell.

Hypochlorous acid is known as an 'active chlorine' compound. That is, it is capable of transferring its chlorine atom to other compounds. The cell proteins and enzymes contain nitrogen atoms that are part of amide functional groups:

example of an amide functional group in a protein or enzyme

These nitrogen atoms are particularly susceptible to attack by 'active chlorine' compounds such as hypochlorous acid, and the hydrogen atom is replaced by a chlorine atom:

a chlorinated amide

Such an apparently trivial change has profound chemical consequences. First, the hydrogen atom is essential for the hydrogen bonding needed for protein structure – remove it, by replacing it with chlorine, and you begin to stop enzymes performing their catalytic work and destroy cell structure. Replace lots of these types of hydrogen and cell structure is completely destroyed. Second, the presence of the chlorine atom changes the chemical reactivity of the amide group. So, whereas the non-chlorinated amide is unreactive, the chlorinated amide is reactive and the carbon–nitrogen bond can be broken easily:

stable                    this bond is easily broken

Breaking the amide bond destroys the protein or enzyme, in just the same way as breaking a link in a chain destroys the chain.

One of the earliest uses of hypochlorite solutions was in the attempt to control the often fatal childbirth fever. In 1835 in Boston, USA, Oliver Wendell Holmes studied the spread of the disease and was certain it was contagious and transmitted by midwives. By insisting that they disinfect their hands using a solution of 'chloride of lime' – actually calcium hypochlorite, made by dissolving chlorine in lime water – he was completely successful in stopping the disease from spreading. He met with considerable antagonism from the medical profession, however, many of whose members considered his ideas insulting to the way they practised. In 1839, the work of Ignaz Semmelweis suffered a similar fate in Vienna. Semmelweis demonstrated that the death rate from childbirth fever was much higher in the ward where the medical students were trained than in the ward in which nurses and midwives were trained. He reasoned that the medical students were infecting patients after they'd carried out post-mortem examinations. He insisted that they disinfect their hands in 'chloride of lime' solution, and was able to reduce spectacularly the mortality from childbirth fever from 12% to 1%. However, the implication that the current medical practice was less than perfect met with hostility and his contract was not renewed. It wasn't until Pasteur had demonstrated that disease was spread by micro-organisms and until Lister had demonstrated the use of carbolic acid as an antiseptic, that disinfectants were accepted as a means of eradicating disease. Today we wouldn't be without them.

Hypochlorites are powerful disinfectants, but they aren't particularly satisfactory for cleaning open wounds or delicate tissues. The basic solutions and any free chlorine tend to irritate the tissues. Even today, only dilute solutions, containing no more than 0.5% active chlorine, should be used for such purposes.

How then to produce a safer milder antiseptic or disinfectant? As ever, we need a compound to provide a clue as to which avenues to develop, and amines, such as ammonia, are one such class of compounds. These are known to react with hypochlorous acid to form chloramines:

$$NH_3(aq) + HOCl(aq) = NH_2Cl(aq) + H_2O(l)$$

This is a very similar reaction to the one described between HOCl and proteins. It is a reversible reaction because chloramine will react with water to generate ammonia and hypochlorous acid. These chloramines have antiseptic properties in their own right, but are too unstable for medical use. However, chloramine B (**3.10**) and chloramine T (**3.11**) are two stable chloro derivatives of amines that have antiseptic properties because they slowly release hypochlorous acid on contact with water.

**3.10**                                    **3.11**

If we abbreviate the structures of chloramines B and T to

then we can write the reaction with water as

$$R-\underset{\underset{O}{\|}}{\overset{\overset{O}{\|}}{S}}-\underset{Cl}{\overset{}{N^-}}\quad Na^+ \quad + \quad H_2O \quad \longrightarrow \quad R-\underset{\underset{O}{\|}}{\overset{\overset{O}{\|}}{S}}-\underset{H}{\overset{}{N^-}}\quad Na^+ + HOCl$$

**3.12** sodium
dichloroisocyanurate

A more commonly known sterilizing reagent, particularly for swimming pools or babies' feeding bottles, is sodium dichloroisocyanurate (**3.12**). It is more likely you know this as Babysafe Tablets, Milton Tablets, Puritabs, Fi-Tab or some other proprietary name (Figure 3.8). Again, this is a relatively stable source of active chlorine that liberates hypochlorous acid in water.

**Figure 3.8**
Commercial products
containing active chlorine
compounds.

So what makes a good chlorine-based disinfectant? We can get a good clue by comparing the molecular structures of the compounds we've been looking at. These are chlorine, hypochlorous acid and hypochlorite anion, chloramine, chloramines B and T and sodium dichloroisocyanurate. All of these compounds are active chlorine agents. If we focus our attention at the 'working part' of each of these molecules, that is the fragment containing the active chlorine, then the following bonding pattern emerges:

Cl—Cl    chlorine

—O—Cl    hypochlorous acid
and hypochlorite ion

$\overset{\diagdown}{\underset{\diagup}{N}}$—Cl    chloramines, sodium
dichloroisocyanurate

active
chlorine atom

In each case, the active chlorine atom is bonded to an atom, Cl, O, or N that, as you may recall from Book 1, strongly attracts electrons. In contrast, when a chlorine atom is bonded to an atom that is not electron attracting, such as carbon in C—Cl, the compound is not an active chlorine compound and is therefore not a disinfectant. For example, 1,1,1-trichloroethane (**3.13**) contains three C—Cl bonds; it is a useful solvent, but it has no disinfectant properties.

$$
\begin{array}{ccc}
\text{H} & & \text{Cl} \\
| & & | \\
\text{H}-\text{C}- & \text{C} & -\text{Cl} \\
| & & | \\
\text{H} & & \text{Cl}
\end{array}
$$

**3.13** 1,1,1-trichloroethane

So, a characteristic of active chlorine disinfectants is that the active chlorine atom is bonded to an electron-attracting atom.

Today, large-scale disinfection of the water supply is carried out with chlorine gas. Chlorine in the water supply is a contentious issue. It gives an unpleasant taste to water, and many people invest in water filters to remove the chlorine. Others choose to drink bottled water. What cannot be in doubt is the vital contribution that the provision of a clean, sterilized water supply has made to people's health.

> **Question 13** Iodine tinctures are often used as antiseptics to clean cuts and grazes of the skin. Iodine occurs in the same Group as chlorine in the Periodic Table and exists as diatomic molecules. Describe the reasons why iodine has antiseptic properties.

## 3.3 Summary of Chapter 3

In Chapter 3 you have found out that:

Phenol (carbolic acid) can be obtained from coal tar by distillation extraction.

Phenol is a derivative of benzene; it contains a six-carbon atom benzene ring attached to an OH group.

Phenol has antiseptic properties because it can denature proteins by forming hydrogen bonds to them as well as by acting as a non-ionic detergent.

Phenols that contain hydrocarbon groups attached to the benzene ring have enhanced detergent and antiseptic properties.

Bleach is an alkaline solution of chlorine water which contains sodium hypochlorite and sodium chloride.

Compounds containing N—Cl bonds, such as chloramine, chloramines B and T, and sodium dichloroisocyanurate, are also effective disinfectants.

Disinfectants are active chlorine compounds; these are compounds that contain a chlorine atom bonded to an electron-attracting atom.

Active chlorine compounds are disinfectants because they replace hydrogen atoms of amide groups in enzymes and proteins with chlorine atoms; this alters the hydrogen bonding properties and chemical reactivity of the amide groups and destroys the biological function of the enzymes and proteins.

You have also seen that:

Reactions that will go in either direction are called reversible reactions.

# Chapter 4
# The search for a cure

This Chapter sketches a preliminary outline of the nature of medicinal chemistry. We begin with the story of quinine; its isolation from the bark of a tree, how it entered conventional pharmacy, its role in the development of homoeopathy, and the limitations that arose from a lack of knowledge of its chemical structure. We continue with the story of cocaine, which illustrates how a better picture of molecular structure provides the necessary clues that enable the development of compounds with specific pharmaceutical action. In the case of cocaine, local anaesthetics are the compounds that arise. Together, the stories of quinine and cocaine provide us with the beginnings of a pattern of drug discovery and development that continues to this present day.

There can be no doubt that proper nutrition and careful hygiene are fundamental to good health. Yet it is quite obvious that these alone cannot procure permanent good health over a person's lifetime. The human body is assailed by a whole host of agents that can cause illness and disease. Viruses, fungi and bacteria are all common external agents of infection, but exposure to certain environmental chemicals also can result in ill health. From within, too, breakdown of the system of chemical reactions that support and maintain life, and which go on in every living cell of our bodies, result in disability, disease and ultimately death. We are extremely unlikely to avoid illness at every stage in our lives, so what can we do to combat ill health?

■    Jot down some of the things you do when you are unwell to try to make you get better.

■    Your list may contain some of the following (it probably contains others too):

Find a quiet place to rest or sleep, listen to peaceful music, visit the doctor, take some medicine, have a herbal drink, practise aromatherapy.

Your list will include some things – listening to music, for example – which could be classified as 'feel-good factors', and there is no doubt that our mental state has an effect on the healing process. Others on the list – like taking a medicine, or a herbal drink – will indicate that some kind of physical intervention is usually necessary. But that immediately raises other questions like 'What should I take for my illness?' and 'How have we come to know what to take?'. In the remaining Chapters, we shall examine some of the ways in which modern medicine has developed, why it has developed in this way, the role that chemistry has in our understanding of issues of health and disease, and the way that chemistry influences the progress of modern healthcare.

## 4.1 From potions to drugs

William Shakespeare, in Romeo and Juliet, describes well – if somewhat facetiously – what it would have been like to have gone to an apothecary with a prescription around 1600:

> *I do remember an apothecary,*
> *And hereabouts a dwells, which late I noted,*
> *In tattered weeds, with overwhelming brows,*
> *Culling of simples. Meagre were his looks.*
> *Sharp misery had worn him to the bones,*
> *And in his needy shop a tortoise hung,*
> *An alligator stuffed, and other skins*
> *Of ill-shaped fishes; and about his shelves*
> *a beggarly account of empty boxes,*
> *Green earthern pots, bladders, and musty seeds.*
> *Remnants of packthread, and old cakes of roses*
> *Were thinly scattered to make up a show.*

Should you think that an extreme description, then the following recipe from the New London Dispensatory (Figure 4.1), published by William Salmon in 1678, should add authenticity:

> *Aqua Divina. Divine water*
>
> *Take the whole carcase of a man violently killed, with the Intrails, cut it in pieces, and mix them; distil it from a Retort twice or thrice.*
>
> *It is reputed to have a Magnetic power: if to one drachm of this water you put a few drops of the Blood of a sick person, and set them on fire, and they mix, the sick recovers; if not, the sick dies.*

Figure 4.2 illustrates the interior of an apothecary's shop in the 17th century. By the mid to late 19th century, the interior of the chemist and druggist's shop has changed beyond recognition (Figure 4.3). Though the drug runs – drawers full of herbs and spices – remain, gone are the tortoises and alligators. Taking their place are row upon row of bottles, jars and pots containing the constituents necessary to compound medicines to the prescription supplied by the physician. A glance around the shop would reveal the equipment of the pharmacist – pill-making machines, pessary makers, measures, pestles and mortars, etc. A modern, late 20th-century, pharmacy is quite different again (Figure 4.4). Gone now are the drug runs, the bottles of individual chemicals and extracts; gone too is all the drug-making equipment, all to be replaced by packets of tablets

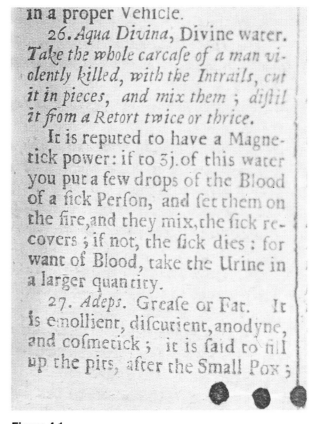

**Figure 4.1**
The recipe for *Aqua Divina* from Salmon's New London Dispensatory.

**Figure 4.2**
An apothecary's shop of the 17th century.

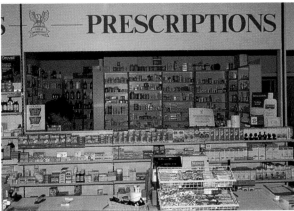

**Figure 4.3**
The interior of Emile Doo's pharmacy shop, preserved in the Black Country Museum, Dudley.

**Figure 4.4**
The interior of a modern pharmacy.

and bottles of medicines already compounded by the pharmaceutical manufacturers ready to be dispensed by the pharmacist as prescribed by the doctor.

This changing role of the local pharmacist over the past 300 years has paralleled the growth of a more sophisticated understanding of what causes ill-health and the means by which ill-health may be remedied. Gone is the semi-superstition of the time when it was considered important to collect herbs under the specific influence of an astrological body, to be replaced by what might be called a 'rational approach', in which a drug is administered because it has a known, specific and quantifiable biological effect.

Perhaps this is best illustrated by comparing three different prescriptions for the same illness, asthma: one taken from Salmon's Dispensatory, another from the 1904 prescription book of Cox and Robinson, a long-established pharmacy in the North Buckinghamshire area, and the third a modern drug (Table 4.1).

**Table 4.1**

| Salmon's Extract of Fox Lungs | Cox and Robinson's Infallible cure for asthma (Figure 4.5) | Glaxo's Ventolin (Figure 4.6) |
|---|---|---|
| Take of Fox Lungs, slice them; Pauls Betony, Hysop, Scabious, of each half a handful; | Senna, $\frac{3}{4}$ oz<br>Flower of sulphur, $\frac{1}{2}$ oz<br>Ginger, 2 drachms | Salbutamol, 100 µg per metered inhalation. |
| Anise and Fennel seeds, of each 1 drachm [about 3.5 g], boyl them in a large glass half a day, or till they turn to water, strain, evaporate, and add to sugar till it comes to the consistency of an Extract. | Saffron, $\frac{1}{2}$ drachm<br>Honey, 4 oz | |
| This Extract is a very good Pectoral, prevalent against....... Asthma's.... | | |
| Dose from 1 to 2 drachms [approx. a teaspoonful] or more. | Use a quantity the size of a nutmeg night and morning. | Dose: two inhalations of 100 µg each, 3 or 4 times daily. [100 µg is about the mass of a grain of salt]. |

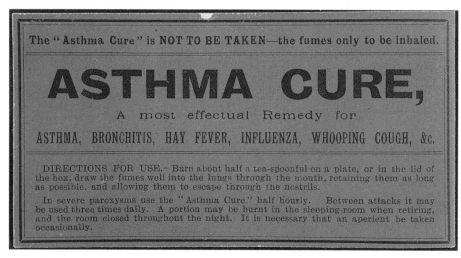

The "Asthma Cure" is NOT TO BE TAKEN—the fumes only to be inhaled.

# ASTHMA CURE,

A most effectual Remedy for

ASTHMA, BRONCHITIS, HAY FEVER, INFLUENZA, WHOOPING COUGH, &c.

DIRECTIONS FOR USE.- Burn about half a tea-spoonful on a plate, or in the lid of the box, draw the fumes well into the lungs through the mouth, retaining them as long as possible, and allowing them to escape through the nostrils.

In severe paroxysms use the "Asthma Cure" half hourly. Between attacks it may be used three times daily. A portion may be burnt in the sleeping-room when retiring, and the room closed throughout the night. It is necessary that an aperient be taken occasionally.

**Figure 4.5**
A label for Cox and Robinson's asthma cure.

**Figure 4.6**
The Ventolin inhaler.

■ Use your general knowledge to try to identify how these three prescriptions might indicate a greater sophistication in the ability to treat an illness.

■ First, the most recent prescription contains only one ingredient; second, the more recent prescriptions contain less esoteric ingredients; third, the more recent prescriptions contain quantities that are much more precise; fourth, the quantities in the most recent drug are much smaller; fifth, the timing of taking the dose is more specific in the recent prescription.

What you probably were unable to propose with your present knowledge, is that salbutamol is a pure chemical compound, whereas the others contain mixtures and extracts of many compounds, as well as plant and animal material.

In fact, salbutamol (Figure 4.7) itself is the product of a research programme that started with a Chinese herbal remedy for asthma – ma huang (Figure 4.8). The plants used in the remedy, various *Ephedra* species, produce two compounds ephedrine (Figure 4.9) and pseudoephedrine (Figure 4.10) that are responsible for the anti-asthmatic properties of the plant. We shall be looking at this story and these molecules in more detail later, so don't worry if at the moment these structures appear rather complex. For now it's sufficient to note the similar features in these three compounds: a benzene ring bonded to a short, two-carbon chain, from which are appended an alcohol OH group and an amine NH group. By altering systematically the various parts of the molecular structure – the precise way in which the atoms are bonded together – through well-designed 'packages' of chemical reactions, salbutamol was produced.

The progress from minced foxes' lungs to salbutamol reflects the greater understanding we have of biology (in particular how cells and the individual components of cells both function and communicate) and of chemistry (particularly in the way that the structures of compounds and materials affect how they behave and react). Here we shall focus on how the greater understanding of chemistry has brought about an improvement in health care for the modern world.

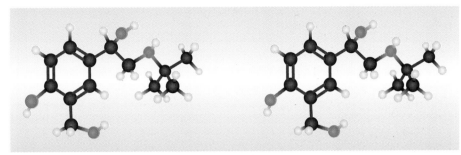

**Figure 4.7**
Stereoscopic model of the structure of salbutamol.

**Figure 4.8**
One of the several ephedrine-containing species of *Ephedra* or ma huang.

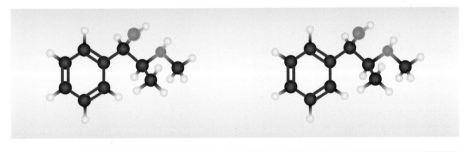

**Figure 4.9**
Stereoscopic model of the structure of ephedrine.

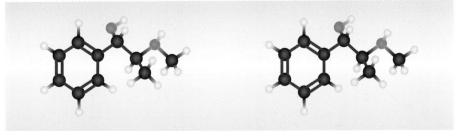

**Figure 4.10**
Stereoscopic model of the structure of pseudoephedrine.

### Box 4.1 Chemist or pharmacist

Many of us these days will talk of 'taking our prescription to the pharmacy'. Even so, we might still say that we obtained a medicine 'from the chemist'. There is a confusion between the words chemist and pharmacist, and we seem to see them as interchangeable terms for the same thing. The confusion has arisen out of the historical development of pharmacy. The term chemist, used in the sense of pharmacist, is a contraction of 'Chemist and Druggist'. This was a term originally applied to those people whose business it was to buy, prepare, compound, dispense and sell 'drugs, medicines and medicinal compounds' either for wholesale or retail. This was to distinguish them from the Apothecaries, who were able to do all those things as well but who were also able to examine patients and prescribe medicines. Apothecaries were the forerunners of the modern general practitioners. Chemists and Druggists obviously dealt in chemicals, but they dealt in herbal and plant materials too. In 1841, the Chemists and Druggists organized themselves into the Royal Pharmaceutical Association and introduced qualifications such as Pharmaceutical Chemist. The use of the word 'pharmaceutical' more correctly describes the profession, in that it explicitly recognizes the fact that it involves working with drugs and medicines – the Greek word for drug is pharmakon, φαρμακον. Today's pharmacies are directly descended from the Chemist and Druggist shops of the 19th century.

The term chemist, used in the sense of a practitioner of chemistry, reflects a much wider field of interest. Some chemists may be interested in drugs, but in general chemists explore the nature of all materials – how substances are constructed, what forces hold them together, how one substance is converted into another – and attempt to explain their properties in terms of the behaviour of atoms.

## 4.2 From cinchona bark to quinine

*If the Colledge mean the Peruvian bark, of which the Jesuites powder is made, it is an excellent thing against all sorts of Agues:*

So wrote William Salmon in the Fourth Edition of the *New London Dispensatory* in 1691. Peruvian bark was something of a wonder drug in 17th century Europe. As its name implies, it hailed from Peru and was the bark of a tree that the Incas called *quina* (Figure 4.11). The first European to mention it was the Augustinian monk Father Antonio de la Calaucha in his *Chronicle of St Augustine* (about 1633):

*A tree grows which they call the fever tree…when made into a powder amounting to the size of two small silver coins and given as a beverage, it cures the fevers and tertians.*

Ague, fevers and tertians are all descriptions of the symptoms of various types of malaria; attacks of the fever take place every two, three or four days and such cycles have been called quotidian, tertian and quartan, respectively. Malaria was then the most widespread disease in the world, and the arrival of a drug that could successfully treat it was hailed as a triumph. The Jesuit missionaries were the first to ship the bark back to Europe – hence the name Jesuit's powder – and the Jesuit Cardinal Johannes de Lugo was one of the first to make the remedy popular:

*…against quartan and tertian fevers accompanied by shivers, two drachms [about 8 g] of the finely ground and sifted bark mixed in a glass of strong white wine three hours before the fever is due.*

**Figure 4.11**
*Cinchona officinalis*, the tree whose bark provides Jesuit's powder and the drug quinine.

By the turn of the 19th century the drug, now called cinchona (pronounced sing-cone-ah), was well established in the pharmacopoeia (the compendium of drugs and the illnesses for which they are used). In 1824, Thomas Cox M.D., in translating the *Pharmacopoeia Londinensis* in his *New London Dispensatory*, could write

> *It [cinchona] acts as a specific in the cure of intermittents; seldom failing where the stomach can retain it in sufficient quantity.*

It was at this time, too, that cinchona, along with several other plants, such as the opium poppy, was beginning to be the focus of attention of pharmacists and chemists. In 1820, having successfully isolated a compound, which they called strychnine, from the seeds of the most potent plant poisons then known, *Strychnos nux vomica* and *Strychnos ignatii*, two French scientists Joseph Pelletier and Joseph Caventou turned their attention to cinchona bark. They isolated two compounds; one, which they isolated from the pale, or grey, bark of *Cinchona lancifolia*, they called cinchonine (pronounced sing-cone-een) (Figure 4.12), the other, isolated from the yellow bark of *Cinchona cordifolia*, they called quinine (pronounced kwin-een) (Figure 4.13). Their achievement was marked 150 years later by the issue of a special postage stamp (Figure 4.14).

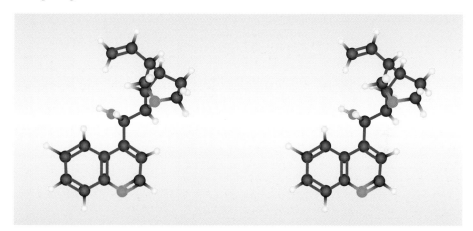

**Figure 4.12**
Stereoscopic model of the structure of cinchonine.

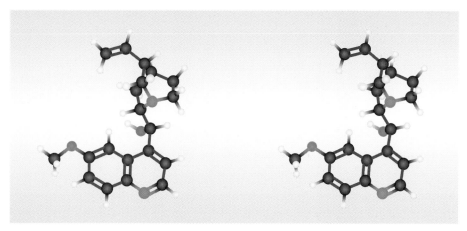

**Figure 4.13**
Stereoscopic model of the structure of quinine.

**Figure 4.14**
French stamp celebrating the isolation of quinine from cinchona bark by the French chemists Joseph Pelletier and Joseph Caventou. The stamp depicts the structure of the quinine molecule.

## Box 4.2  Looking at large organic molecules

Many organic compounds have molecular structures that are relatively simple. This might be because they contain only a few atoms or it may be that they only contain one, or at most two, functional groups. However, most organic compounds have large molecular structures containing several functional groups. These can appear rather complex, and seem rather difficult to understand, particularly if we try to take in every detail. The trick to looking at large molecular structures is to fade out of the picture the unimportant detail and focus attention on the framework of the molecule and the arrangement of the functional groups with respect to the

framework. We began this process when we simplified the structure of lauryl alcohol (**2.7**). Let's develop the method by taking quinine as an example.

The ball-and-stick model of quinine in Figure 4.13 appears complicated because it contains all of the atoms and bonds involved in forming the molecular structure. To use such a picture every time we wished to talk about the structure of quinine would be tedious. We need to remove the clutter and simplify the structure by adopting the method we used for benzene. If we were to represent the atoms by the letters of their chemical symbols, the structure would look like **4.1**, but even that looks cluttered.

**4.1**

A simplification is to 'fade out' the carbon atoms as well as the hydrogen atoms bonded to carbon. This doesn't mean that these atoms are not present in quinine (or any other structure for that matter). Rather, we have to assume that whenever

a bond meets another and no atom is specified then a carbon atom is present, and that for each carbon atom the correct number of hydrogen atoms is present to maintain the valency of carbon as four. An exception is often made for carbon atoms that are part of functional groups and for the hydrogens of $CH_3$ groups. The simplified structure of quinine looks like **4.2**, and the benefit of using this type of representation is that it allows the molecular features that are present to be more clearly discernible.

**4.2**

■ Look at the structure of quinine depicted in **4.2**. What molecular fragments does it contain?

■ The quinine molecule contains the following fragments: a planar ring similar to benzene, with a $CH_3O$ group attached;

an alcohol; two amine groups, one part of the planar ring system, the second in the other ring system; a carbon–carbon double bond.

These are almost impossible to identify in the ball-and-stick structure in Figure 4.13.

Both these compounds have highly complicated, but very similar, three-dimensional structures. Although the ability to determine their molecular structures was far beyond the capability of chemists of the time – it took another century before the structures were determined, and only in 1944 were they first synthesized – the isolation of quinine and cinchonine proved a landmark in the role of chemistry in pharmacy and medicine. Why? Because when they isolated these pure compounds, Pelletier and Caventou suggested that their therapeutic properties should be studied. This was the first time that such an approach to drug discovery had been used, and it would appear that little time was lost. Both quinine and cinchonine were found to have anti-malarial activity, quinine having the greater potency. So the anti-malarial activity was not a property of the bark as a whole, but apparently came from a few active ingredients. Within four years Cox could write

> *The sulphate of quinine, of late, has been much extolled in this disease, and is truly valuable.*

and, moreover, include in his Dispensatory Pelletier and Caventou's method for obtaining both quinine and cinchonine:

> *The alkaloid, first called Cinchonin, by Dr Duncan, Jun., is prepared by M. M. Pelletier and Caventou, in the following manner: Dissolve the alcoholic extract, prepared from the pale bark, in distilled water, strongly acidulated with muriatic [hydrochloric] acid; add to the solution calcined magnesia [magnesium oxide] in excess, and boil for a few minutes; when cold, filter, and wash the precipitate with cold water, digest it in boiling alcohol, and evaporate this spirituous infusion until crystals are deposited, of a white needle-like form; they have an intensely bitter taste, and are very sparingly soluble in water.*

> *The sulphate of cinchonine possesses the active properties of bark, and is very soluble in water.*

> *Quinine is obtained from yellow bark, by a similar process to the above, with somewhat different qualities; and it is the sulphate of quinine, which has been lately so much used, as a substitution for the powder of bark, in intermittents, &c.*

The alcoholic extract is prepared simply:

> *Take of…cinchonas bark, bruised, two pounds, Rectified spirit, a gallon;*

> *Macerate for four days, and strain. Distil the tincture by a water-bath, until it has acquired a proper consistence.*

## Box 4.3  Alkaloids

Alkaloids is a term used to describe substances that behave like alkalis, that is they form basic aqueous solutions. The term is usually applied to compounds isolated from plants, and these compounds all have one common feature – their molecular structures contain at least one amine group. So heroin, morphine and codeine – all obtained from the poppy *Papaver somniferum* – are alkaloids. So too are cocaine, quinine and strychnine.

**Figure 4.15**
The opium poppy *Papaver somniferum*, and stereoscopic models of the structures of (a) heroin, (b) morphine and (c) codeine.

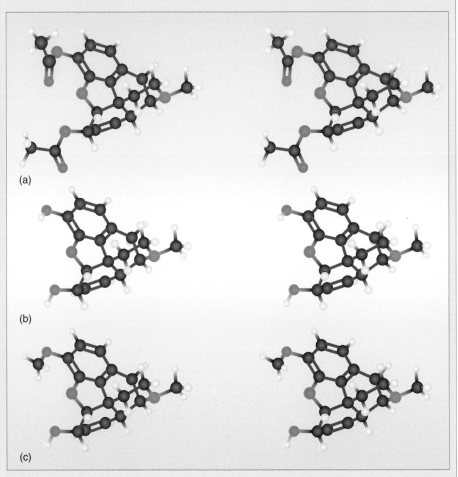

In this way, the pure compound quinine rapidly displaced cinchona bark as the drug of choice (Figure 4.16).

■   Try to list some advantages of extracting and using a pure compound as opposed to the plant material. What disadvantage might such an approach have?

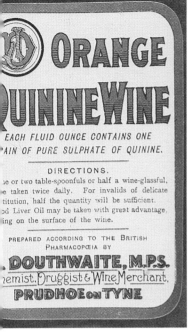

**Figure 4.16**
A label for a quinine preparation.

First, the amount of the substance in the plant might vary depending on the conditions under which it was grown. So the place or the time of year might affect just how much of the active ingredient is available. Standardizing different lots of plant material, therefore, becomes a difficult task, which makes administering a precise dose difficult. Having the pure compounds avoids this entirely, and allows precise dosing to be achieved easily. Because of this, there is greater control over what is taken so it is potentially safer.

Second, the use of pure compounds allows their individual efficacy to be determined; with plant material it is difficult if not impossible to ascertain precisely which of the components are the active ingredients.

Third, it reduces the risk of imbibing something nasty from a plant.

A possible disadvantage is that extracting and using the major active ingredient(s) may cause some active minor components to be overlooked. So pure compounds may not reproduce entirely the medicinal effect of the original material.

This disadvantage seems to be a criticism that is currently prevalent, as many people turn to herbal remedies. However, the range of effective medicines that have been isolated from plant species worldwide shows that the advantages are also considerable.

How did Pelletier and Caventou know that they had a pure compound? By today's standards and techniques they had very few means of determining the purity of an unknown compound. One is to record the melting temperature.

Pure compounds have melting temperatures that fall within quite narrow ranges, usually one or two degrees Celsius. Quinine, for example, melts between 173 and 175 °C. Any impurities that might be present tend to lower the melting temperature and increase the range over which melting occurs. So the melting temperature of quinine produced initially could have been recorded, then the crystals could have been purified by being redissolved and allowed to crystallize once more and the melting temperature recorded again. If the two determinations differed by less than one degree Celsius then the compound could be considered to be pure. If not, the compound would have to be purified further by crystallization until successive determinations of the melting temperature differed by less than one degree Celsius.

So, the first major leap forward towards the modern development of drugs came with the ability to extract and purify compounds from the herbal remedies already available. However, for some time progress was halted at that point. It proved impossible, for example, to develop other drugs similar to quinine because no-one knew what the structure of quinine was. Although the chemical composition of quinine could be determined by combustion analysis (see Box 4.4), and was found to be $C_{20}H_{24}N_2O_2$, the molecular structure remained an enigma. This is most clearly seen in W.H. Perkin's futile attempt to synthesize quinine from allyltoluidine. Simply basing his approach on atomic composition, he arrived at the following reaction:

$$2C_{10}H_{13}N + 3[O] = C_{20}H_{24}N_2O_2 + H_2O$$

allyl toluidine          quinine

This looks fine on paper, but never stood any chance of success because of the enormous differences in the structures (which, of course, were unknown to him). If you compare the structure of allyltoluidine (**4.3**) with that of quinine (**4.2**), it will be obvious that the synthesis would require an enormous and impossible reorganization of the bonding pattern. Even so, Perkin struck lucky. The reaction produced a mixture of compounds from which he was able to extract a beautiful mauve dye. Perkin devoted the next few years of his life to manufacturing dyes and made a personal fortune that enabled him to retire at 35. You will discover more about this in Book 4.

$$CH_3 - \bigcirc - NH - CH_2 - CH = CH_2$$

**4.3** allyltoluidine

## Box 4.4 Combustion analysis and molecular structure

To determine the precise structure of an organic compound it is usually necessary first to determine the elements that are present, and their relative proportions. One way of doing this is to burn a known amount of the compound with an excess of oxygen. This combustion process converts any carbon atoms in the molecule into carbon dioxide, $CO_2$, and the hydrogen atoms are converted into water, $H_2O$; any nitrogen atoms form nitrogen gas, $N_2$.

The actual amounts of each of these three products formed are then separately determined. By correcting for the known percentages of the elements in these products, their relative percentage proportions in the compound can be calculated. If these proportions do not add up to 100% the remainder is assumed to be due to oxygen contained in the compound, unless of course the compound is known to contain sulfur, chlorine or some other element.

However, knowing the atomic composition of a compound doesn't tell you anything about its structure.

Prior to 1950, determinations of molecular structures were made by carefully subjecting a compound to reactions that broke the molecule up into fragments, which were identified by comparison with known compounds. From a knowledge of the types of reaction involved, these fragments provided the pieces of a molecular jigsaw that could be re-assembled to provide a picture of the structure of the compound.

Since 1950, techniques have been developed that don't require breaking up the molecules. These techniques rely on the way atoms, or groups of atoms, in molecules absorb characteristic types of energy from the electromagnetic spectrum. They are called **spectroscopic techniques**. No single one of these techniques is able to give a complete molecular structure, but when information from several is combined the structures of even very complex molecules can be unravelled. For example, in Book 2 Part 2 you met the infrared spectrum of $CCl_2F_2$, which displayed how this compound absorbed infrared radiation. Figure 4.17 shows the infrared spectra (spectra is the

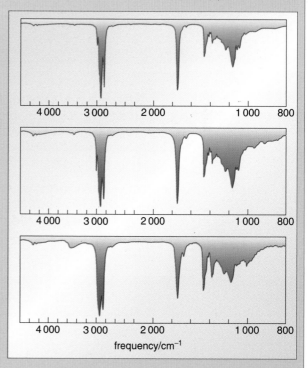

**Figure 4.17**
The infrared spectra of olive oil, cottonseed oil and lanolin.

plural of spectrum) of olive oil, cottonseed oil and lanolin. Although these spectra are not precisely the same they contain regions where energy is absorbed that are common to all three. In particular, the absorptions in the regions of 3 000 cm$^{-1}$ and 1 740 cm$^{-1}$ are particularly strong and present in each spectrum.

- Olive oil, cottonseed oil and lanolin all contain one type of functional group. From your earlier studies, recall which type of group this is.

- It is the ester functional group.

The absorption close to 1 740 cm$^{-1}$ in the above spectra is due to the ester group in these substances (the absorption close to 3 000 cm$^{-1}$ turns out to be due to the C—H bonds). *All* esters give rise to an absorption in this region of the infrared spectrum. So, for example, if you are presented with the spectrum of an unknown fat or oil that has an absorption close to 1 740 cm$^{-1}$ you could be fairly confident that it is an ester and not a hydro-carbon. Unfortunately, the spectrum doesn't tell us precisely where in the molecule the ester group is to be found – we need the information obtained from other types of spectroscopy to tell us that (but we won't be dealing with these in this Course). All functional groups have characteristic regions of the infrared spectrum in which they absorb radiation.

**Question 14** Which of the infrared spectra in Figure 4.18 would you assign to methyl butanoate, an ester isolated from pineapples?

**Question 15** The three infrared spectra shown in Figure 4.19 were obtained from the alcohols glycerol, petroselinyl alcohol (an alcohol obtained from parsley, *Petroselinum crispum*) and nerol (an alcohol obtained from orange blossom). Which absorption region in the spectra would you say was characteristic of the alcohol, OH, group?

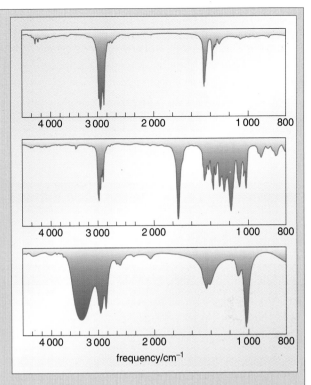

**Figure 4.18**
Possible infrared spectra for methyl butanoate.

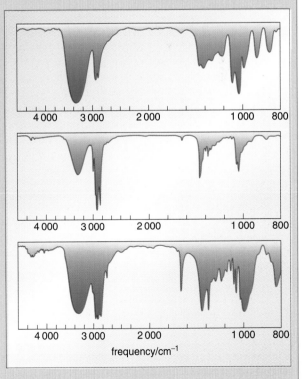

**Figure 4.19**
The infrared spectra of (top) glycerol, (centre) petroselinyl alcohol and (bottom) nerol.

However, once the structure of quinine was established, and a synthesis achieved, a range of new anti-malaria drugs based on quinine rapidly became available. Those of you who have required anti-malaria treatment for a visit to a tropical country may recognize drugs such as primaquin, chloroquin, mepacrine and mefloquin, which are the outcome of this knowledge.

At this stage, you could usefully undertake a Home Experiment, the isolation of caffeine from tea leaves. Caffeine, of course, has biological activity of its own. It is a well-known stimulant, and is contained in several pain-relieving preparations because it enhances the action of paracetamol and aspirin.

## Experiment 3.4  Isolation of caffeine from tea

Before we leave the story of how quinine revolutionized the development of human medicine, there is another aspect to its history that has led to a quite different approach to treating illness. **Homoeopathy** owes its foundations to the ideas of the German doctor Samuel Hahnemann (Figure 4.20). Having read an account of how Peruvian bark (called *China* by homoeopaths) was used to treat malaria, he disagreed with the proposed explanation and set about carrying out experiments on himself.

**Figure 4.20**
Samuel Hahnemann (1755–1843), the originator of homoeopathy.
(This image has been electronically generated from an original of poor quality.)

> *I took by way of experiment, twice a day, four drachms of good China. My feet, finger ends, etc., at first became quite cold; I grew languid and drowsy; then my heart began to palpitate, and my pulse grew hard and small; intolerable anxiety, trembling, prostration throughout all my limbs; then pulsation, in the head, redness of my cheeks, thirst, and, in short, all these symptoms which are ordinarily characteristic of intermittent fever, made their appearance, one after the other, yet without the peculiar chilly, shivering rigour. Briefly, even those symptoms which are of regular occurrence and especially characteristic – as the stupidity of mind, the kind of rigidity in all the limbs, but above all the numb, disagreeable sensation, which seems to have its seat in the periosteum, over every bond in the whole body – all these made their appearance. This paroxysm lasted two or three hours each time, and recurred, if I repeated this dose, not otherwise; I discontinued it and was in good health.*

So, in a healthy person, Peruvian bark produced what appeared to be the symptoms of malaria. Since quinine cured malaria, this led Hahnemann to develop a system of medicine that involves treating a patient not with drugs that *opposed* this illness but with 'medicines that can excite *similar* symptoms in a healthy body'. This is precisely the opposite approach to conventional medicine. In homoeopathy, the healing properties of a substance are determined by the effect it has on a healthy person; in conventional medicine, although drugs are tested for safety on healthy human beings, their efficacy is determined by their ability to heal the sick.

In another, radical, departure from conventional medicine, the homoeopathic approach states that the more a remedy is diluted the stronger are its curative powers. This idea developed out of Hahnemann's laudable desire to minimize the side-effects of his medicines. At first, he found that simply diluting his samples eventually resulted in them losing the ability to effect a cure. So instead of stirring his solutions on diluting them, he shook them vigorously. These 'potentized remedies' were found to be effective medicines, and the more he diluted them the more effective they became.

■ How does this understanding of increased potency upon greater dilution differ from your understanding of basic chemical principles?

■ The physical and chemical properties of a substance arise out of its molecular structure directly, so the more you have of it the greater the particular property – the more sugar, the sweeter the cup of tea. Homoeopathy appears to suggest the opposite.

An equally difficult homoeopathic concept to understand also arises out of the dilution of active ingredients. In homoeopathy, the starting remedy is a 'mother tincture', made by steeping the active substance in alcohol. This tincture is then diluted according to either the decimal or the centesimal scale. In the decimal scale, one part of the tincture is added to nine parts of alcohol, so this first dilution – called 1X – is a tenth as concentrated as the original tincture. This 1X solution is then diluted in exactly the same way to form the second decimal dilution, 2X, which is one hundred times less concentrated than the original mother tincture. In the centesimal scale a similar procedure is adopted except that one part of the tincture is diluted to one hundred parts with alcohol. This dilution is called 1C; in purely concentration terms 1C is identical with 2X. The next centesimal dilution 2C, is one ten-thousandth ($1/100 \times 1/100 = 1/10\,000$) the concentration of the original.

Now, let's see if you can identify a potential source of conflict between homoeopathy and conventional science by attempting the following calculations.

■ Assume that the mother tincture is a 1.0 mol l$^{-1}$ solution of the active ingredient. (Actually, such tinctures are more likely to contain $1.0 \times 10^{-3}$ mol l$^{-1}$.) Among the most potent homoeopathic remedies are those that are called 30X and 12C. If you started with one litre of the mother tincture, calculate how many one-litre portions in principle would be obtained on making these dilutions. Then use Avogadro's constant to identify how many molecules of the active ingredient are distributed between these diluted solutions. Does your answer alert you to a major difficulty to understanding how homeopathic medicine works?

■ If 1X is a 10 fold dilution, and 2X is $10 \times 10$ fold dilution, then 30X must be a $10^{30}$ fold dilution, which means in principle there would be $10^{30}$ one-litre portions formed on dilution.

Similarly, if 1C is a $1 \times 10^2$ fold dilution and 2C is a $10^2 \times 10^2$ fold dilution, then 12C is $10^{24}$ fold dilution, so there would be $10^{24}$ one-litre portions formed.

Avogadro's constant tells us that one mole of any substance contains $6.02 \times 10^{23}$ molecules. Since the mother tincture is a 1.0 mol l$^{-1}$ solution then this is also the number of molecules of active ingredient distributed between the $10^{30}$ and $10^{24}$ litre portions. It is quite clear that there aren't enough molecules to distribute between these portions such that there is even one molecule per portion. For the 12C dilution about one in every two portions $\left(\dfrac{10^{24}}{6.02 \times 10^{23}}\right)$ will contain a molecule of the active ingredient, while for the 30X dilution only one portion in roughly two million $\left(\dfrac{10^{30}}{6.02 \times 10^{23}}\right)$ will contain one molecule of the active ingredient.

We are drawn to the inevitable conclusion that by dilutions such as 12C (or 24X) no more than half of the portions of the remedies can contain any molecules of the active ingredient whatsoever, and for greater dilutions the proportion reduces dramatically!

How then do they exert their effect? One suggestion is the following:

> ...the succussion [the process of dilution using vigorous shaking rather than stirring] creates an electrochemical pattern which is stored in the dilutant and which then spreads like liquid crystal through the body's own water.
>
> (Miranda Castro, The Complete Homoeopathy Handbook, MacMillan, London, 1990)

I am not at all clear what this means, but I interpret it to mean that the molecular structure of the active ingredient imparts to the alcohol an order that is then transferred, on taking the remedy, to the water within the body.

■   With your understanding of the nature of liquids, consider the likelihood of this possibility.

■   The molecules of a liquid are in constant motion, such that there is no overall organized structure to the liquid. Even in liquids like water, where hydrogen bonds can generate local order, the random movements of the individual molecules are such that any local organization lasts for extremely small fractions of a second only. Water and other such liquids can be made to be ordered by the presence of other substances – such as gelatin – whose large molecules are relatively rigid, but in the absence of such substances the order disappears. So, if homoeopathic remedies involve solutions that contain no drug, the random movements of the solvent molecules are sufficient to remove any structure that might have been present in more concentrated solutions.

The homoeopathic principles were derided by the practitioners of conventional medicine when they were first used by Hahnemann, and today they continue to be looked at with a great deal of scepticism for some of the reasons outlined above.

## 4.3 From cocaine to local anaesthetics: a pattern for inventing drugs

The story of the isolation of quinine illustrates how pure, standardized, compounds entered into medicinal use, ushering in a new era of pharmacy. Other compounds, such as morphine and codeine from the opium poppy *Papaver somniferum* and strychnine from *Strychnos nux vomita*, also became part of the pharmacist's armoury. Cocaine illustrates well the next step in the development to modern medicine – with some knowledge of molecular structure it is possible to devise new compounds, not found in nature, that have similar but improved biological activity.

**Figure 4.21**
*Erythroxylum coca*, the shrub from which cocaine is obtained.

High in the Andes mountains of Columbia, Peru and Bolivia grows a shrub, *Erythroxylum coca* (Figure 4.21). For at least 1500 years the leaves of this shrub have been known to have stimulant properties. Indeed, archaeologists have recovered several bags of coca leaves from the grave of one Peruvian ruler who lived about 500 BC. Despite coca's use being limited to the royal classes and religious ceremonies, the Inca civilization had high regard for it, and claimed that

> *God's angels had presented man with the coca leaf to satisfy the hungry, provide the weary and fainting with new vigour, and cause the unhappy to forget their miseries.*

With the arrival of the Spanish in 1533, the use of coca by the common indigenous people became widespread, no doubt because the Spanish had observed that

> *This herb is so nutritious and invigorating that the Indians labour whole days without anything else, and on the want of it they find a decay in their strength.*

and therefore encouraged its use so as to extract more work from the indigenous population.

Surprisingly, coca leaves made little impact in Europe till the mid 19th century. Then in 1863 a Corsican chemist, Angelo Mariani, launched a tonic that was to become Europe's favourite drink, Vin Mariani (Figure 4.22). This beverage was an extract of coca in wine and as well as being a stimulant was claimed to be an effective painkiller, anaesthetic and remedy for flatulence. It was a runaway success, even receiving a special medal from Pope Leo XIII. Inspired by Vin Mariani, in the USA the pharmacist John Pemberton invented 'Pemberton's French Wine Coca'. This drink, sold initially as a headache remedy and stimulant, contained extracts of coca leaves, together with wine and the extracts of the seeds of the tree *Cola nitida*, which contain caffeine (Figure 4.23).

**Figure 4.22**
An advertisement for Vin Mariani.

**Figure 4.23**
*Cola nitida*, the seeds of which contain caffeine.

**Figure 4.24**
An early advertisement for Coca-Cola.

In 1886, the prohibition of alcohol meant that the wine had to be removed from the recipe. Sugar syrup was used instead, and the drink became known as Coca-Cola (Figure 4.24). Advertisements called it 'the intellectual beverage and temperance drink'. Two years later, soda water replaced ordinary water, and in 1904 the coca extracts were removed and replaced with increased amounts of caffeine. This is essentially the form of Coca-Cola we have today.

The renewed interest in the stimulating properties of *Erythroxylum coca* leaves provided the encouragement needed to attempt to extract the ingredient(s) responsible for the biological activity. In 1860, the German chemist Albert Niemann successfully obtained pure crystals of cocaine, which is the compound that is mainly responsible (but not solely so) for the biological effects of coca leaves.

One of the first scientists to experiment with cocaine was Sigmund Freud. He quickly discovered the sensations that had long been known to South Americans: euphoria, alertness, energy, and lack of appetite for food. This led him to publish his findings in 1884 in an article entitled *Über Coca* (see Box 4.5)

---

### Box 4.5 Über Coca (On Cocaine)

...There is ample evidence that Indians under the influence of coca can withstand exceptional hardships and perform heavy labour, without requiring proper nourishment during that time...

...A few minutes after taking cocaine, one experiences a sudden exhilaration and feeling of lightness. One feels a certain furriness on the lips and palate, followed by a feeling of warmth in the same areas; if one now drinks cold water, it feels warm on the lips and cold in the throat.

On other occasions the predominant feeling is a rather pleasant coolness in the mouth and throat.

...I have tested this effect of coca, which wards off hunger, sleep, and fatigue and steels one to intellectual effort, some dozen times on myself; I had not opportunity to engage in physical work.

...The main use of coca will undoubtedly remain that which the Indians have made of it for centuries: it is of value in all cases where the primary aim is to increase the physical capacity of the body for a given short period of time and to hold strength in reserve to meet further demands – especially when outward circumstances exclude the possibility of obtaining the rest and nourishment normally necessary for great exertion. Such situations arise in wartime, on journeys, during mountain climbing and other expeditions, etc. – indeed, they are situations in which the alcoholic stimulants are also generally recognized as being of value. Coca is a far more potent and far less harmful stimulant than alcohol, and its widespread utilization is hindered at present only by its high cost.

...Cocaine and its salts have a marked anaesthetizing effect when brought in contact with the skin and mucous membrane in concentrated solution; this property suggests its occasional use as a local anaesthetic, especially in connection with affections of the mucous membrane...Indeed, the anaesthetizing properties of cocaine should make it suitable for a good many further applications.

---

Freud's observation, that cocaine's anaesthetizing effect could result in it being a useful local anaesthetic, was taken and developed by one of his colleagues, Carl Koller. Chewing coca leaves makes the mouth numb. Koller noticed that pure cocaine invariably has this effect on the tongue. Koller had been searching for a local anaesthetic to use in eye surgery, so he tested cocaine first on a frog, then on a rabbit and a dog, then on himself. He found that, by trickling a solution of cocaine into his eye, he was able to touch the cornea and make a dent in it with a pin head without any awareness of the touch. This observation proved a landmark in the development of local anaesthetics. However, the growing awareness that cocaine had unwanted side-effects, particularly its effect on the brain, generated a search for drugs that would have only a local anaesthetizing effect.

But where to start? We now know the molecular structure of cocaine (**4.4**), but in the latter half of the 19th century this had not been determined.

**4.4** cocaine

With a knowledge of the structure of cocaine, today probably the first move would be to find out which of the structural features in the molecule are responsible for the biological effects. (Of course, an alternative possibility might be that it is the *overall* molecular structure that confers activity.) A logical approach would be to test other compounds that were similar to cocaine but lacking one or more of the fragments or groups that might be responsible for its biological activity. If these compounds still have activity then it is probably safe to assume that the omitted fragments are not important biologically. However, if the amended compounds are not active, then it's probable that the missing bits *are* important. In fact, despite the lack of a complete understanding of its structure, this is exactly the approach that was adopted for cocaine. Over a century later, though the methods are somewhat more sophisticated, it is still the major strategy employed in drug discovery. So, let's discover, through an investigation of cocaine, how local anaesthetics were developed.

By the mid-1880s it was appreciated that a simple chemical reaction – hydrolysis – broke the cocaine molecule into two fragments: benzoic acid and an amine-containing fragment. Although the structure of benzoic acid was known exactly, the structure of nitrogen-containing fragment was not. With hindsight, we can understand this reaction as the hydrolysis of an ester, just like those used to make soaps from fats (Equation 4.1). The formation of benzoic acid indicates that cocaine contains a *benzoyl* fragment.

$$\text{hydrolysis} \qquad + \qquad + \qquad CH_3OH \ (4.1)$$

amine-containing        benzoyl            amine-containing            benzoic acid
   fragment           fragment              ring system

Another compound under study at the same time was atropine. Atropine (**4.5**) is a poison obtained from the deadly nightshade, *Atropa belladonna* (Figure 4.25), and is well known for its ability to dilate the pupil of the eye.

**Figure 4.25**
*Atropa belladonna*, a source of atropine.

When atropine is subjected to hydrolysis, it, too, forms two fragments: an alkaloid called tropine (**4.6**) and tropic acid (**4.7**) (Equation 4.2).

(4.2)

**4.5** atropine                 **4.6** tropine                 **4.7** tropic acid

Initially, the alkaloid was thought to be the same as that in cocaine. Several compounds similar to atropine were synthesized by covalently linking tropine with other carboxylic acids. Among the compounds made were homatropine (**4.8**) and benzoyltropine (**4.9**).

**4.8** homatropine                 **4.9** benzoyltropine

▨ As you can see from their structures, benzoyltropine (**4.9**) and cocaine (**4.4**) are different compounds. What does this tell you about the amine-containing fragments in both compounds?

▨ Since the benzoyl fragments are identical, the amine-containing fragments in cocaine and benzoyltropine must be different, not the same as originally supposed.

Atropine, homatropine and benzoyltropine were all tested for their local anaesthetic activity; atropine was a feeble anaesthetic, homatropine was more potent and benzoyltropine was a powerful local anaesthetic, like cocaine.

▨ Compare the structures of these three compounds, and that of cocaine. What do the results of the tests for local anaesthetic activity suggest to you about the structural factors necessary for the activity?

▨ Since benzoyltropine and cocaine have greatest activity the benzoyl fragment seems to be important. Also, this suggests that the ester fragment in the amine-containing fragment of cocaine seems not to be important (Figure 4.26).

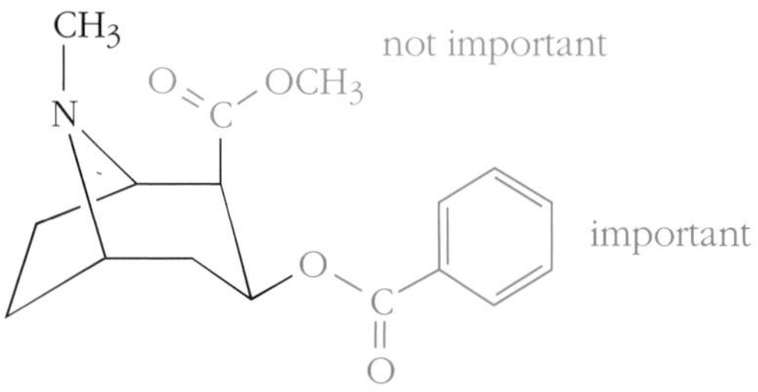

**Figure 4.26**
The structure of cocaine showing the relevance of the ester groups to local anaesthetic activity.

The deduction that the benzoyl group was important led to the synthesis and testing of the benzoyl derivatives of many other compounds, quinine and cinchonine among them. While all were active, many proved to be irritant too, but the approach led to a concentration of effort on benzoyl compounds, particularly simple esters of benzoic acid (**4.10**). By simple, we mean esters in which the R group is structurally less complex than that of, for example, tropine. One such compound was ethyl 4-aminobenzoate (**4.11**), which was found to numb the tongue. This compound, more commonly called benzocaine, is a compound that contains an amine group in the benzoyl fragment. This is the local anaesthetic contained in throat lozenges such as Merocaine.

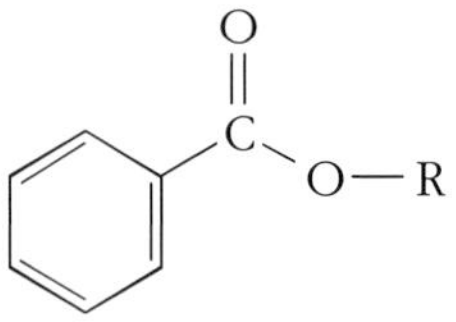

**4.10** 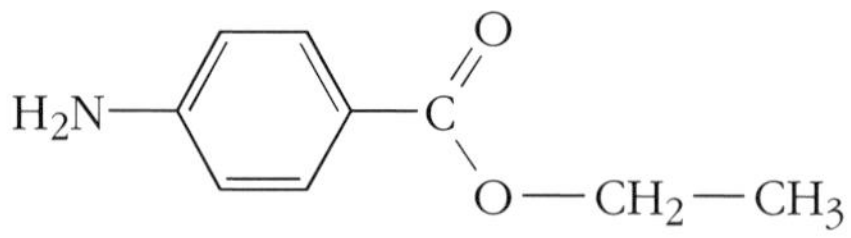                         **4.11** benzocaine

Alongside the activity concerned with the benzoyl fragment, the other half of the molecule – the amine-containing fragment – was also subjected to further investigation. By the early 1890s it was known that this fragment contained two rings, one of them based on the piperidine ring (**4.12**). Because simple derivatives of piperidine were available, an obvious question to ask was 'Do benzoyl piperidines have anaesthetic activity?'

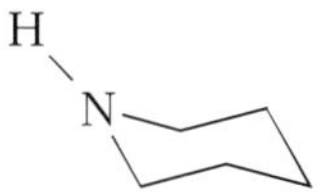

**4.12** the piperidine ring

To answer this question, several benzoyl esters were synthesized, including compounds **4.13**, **4.14** and **4.15**. All three had significant local anaesthetic activity, even though they all contain different combinations of ring substituents – the $CH_3$ and $COOCH_3$ groups – compared with cocaine. So, it became clear that the complex ring system of cocaine is unnecessary.

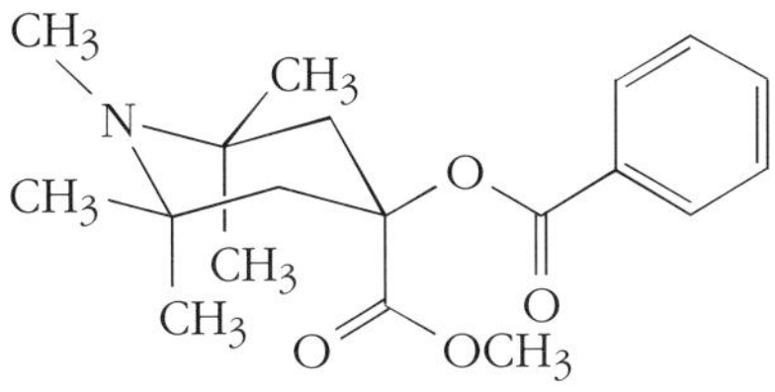

**4.13**

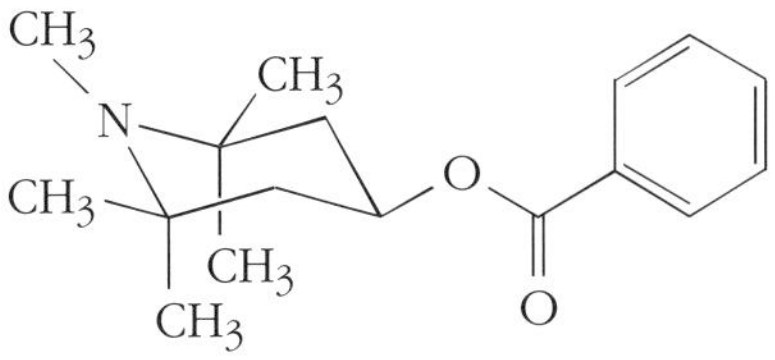

**4.14**

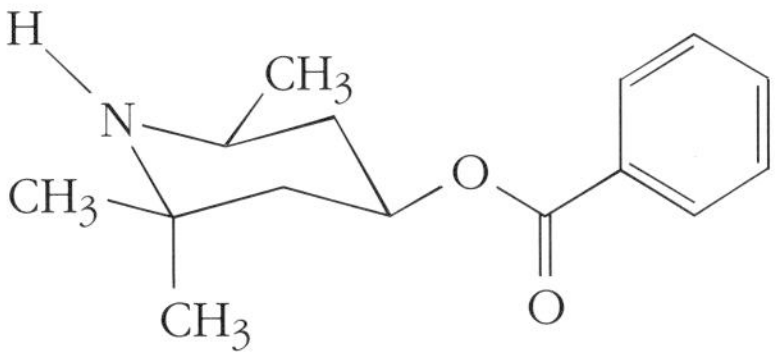

**4.15**

▨ If biological activity is a result of the functional groups that a molecule contains, what seem to be the common criteria needed for compounds related to cocaine to have local anaesthetic action?

▨ All the compounds with activity contain an ester of benzoic acid, as well as an amine group that is part of a ring that contains six atoms.

Of course, having simplified the ring structure of the amine-containing fragment of cocaine without losing biological activity, a logical extension is to determine whether or not the ring system of piperidine is also needed.

Possibly the simplest compound that might be used to test if this is so is **4.16**. This retains the benzoyl ester and amine groups, and keeps them separated by three carbon atoms, as in cocaine. Other possibilities might include molecules that have methyl groups, CH$_3$, either on the nitrogen atom or on the 'spacer' carbon atoms, such as **4.17**. This would keep the substitution pattern of the nitrogen atom similar to that in cocaine; that is, it is bonded to three carbon atoms.

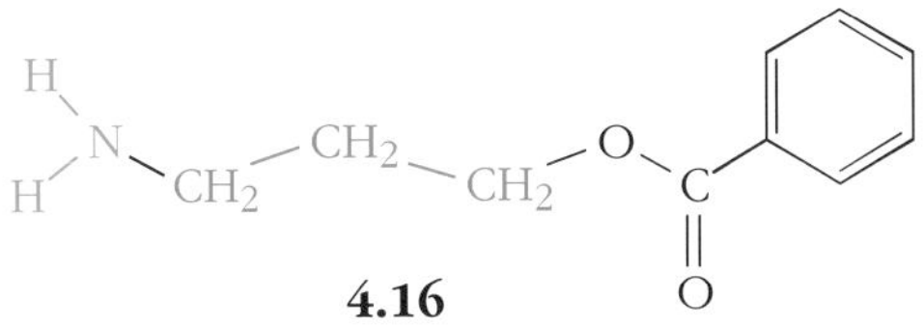

**4.16**

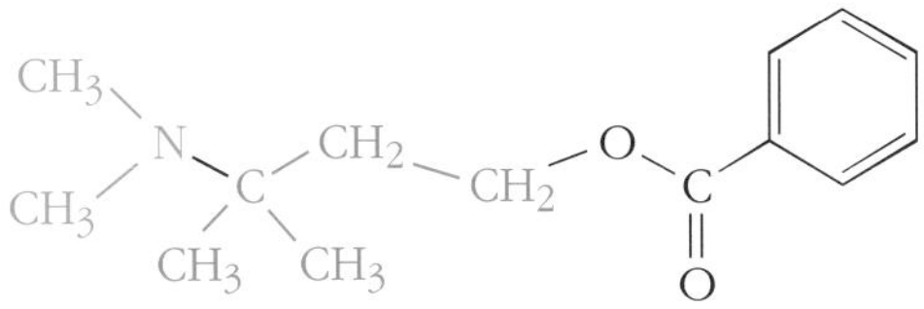

**4.17**

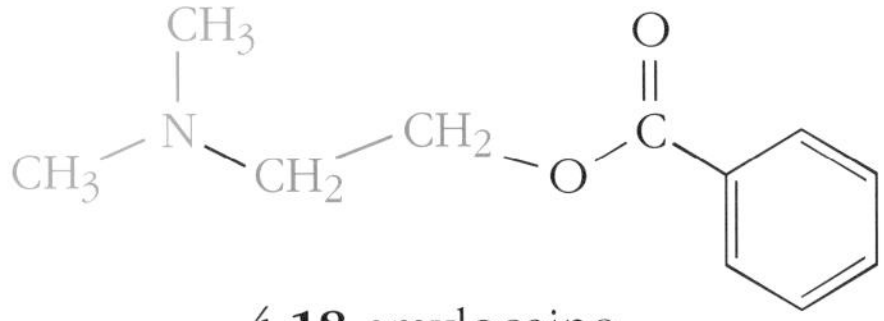

**4.18** amylocaine

Ernest Fourneau, of Poulenc Frères (later to become the industrial giant Rhône Poulenc), developed one such compound, amylocaine (**4.18**). This compound has powerful local anaesthetic action, with the added benefit that it is non-irritant; it rapidly became a substitute for cocaine.

■ Compare the structure of amylocaine with the one that we proposed, **4.16**. What difference do you notice between them?

■ Amylocaine has one 'spacer' carbon atom fewer between the benzoic acid ester fragment and the amine group than does our proposed molecule. It also has the nitrogen atom attached to two $CH_3$ groups, so the bonding pattern of the nitrogen atom is similar to that in cocaine.

It would seem, therefore, that the bonding arrangement need not mimic that in cocaine exactly. As a prelude to later Chapters, we can begin to see why this might be so if we carry out the following molecular model exercise. You should be aware that what we are about to do is an after-the-event rationalization, done with a modern understanding of structure.

---

### Activity 3  Comparison of cyclic and non-cyclic bonding arrangements in cocaine and amylocaine

Take two black C centres, one blue N centre and one red O centre, together with three short inflexible bonds, from your molecular model kit and make the structure shown in Figure 4.27, which represents the relationship between the ester group and the amine group in amylocaine.

Keep your model of the partial structure of amylocaine intact. Now take five more black C centres, one blue N centre, one red O centre and seven short bonds, and make the structure shown in Figure 4.28, to represent the relationship between the same two groups in cocaine.

Holding one model in your left hand, and the other in your right, see if you can manipulate them so that the oxygen atom of one model overlaps with the oxygen atom of the other and, at the

**Figure 4.27**
A partial molecular model of amylocaine to show the relationship between the ester group and the amine group.

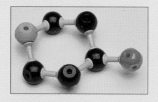

**Figure 4.28**
A partial molecular model of cocaine to show the relationship between the amine group and the ester group.

same time, the nitrogen atom of one overlaps with the nitrogen atom of the other. When I tried this exercise, I found it was possible to achieve this overlap of atoms if the molecules were arranged as in Figure 4.29.

Since many of the carbon atoms do not overlap, it seems that their positions are not important for local anaesthetic activity.

■ What does this tell us about the relationship of the amine and ester groups in local anaesthetics?

■ That it is not the exact *bonding pattern* that matters, but the *distance* between the two groups.

You might like to make another model to see whether the sequence $O-CH_2-N$ would be a sequence likely to give local anaesthetic properties (if the analysis above is correct, of course!). Your answer should be 'No'.

You should keep your partial model of cocaine to help you to answer Question 17.

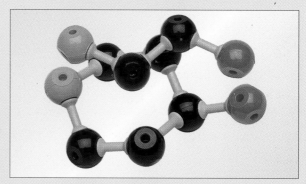

**Figure 4.29**
Comparison of the partial molecular models of amylocaine and cocaine.

Further development of local anaesthetics from cocaine comes from the logical suggestion that combining the best features of amylocaine and benzocaine into one molecule ought to provide a new compound that should be a more powerful anaesthetic than either.

■    What do you think are the molecular features of the individual molecules that are worth combining?

■    From amylocaine, the amine group and the ester group, which need be separated by only two carbon atoms, as in fragment **4.19**:

**4.19**

and from benzocaine the aminobenzoyl fragment **4.20**:

**4.20**

**Figure 4.30**
Having an injection at the dentist's. The local anaesthetic used to numb the nerves in the gums is procaine

Assembling these fragments using our Lego-brick approach does take us very close to a compound that has powerful local anaesthetic action, as you will have experienced if you've ever had an injection at the dentist's (Figure 4.30). The compound, procaine (**4.21**) – better known as Novocaine – has been in use as a local anaesthetic for most of the 20th century. (It has ethyl, rather than methyl, groups on the nitrogen atom.) Because procaine is an amine, it has the ability to form ammonium compounds. These are water soluble, which allows procaine to be injected directly into the site of application.

**4.21** procaine

The discovery of local anaesthetics from initial observations of the effects of cocaine illustrates clearly how a knowledge of chemistry is central to the development of new drugs (Figure 4.31): first, in the isolation and purification of active compounds from known remedies; second, in identifying features of the molecular structure that give rise to biological activity; and third, in generating new compounds with specific biological activity. This pattern is remarkably similar to that used in the discovery of new detergents (Chapter 1) and it encapsulates the chemical approach to most problems.

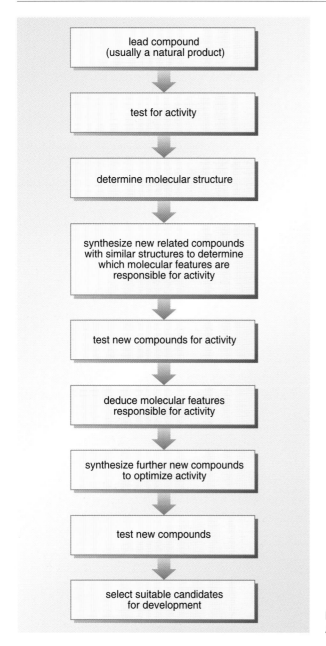

**Figure 4.31**
A pattern for drug discovery.

The progress to procaine from cocaine occurred without there being a full understanding of its molecular structure, and almost no understanding of how local anaesthetics actually bring about their biological effect. Even today it isn't entirely clear how they work. (A current description is given in Box 4.6 – you may find that it is better to read this after you have finished the next Chapter.)

Greater and more rapid progress came with a better understanding of animal biochemistry – the reactions that go on inside the body to maintain life – as well as with a greater ability to determine the structures of molecules more readily. In the following Chapters we shall see how a combination of this pattern for drug discovery together with a greater biochemical understanding of what makes us 'tick', results in a much more successful approach to the treatment of disease.

## Box 4.6 Local anaesthetics

Nerve cells are the means by which our brains communicate with the various parts of our bodies. The messages are tiny pulses of electric charge, which are transmitted along nerve fibres. The information is coded in the frequency and size of the pulses. Nerve cells transmit these pulses by changing their ability to allow ions, such as $Na^+$, $K^+$ or $Cl^-$, to enter or leave the cell. The cells have channels through which the ions can travel, each ion having a specific channel. When the ions move across the cell wall they take their charge with them, altering the charge balance inside and outside the cell.

Sometimes the channels are shut so no ions pass, sometimes they are open so ions pass through. The cells therefore need some kind of switching mechanism to tell them when the channels should be open and when shut. Although the mechanism of action of local anaesthetics is still poorly understood, it is thought that the chemical acetylcholine (**4.22**) (pronounced ass-e-tile-co-leen) is the natural compound that controls the transport of $Na^+$ ions through the cell wall.

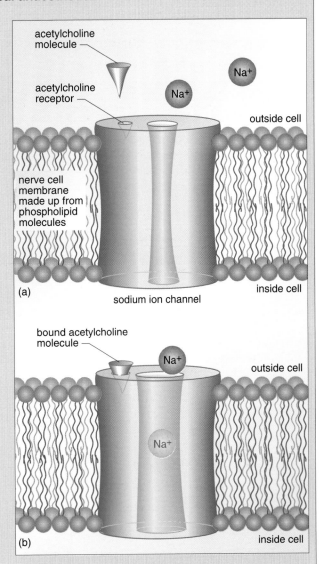

**4.22** acetylcholine

At the surface of the cell is a large protein molecule that 'recognizes' the molecular shape and charge of acetylcholine and can bind to it. Such a protein is called a receptor. When acetylcholine binds to its receptor, the receptor protein changes its shape to accommodate the bound molecule, and this change in shape determines whether the channel is open or closed. Both cocaine and the local anaesthetics have molecular features similar to acetylcholine so they too can bind to the receptor. These molecules don't have identical shapes to acetylcholine though, so the change in the shape of the receptor protein is different and so the effect on the channel is different. What's more, when a cocaine molecule is bound to the receptor a molecule of acetylcholine can't because its site is already occupied. So as well as having a different effect from acetylcholine, the local anaesthetics block the normal effect of acetylcholine.

**Figure 4.32**
A schematic drawing of the sodium ion channel. In (a) the channel is closed so sodium ions can't get through. In (b) an acetylcholine molecule has bound to a receptor, which allows the channel to open enabling sodium ions to pass through.

This brings about a change in the ability of the nerve cells to conduct electrical charge, which in this case is perceived by the brain as a lack of pain.

**Question 16**  The infrared spectrum of cocaine is shown in Figure 4.33. From this spectrum, which functional group can you identify as being present in the molecule?

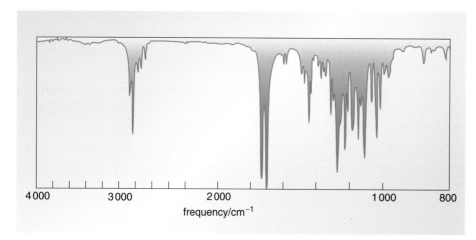

**Figure 4.33**
The infrared spectrum of cocaine.

**Question 17**  Use your molecular model kit to decide which of the two compounds **4.23** and **4.24** you'd expect to have the greater local anaesthetic activity. For compound **4.23** you need only build the fragment shown in Figure 4.34 and for **4.24** that shown in Figure 4.35. You will need to compare these models with partial structure of cocaine you built earlier (Figure 4.28).

**4.23**

**4.24**

**Figure 4.34**
A partial molecular model of compound **4.23**.

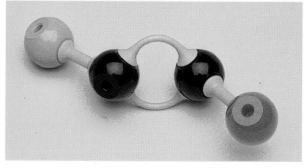

**Figure 4.35**
A partial molecular model of compound **4.24**.

## 4.4 Summary of Chapter 4

In this Chapter you have found out that:

The most 'powerful' remedies used in homoeopathy appear to contain no active ingredient.

A knowledge of molecular structure provides the basis for developing novel compounds with potentially useful biological activity.

Fragments of molecular structures can be compared using molecular models to identify relationships between atoms, or groups of atoms, that may be responsible for the biological activity of the compounds concerned.

The process of drug development follows a stepwise path from the initially discovered compound, via a knowledge of its molecular structure and an understanding of the molecular features that provide activity, to the synthesis of new compounds with optimum activity.

Cocaine has been the basis for developing local anaesthetics.

You have also seen that:

Infrared spectroscopy can be used to identify functional groups in a molecule; for example, esters have a characteristic absorption at $1\,740\ \text{cm}^{-1}$, and alcohols have one centred at $3\,350\ \text{cm}^{-1}$ but extending from $3\,000\ \text{cm}^{-1}$ to $3\,500\ \text{cm}^{-1}$.

**Question 18** Analyse the development of the local anaesthetic procaine (**4.21**) from cocaine, according to the pattern of drug development set out in Figure 4.31. Express your answer as a flow chart in the style of Figure 4.31.

# Chapter 5
# Molecular targets and magic bullets

In this Chapter we shall examine the nature of the major biological targets at which drugs are aimed. Specific emphasis will be given to the types of bonding interaction that are possible between the biological targets and the drugs.

In 1988, C. J. Coulson made the following admission in the textbook called *Molecular Mechanisms of Drug Action*:

> *It would have been impossible to write a book of any length detailing mechanisms of drug action more than 20 years ago, because very little was known at that time. Penicillin, for example, had been on the market for 20 years, but we were still far from detailing its precise mode of action. The philosophical attitude, prevalent in those days and still common now, was that drugs were just used because they worked: enquiry into their mode of action was deemed unnecessary. The fact that, at that time, our detailed understanding of biological processes was very limited, may not be unconnected. Many of us entering the drug industry in the 1960s hoped, however, to be able to design drugs more effectively on the basis of molecular structure...*

*(C. J. Coulson,* Molecular Mechanisms of Drug Action, *Taylor and Francis, 1988, p. 1)*

This seems remarkable. More than half a century had passed since procaine had been developed, and in the interim many other drugs had been developed using the same strategy of **rational design**. This is, the process of taking a **lead compound** – not a compound of the element Pb, but a compound from which leads (pronounced leeds) are developed – making closely related compounds to find out which molecular features are responsible for the biological activity, and then designing new compounds that have all the active features incorporated into them. The lack of understanding of how the drugs actually worked was a result of the poor understanding of the chemistry of the body, in particular the chemistry of the cell. As a knowledge of this chemistry has accumulated, so an understanding of how drugs bring about their biological effect has been developed. In turn, this has led to a more powerful approach to drug development.

What, then, are the major biological targets? All forms of life, from protozoa to human beings, use cells – in the case of protozoa, just one cell – to divide up into compartments the chemical processes that are required for energy and for the maintenance and propagation of life. Cells are organized so that these processes can be carried out efficiently. Although cells from different forms of life have different characteristics, and even cells from the same organism can be very different, most cells have some features in common, namely a cell membrane, a nucleus and a fluid called cytosol (Figure 5.1).

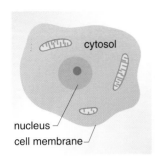

**Figure 5.1**
A simplified drawing of a cell.

At its most simple, the cell membrane is a barrier that holds the cell together; some cells have a cell wall outside the membrane to reinforce this function. The membrane makes sure that wanted materials are allowed into the cell and kept there, while unwanted ones are allowed out and harmful ones are not allowed in.

The membrane is made up from roughly equal amounts of lipids and proteins. The lipids, the fatty substances, form the basic structure of the membrane into which are embedded the proteins (Figure 5.2).

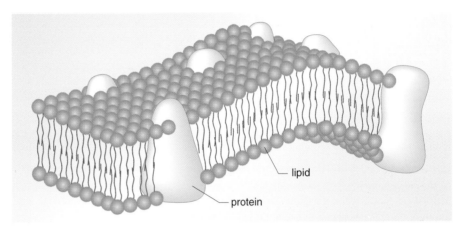

lipid

protein

**Figure 5.2**
A representation of the structure of the cell membrane. Proteins are embedded into the double layer of lipids.

The membrane proteins have several functions. One of these is to be able to recognize and respond to specific chemicals. The result is a series of effects, such as allowing substances required for cell maintenance to pass through the membrane, or perhaps initiating a series of chemical reactions. This type of protein is called a **receptor**. Others catalyse specific chemical reactions. These proteins are called enzymes, which we looked at in Chapter 3 of Part 1. Enzymes are actually found throughout the cell, not just in the membrane. The difference between an enzyme and a receptor is the following: *enzymes* transform specific chemicals into new substances through bond-making and bond-breaking processes; *receptors* respond to specific chemicals, but the chemicals are not transformed. Both enzymes and receptors remain unaltered when they have carried out their functions.

Within the cell lies the nucleus. This is where the **nucleic acid** resides. The nucleic acid deoxyribonucleic acid, or DNA for short, is the molecule that carries all the information for the cell. DNA encodes the plans for making all the molecules that are needed for the processes that go on in the cell. Most importantly, DNA carries the information to replicate itself, which means that all of the information for the life of the cell is passed on at cell division.

As well as a membrane and a nucleus, most cells have other features that are important to maintaining life. These, too, are usually made up of lipids and proteins, and another type of biomolecule – polysaccharides (Part 1, Section 2.3). Surrounding all of these features is the cytosol, which contains water-soluble enzymes, proteins and the small molecules and ions required for the various processes of the cell.

Although cell structure is much more complex than the brief description given here, we are now in a position to identify potential molecular targets for drug action. First, there are the enzymes. Cells contain many different enzymes, each usually able to catalyse only one reaction. Many diseases, or their symptoms, are caused by an excess or deficiency of the compounds involved in these enzyme-catalysed reactions. If that is the case, one possibility for medical treatment might be to develop a drug that blocks the action of either the enzyme that produces the compound responsible, or alternatively, the enzyme that uses the compound. We might achieve that by designing a molecule in such a way that it resembles the compound that the enzyme normally transforms, but which then cannot take part in the enzyme-catalysed process. However we decide to block – or inhibit – the enzyme-catalysed process, the fact that we can do so means that we can interfere with cell biochemistry and therefore cell processes. We shall examine two such examples in Chapter 7.

The second target is the receptors. Because receptors operate in the presence of a particular compound by triggering a series of chemical responses, it ought to be possible to influence the way that the receptor interacts with the triggering compound. We could, for example, design a compound that will interact more strongly with the receptor. This would block the usual compound and therefore diminish its effect. Alternatively, we might try to design a compound that will interact with the receptor to bring about a greater effect than the normal compound. We shall be studying an example of a drug interacting with a receptor in Chapter 6.

The third target is DNA. Because DNA is the genetic material, carrying all of the information for the life of the cell, if we interfere with the way that the information is passed on – or stop it being passed on altogether – or in the way it is decoded, then we ought to be able to disrupt the cell processes. However, attempting to interfere with DNA is fraught with danger. Any drug that interacts with DNA must be specific, otherwise it is likely to affect all of the cell processes. Moreover, since the difference between DNA from normally functioning cells and that from malfunctioning cells is often very small, drugs that interact with DNA are usually toxic to normal cells too, which is why drugs designed to interact with DNA are usually reserved for life-threatening illnesses, such as the various cancers and viral infections.

Although they are not the only targets at which drugs can be aimed, enzymes, receptors and nucleic acid are arguably the three most important. They are certainly the most common both when it comes to designing new drugs and in understanding how older drugs work. In this Course we shall examine examples of drugs that interact with receptors and enzymes.

The quest of pharmaceutical chemistry (Figure 5.3) is to discover or develop an arsenal of 'magic bullets', a range of drugs that can be specifically aimed at any one of the biological targets without straying off-target and hitting the others. These drugs, it is hoped, will have a precise mode of action, treating the illness but not affecting any of the processes involved in staying alive. This quest may seem hopelessly optimistic, but it has had, and continues to have, notable successes, as you shall discover.

**Figure 5.3**
The major targets of
pharmaceutical chemistry.

What then are the features of enzyme and receptor molecules that allow us to design compounds that can interact with them? As you may recall from Part 1, Chapter 3, both are protein biopolymers made from the same building blocks, amino acids:

$$\text{amine group} \qquad \begin{array}{c} R \quad H \\ H \diagdown \ \ | \ \diagup \\ N-C \ \ C{=}O \\ \diagup \qquad | \\ H \qquad OH \end{array} \qquad \text{acid group}$$

The general structure of enzymes and receptors is formed by linking the amine group of one amino acid to the acid group of another:

$$\begin{array}{c} R^1 \ H \quad H \qquad O \\ H \diagdown \ \ \diagup \ \ | \qquad \| \\ N-C-C-N-C-C-OH \\ \diagup \qquad \| \qquad | \\ H \qquad O \quad R^2 \ H \end{array}$$

amino acid
residue          amino acid
residue

and so on until fifty to several hundred amino acids have been linked together. The precise role that this giant molecule will have, either as an enzyme or a receptor, depends on how many amino acid groups are used to build up its structure, which of the 20 amino acids are used and, crucially, the order in which they are linked together. But no matter what their function, all of these biological molecules use a few simple forces both to hold together their own three-dimensional structure and to bind to other molecules. You have already met these forces in Chapter 8 of Book 1; they are hydrogen bonding, ionic interactions and London forces.

▨    To what type of group in a drug molecule would a positively charged
      ammonium cation on the enzyme or receptor protein bind?

■    Such a positively charged ion could bind to a negatively charged
      carboxylate ion on the drug.

Of course, the reverse is also true, with the drug carrying the ammonium
cation and the protein the carboxylate anion. Another possibility is that a
nitrogen or an oxygen atom on the protein can form a hydrogen bond to a
suitable hydrogen atom on the drug – in an OH group for example. Again,
the reverse is true – with the drug containing the nitrogen or oxygen atom
and the protein the hydrogen atom. The third type of interaction is London
forces, in particular those between hydrocarbon chains and between
aromatic rings. All these interactions are illustrated in Figure 5.4.

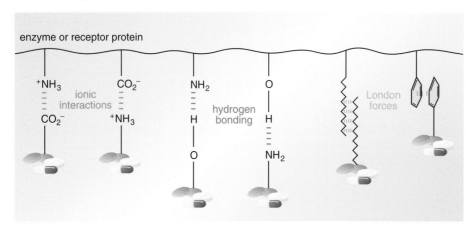

**Figure 5.4**
Potential interactions
between enzymes or
receptors and drugs, shown
in a schematic manner.

Usually, binding of molecules to proteins requires a combination of these
interactions rather than just one. Moreover, because the proteins have precise
three-dimensional structures, the functional groups in a potential drug have to
be correctly positioned in the molecule for the interactions to be favoured
(Part 1, Chapter 6). The challenge of drug development is to discover how to
position the appropriate groups correctly to maximize drug action.

## 5.1  Summary of Chapter 5

In this Chapter you have found out that:

The three major targets for drug action with cells are enzymes, receptors and
nucleic acid.

Enzymes and receptors are proteins made from amino acids; the major forces
that enable these proteins to bind to other molecules are hydrogen bonding,
ionic interactions and London forces.

# Chapter 6
# From *Ephedra sinaica* to Ventolin

In this Chapter it becomes apparent that having a clear picture of molecular structure is invaluable to the logical development of compounds with specific biological activity. Our story follows the stages in the development of the anti-asthmatic drug salbutamol (Ventolin); the leads were provided by the compound ephedrine, isolated from the herbal remedy ma huang, and by the hormone adrenaline. Along the way, the kinds of molecular change that can be used to identify which parts of molecules are responsible for biological activity will be introduced.

Ma huang (Figure 4.8) is a herb that has been used in Chinese medicine since around 3100 BC. It was recorded in the Pen Ts'ao (Great Herbal) of Shen Nung in 1760 BC, and in 1596 AD a Chinese apothecary, Kang Mu, reported that it reduced fever, improved circulation, induced sweating and eased coughing.

An aqueous extract of ma huang, which consists of the dried, young branches of several *Ephedra* species, produced by boiling the plant in water, was found on injection into a dog to raise the blood pressure, increase the heart rate, constrict the blood vessels of the kidneys and bring about bronchodilation (that is, a widening of the bronchial airways). A pure compound, ephedrine (eff-ed-reen) (Figure 6.1), can be isolated from the extract. This substance has the power to dilate the airways of the respiratory tract, and this rapidly led to ephedrine being used as a treatment for asthma. The great benefit of ephedrine is that it can be taken orally. Unfortunately, an undesirable side-effect is its ability to raise the blood pressure significantly. Ma huang itself does not raise blood pressure so markedly because it contains other compounds, one of which – pseudoephedrine – actually reduces the rate of heart beat and lowers blood pressure. Pseudoephedrine (Figure 6.2) and ephedrine are related compounds, in that they contain the same number and same types of atoms, but these atoms are arranged slightly differently in space (see Box 6.1). If you take a look at the carbon atoms immediately attached to the benzene rings in these two compounds you should notice that the H and OH groups are arranged in the opposite sense. Biological systems experience these two substances as having distinct properties and respond differently to each.

This is a classic example of how isolating a pure compound from a herbal remedy can lead to a drug that has a different spectrum of biological activity, simply because the herbal remedy contains several compounds with differing activities. In this case the biological effect of pseudoephedrine counteracts to some extent that of ephedrine.

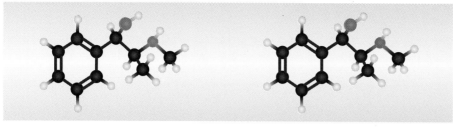

**Figure 6.1**
Stereoscopic model of the structure of ephedrine.

**Figure 6.2**
Stereoscopic model of the structure of pseudoephedrine.

## Activity 4  Molecules and handedness

We all know that, except to the finest detail, our hands are mirror images of each other. They have the same features and same shape yet they are not identical. If you put one hand flat on a table and then place the other hand on top, it is obvious that you cannot arrange them such that all of the features of one hand occupy *exactly* the same positions and space as those of the other. Our hands are therefore not superimposable, and we say that they are non-superimposable mirror images.

It may come as a surprise to learn that certain molecules have 'handedness' too. Molecular handedness arises because of the way four atoms, or groups of atoms, can be arranged around a tetrahedral carbon atom. To find out how this is so, make two models as shown in Figure 6.3. This represents a carbon atom surrounded by four groups, two of which are identical. See if you can determine whether or not these models are identical. You should be able to see that they are if you manipulate them so that each atom or group occupies exactly the same position in space.

Now, use the two models to make two further models like those in Figure 6.4. Notice that this time all of the groups around the carbon atom are different.

These models have been arranged in the picture to help you see that they are mirror images of each other. But are they identical? Try to manipulate the models so that the four groups occupy *exactly* the same positions in space. You should find that it is impossible to achieve. The models will never be superimposable. This is a general result; *whenever a*

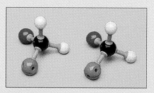

**Figure 6.3**
Models of a carbon atom surrounded by four groups, two of which are the same.

**Figure 6.4**
Models of a carbon atom surrounded by four different groups.

*tetrahedral carbon atom is surrounded by four different groups there are always two ways of arranging the groups around the carbon atom.* This means it is possible to obtain molecules that are, like our hands, identical in every respect except that they are mirror images of each other. The

Greek word for hand is chiros (ki-ros), so carbon atoms with four different groups around them are said to be **chiral** (ki-ral). The two mirror image compounds are called **stereoisomers** (from iso = same, meros = part and stereo = space).

Until quite recently, the methods used to synthesize drugs invariably produced both stereoisomers. However, stereoisomers often bring about different biological responses, which may be the reason why some drugs have side-effects. Sometimes, it is only one stereoisomer that is active while the other has no biological effect. In this situation, to use methods that make both stereoisomers would be wasteful. Not surprisingly, a lot of effort is now being expended in devising methods that produce only the desired stereoisomer.

## Box 6.1  Representing molecules in space

Ephedrine and pseudoephedrine are stereoisomers. They are therefore different compounds, but if we draw them using the abbreviated style we've used up till now they'd have structures **6.1** and **6.2**, which look identical.

So, we need a way of showing that they are indeed different in the way that the groups are arranged in space. Take another look at Figure 6.1; what we'd like is a method that shows, as we look at the molecule, how certain groups appear to be coming towards us (the OH and $CH_3$), while others appear to be going away from us (the two H

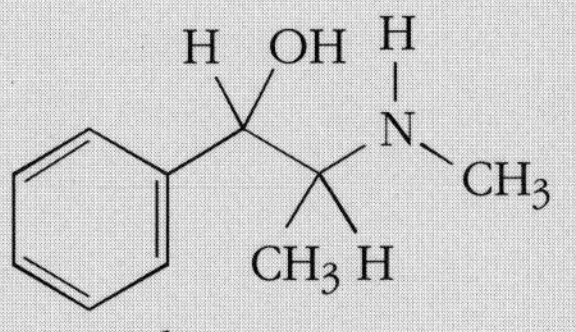

**6.1** ephedrine

**6.2** pseudoephedrine

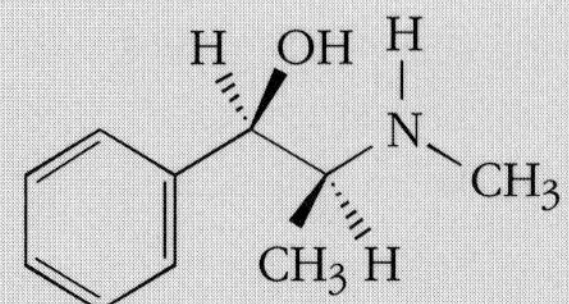

atoms). The method that has been adopted is to use a ▬ symbol for groups coming toward us, and a ⅏ symbol for those going away from us. An abbreviated structure of ephedrine drawn like this looks like structure **6.3**.

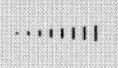

**6.3**

■ Draw an equivalent structure for pseudoephedrine.

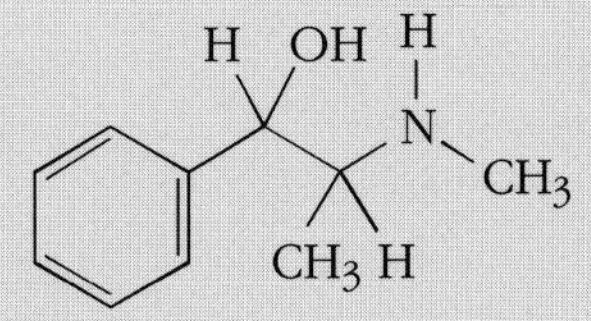

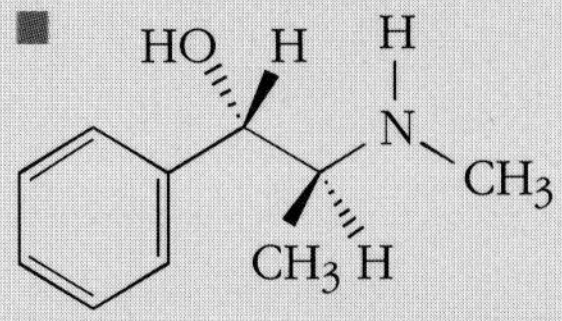

■ **6.4**

We shall use this notation from now on whenever the precise spatial arrangement of atoms is important.

The scarcity of ma huang, together with the great demand for, and undesirable side-effect of, ephedrine, led to a drive to synthesize an effective substitute.

■   Study the structure of ephedrine and try to identify four structural fragments that might contribute to its biological activity.

■   Ephedrine contains an benzene ring system, an alcohol group, an amine group, and what we shall call a branching methyl group (Figure 6.5).

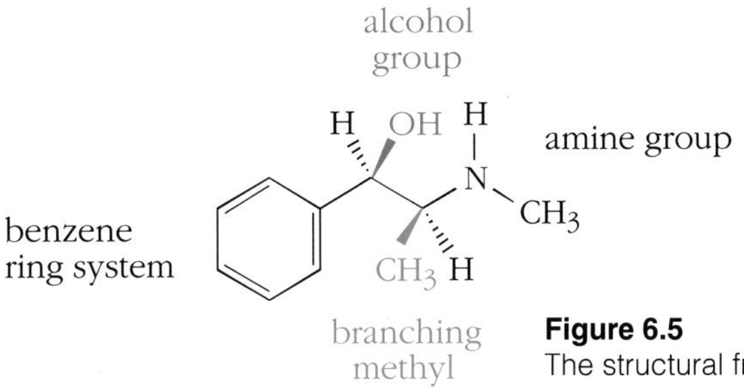

alcohol group

amine group

benzene ring system

branching methyl

**Figure 6.5**
The structural fragments of ephedrine.

As we discovered with cocaine, the best way forward – when it is unclear why a compound has a particular biological activity – is to make simpler substances which contain only two or three of these features and test them for biological activity. Now, carbon atoms and hydrogen atoms are the basic building blocks of organic molecules, and fragments of molecules containing carbon–hydrogen (C—H) bonds generally have little chemical activity. So, when we want to investigate compounds to identify what contributes to their reactivity a common approach is to design simpler substances by replacing a functional group in an active molecule by a hydrogen atom and observing the result.

For example, if we wanted to examine what features might be responsible for some identified biological activity of ethanolamine, $HO—CH_2—CH_2—NH_2$, then there are two simpler compounds that we could study, ethylamine (pronounced eeth-isle-am-een), $H—CH_2—CH_2—NH_2$, and ethanol, $HO—CH_2—CH_2—H$. In ethylamine, the amine fragment of ethanolamine has been preserved but the alcohol group, OH, has been replaced by H:

replace by H

$$HO—CH_2—CH_2—NH_2 \implies H—CH_2—CH_2—NH_2$$

ethanolamine                                    ethylamine

▪ What would the difference, if any, in activity between ethanolamine and ethylamine reveal?

◼ Such a difference would reveal the contribution of the OH alcohol group to the biological activity of ethanolamine.

Similarly, in ethanol the alcohol fragment of ethanolamine has been preserved, while the amine group has been replaced by H:

replace by H

$$HO—CH_2—CH_2—NH_2 \implies HO—CH_2—CH_2—H$$

ethanolamine                                    ethanol

and now the difference in activity would give us an idea of the extent to which the amine group contributes to the biological activity of ethanolamine.

When we study a compound in this way, we cannot simply remove a group like OH or $NH_2$ without replacing it with something else. If we didn't replace it, we'd have a carbon atom that had too few groups bonded to it, such as

$$HO—CH_2—\overset{\overset{\displaystyle H}{|}}{\underset{\underset{\displaystyle H}{|}}{C}}—NH_2 \implies HO—CH_2—\overset{\overset{\displaystyle H}{|}}{\underset{\underset{\displaystyle H}{|}}{C}} \longleftarrow \text{this C atom has only three bonds when it needs four}$$

ethanolamine

The simplest group we can add to satisfy the bonding requirements of the carbon atom, and which is unlikely to have any activity of its own, is hydrogen.

▪ Using the structure of ephedrine as your guide, apply the approach we've just discussed to design one molecule (there are six possibilities) that contains only two of the features that we identified as being potentially important for ephedrine, and another that contains three (there are four possibilities).

■ Any of the following molecules would be an acceptable candidate containing only two of the features of ephedrine:

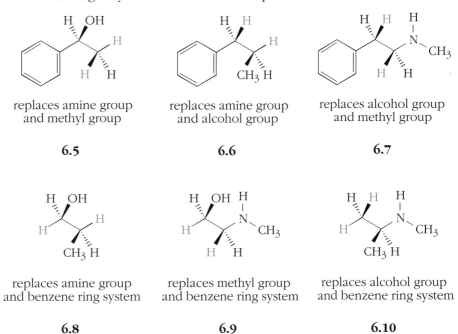

| replaces amine group and methyl group | replaces amine group and alcohol group | replaces alcohol group and methyl group |
|---|---|---|
| **6.5** | **6.6** | **6.7** |

| replaces amine group and benzene ring system | replaces methyl group and benzene ring system | replaces alcohol group and benzene ring system |
|---|---|---|
| **6.8** | **6.9** | **6.10** |

and any one of the following would be acceptable as a candidate containing three of the features of ephedrine:

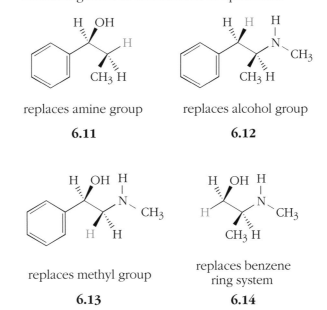

| replaces amine group | replaces alcohol group |
|---|---|
| **6.11** | **6.12** |

| replaces methyl group | replaces benzene ring system |
|---|---|
| **6.13** | **6.14** |

Once more we have used the Lego-brick approach to *designing* potentially useful compounds – using our imagination (and our models!) to remove molecular fragments and replace them with other groups. We haven't begun to tackle how we might *make* any of these compounds experimentally, nor is it possible in this Course to do so.

One of the compounds that has been actually tested, phenylethanolamine
(**6.15**) (pronounced feen-isle-ethanol-am-een), is a useful ephedrine
analogue, but it isn't active when taken orally. Phenylethanolamine resembles
structure **6.13**; it contains three fragment groups from ephedrine, but the
nitrogen atom of the amine group in ephedrine carries a methyl group,
whereas that in phenylethanolamine doesn't.

**6.15** phenylethanolamine

Other compounds found to have activity are phenylethylamine (feen-isle-
eeth-isle-am-een) (**6.16**), amphetamine (**6.17**) and methylamphetamine
(**6.18**).

**6.16** phenylethylamine          **6.17** amphetamine          **6.18** methylamphetamine

Phenylethylamine carries only two of the fragments of ephedrine – the
benzene group and the amine group (although this does not bear a methyl
group) – whereas amphetamine and methylamphetamine contain three of the
fragments of ephedrine – the benzene, amine and branching methyl groups.

Of the three, the two amphetamines are by far the more active, with
methylamphetamine the most potent.

▨    What can you deduce from this information about the structural features
     required for activity?

▨    Since amphetamine is more active than phenylethylamine it would
     appear a branching methyl group is important, and by comparing the
     activities of methylamphetamine with amphetamine it would appear
     that the amine nitrogen atom should bear a methyl group.

Both amphetamine and methylamphetamine have been used to treat asthma;
amphetamine was marketed as Benzedrine and methylamphetamine as
Methedrine, being inhaled directly through the use of a nasal inhaler.
Unfortunately, like ephedrine, the amphetamines also produce an increase in
blood pressure. An equally serious drawback is their ability to act as addictive
stimulants when they enter into the brain from the bloodstream.

So, the need for a suitable alternative is apparent, but where to start? The
structure of ephedrine has provided some leads, but these have dried up.
Until recently, the major problem with any approach of this sort, which is
based on a lead compound isolated from a natural source, is that an
understanding of how it interacts with the molecules of the body is usually

unknown. If we knew, even in a crude way, how ephedrine interacts with these biomolecules then the design of more efficient pharmaceuticals would be possible.

Real progress in the development of an anti-asthmatic drug came following the discovery of the molecule that the body itself uses to dilate the smooth muscle of the respiratory tract, adrenaline (**6.19**).

**6.19** adrenaline

■ Compare the molecular structures of adrenaline (**6.19**), ephedrine (**6.3**), and methylamphetamine (**6.18**). What similarities between adrenaline and the other two compounds can you discern, and what differences?

■ Adrenaline contains the following groups:

all three molecules contain this group

ephedrine and adrenaline, but not methylamphetamine, contain this group

only adrenaline contains this type of benzene ring substituted with two OH groups

Adrenaline does not contain a branching methyl group, whereas both ephedrine and methylamphetamine do.

Not surprisingly, these similarities and differences are precisely the features that can be exploited to generate new, and more specific, drugs to treat asthma.

Adrenaline is a natural hormone; it is secreted into the bloodstream by the adrenal gland and acts at distant organs, such as the lungs, heart, uterus and alimentary tract. It brings about its biological effects by binding to receptors on the cell surface of the organ. When adrenaline binds to these receptors, it triggers a cascade of reactions inside the cells, and it is this cascade of reactions that causes the biological response. This is crudely represented in Figure 6.6. So, if we can work out how adrenaline binds to its receptor then we might to be able to design a molecule that incorporates these features that should have a greater biological activity. Easy to say, less easy to carry out in practice!

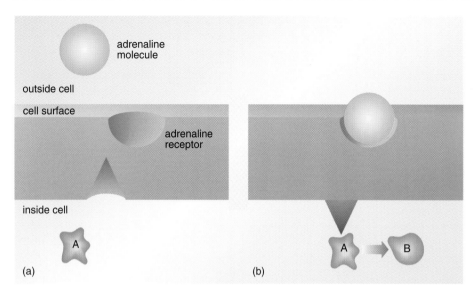

**Figure 6.6**
A representation of how adrenaline brings about its biological action.

It may have crossed your mind to ask the question 'If adrenaline is the naturally occurring compound that can dilate the smooth muscle and open up the airways, why not administer adrenaline?' You may be able to answer this question yourself from your own experience. It is common usage to talk about 'getting the adrenaline flowing' when we need to carry out a physically or emotionally demanding activity. In such stressful situations, what usually happens to your body *physically before* you undertake the activity? I usually find that my heart begins to pound and beats faster. Adrenaline is indeed responsible for these effects.

▨   So, why would the administration of adrenaline be inappropriate to people with asthma?

▦   As well as affecting the lungs and bronchial tract, adrenaline would also affect the heart.

There are obviously adrenaline receptors on the heart muscle cells as well as on lung cells. Any useful treatment for asthma must centre on a drug that is *selective* for the lung receptors rather than the heart receptors. Not a simple task to achieve! Of course, this also identifies a probable reason for any side-effects that may arise from drugs derived from adrenaline.

Further reasons, other than a lack of selectivity, for not using adrenaline directly are first, it is inactive when given by mouth, and second, it has only a short duration of action. Its lack of activity when given orally stems from its poor absorption from the intestines into the bloodstream. Its short duration of action arises naturally because the compound is chemically deactivated by enzymes in the body – this is the body's way of preventing the heart from being in a permanently stressed state!

Despite these drawbacks, adrenaline has one major advantage over methylamphetamine; it is not addictive. This is because it does not enter into the brain from the bloodstream. The blood is a water-rich medium, whereas the brain is a lipid-rich (fat-rich) medium. The two OH groups on the aromatic ring of adrenaline make it much more soluble in the water-rich environment and much less soluble in the lipid-rich environment. However, this does provide a good clue to successful drug design – to avoid problems relating to addiction it would make sense to include the OH groups in any new drug.

**6.20** isoprenaline

One such compound is isoprenaline (**6.20**). Its structure is almost identical with that of adrenaline, except that the $CH_3$ (methyl) group bonded to the nitrogen atom has been replaced by the $CH(CH_3)_2$ (isopropyl) group (hence the name, a contraction of *isop*ropyl and adr*enaline*). Until the early 1970s, isoprenaline was the drug of choice in the treatment of asthma. The replacement of the methyl group by isopropyl made the compound more able than adrenaline to bind to lung receptors. However, isoprenaline doesn't discriminate between lung receptors and heart receptors; its ability to bind to the heart receptors is the same as its ability to bind to the lung receptors. This lack of selectivity between heart and lung receptors not surprisingly gives rise to some unpleasant side-effects, such as palpitations or uneven beating of the heart. For some people these side-effects proved to be lethal; it is estimated that in the UK approximately three thousand asthmatic teenagers died as a consequence of the side-effects that isoprenaline has on the heart. Another disadvantage of isoprenaline is that, like adrenaline, it has a short duration of activity because the enzymes that deactivate adrenaline also deactivate isoprenaline. So, there's a need to understand both how adrenaline binds to its receptor – by identifying which molecular features are needed for binding – and how it is deactivated.

■ What method might you use to identify which of the functional groups in adrenaline are needed for biological activity?

■ One possibility would be to design and test other compounds in which one of the groups had been replaced by a hydrogen atom.

■ Design two compounds based on the structure of adrenaline that would test the role of the two OH groups attached to the benzene ring.

■ Two such compounds are **6.21** and **6.22**; these compounds are identical with adrenaline except that in each case a hydrogen atom (marked in red) has been used to replace one of the two OH groups attached to the aromatic ring. (Repacing both OH groups would amount to changing two features at the same time.)

**6.21**          **6.22**

Compound **6.21** has no biological activity, and compound **6.22** has no anti-asthmatic activity. So, it would appear that both groups in conjunction are necessary for a compound to have anti-asthmatic activity.

We can then ask ourselves 'Are the OH groups themselves necessary, or can we replace them by some other similar groups?'. There are several ways of trying to answer this question. First, we could replace either or both of the OH groups with some other group, for example an amine group $NH_2$.

Alternatively, we could choose to investigate whether or not the OH groups have to be attached directly to the aromatic ring. We can do that by replacing the OH group with $CH_2OH$, effectively by inserting a $CH_2$ fragment – a *spacer* group – between the ring and the OH as in structure **6.23**. In the same way as H atoms are often used to *replace* a group within a molecule, $CH_2$ groups are often used in this way so that the distances between groups that are thought to be biologically important can be altered and investigated.

CH$_2$ group inserted between ring and OH group

**6.23**

**Table 6.1** Groups that can be used to replace each other in drug design.

| | |
|---|---|
| Groups that can be interchanged | (a)  $-OH$, $-NH_2$, $-SH$, $-CH_3$, $-Cl$ <br> (b)  $-O-$, $-CH_2-$, $-NH-$, $-S-$ |
| Spacer that can be inserted between groups | $-OH \implies -CH_2-OH \implies -CH_2CH_2-OH$ |
| Atoms that can be used to replace groups | $C-NH_2 \implies C-H$ <br><br> $C-OH \implies C-H$ |

Table 6.1 lists some groups that we can consider as structurally equivalent and can use to replace others in a molecular structure. You are *not* expected to remember this Table; if you ever need to use information contained in it we will provide it for you. As well as showing groups that can be interchanged, the Table includes the spacer groups that can be inserted between groups and also summarizes the replacement strategy we covered earlier.

By varying both of the ring OH groups in these ways it was found that one is absolutely essential to biological activity, whereas the other can be varied to $CH_2OH$ or $CH_2CH_2OH$ but not to $CH_2CH_2CH_2OH$ (Figure 6.7). Obviously this OH group is necessary, but its distance from the ring can be varied within a limited range.

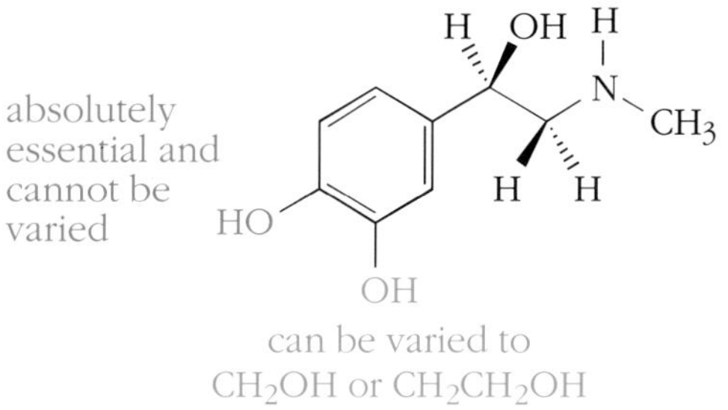

**Figure 6.7**
Variability of the ring OH substituents of adrenaline.

As it turns out, changing the OH group to $CH_2OH$ has another profoundly beneficial effect on the biological activity of the molecule: the molecule becomes resistant to the major pathway of deactivation by enzymes, which means that the drug has a much longer duration of action (Box 6.2).

---

**Box 6.2  Deactivation of adrenaline**

The enzymes that deactivate adrenaline-like compounds do so because they convert one of the ring OH groups into an $OCH_3$ group:

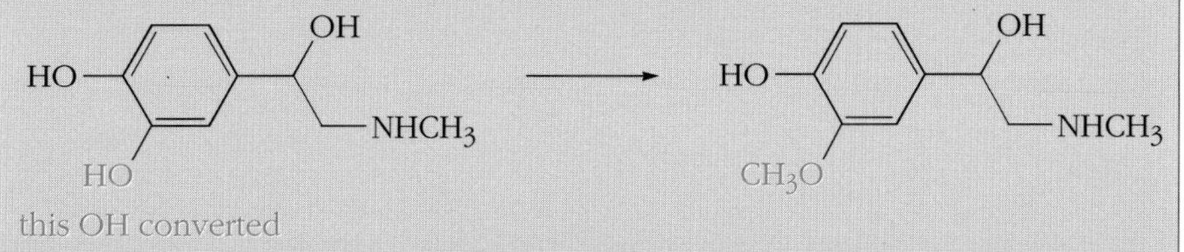

This substitution apparently blocks the ability of the product to bind to the adrenaline receptor. Since this reaction is catalysed by enzymes it is specific for the OH group shown. Neither of the other two OH groups is affected, nor indeed is the OH of the $CH_2OH$ group.

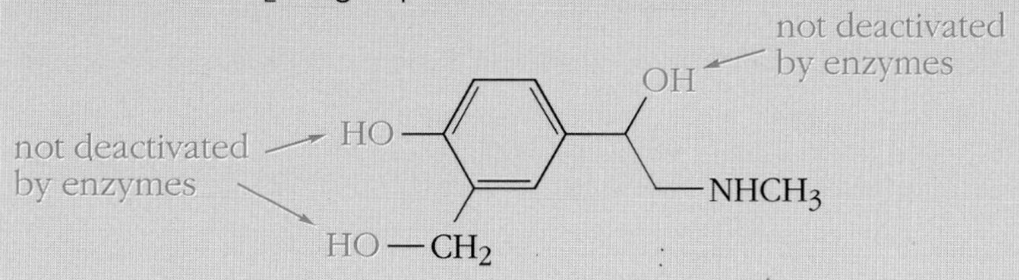

---

We can now begin to build up a crude idea of what is required for a molecule to bind to the adrenaline receptor. First, all of the molecules we have been considering contain an aromatic ring. Second, they all contain an amine group. So, as a very minimum, these two groups seem to be essential and it is possible to imagine that each has an area of the receptor that will recognize it and bind to it (Figure 6.8a). But this picture can be modified, because we know that compounds with OH groups attached to the aromatic ring are more potent molecules than ephedrine-like molecules that lack these groups (Figure 6.8b).

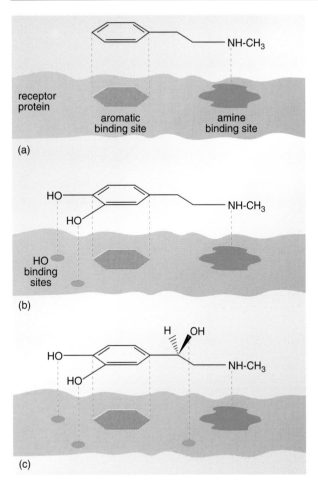

**Figure 6.8**
A two-dimensional
representation of the
adrenaline receptor
(a) taking account of the
aromatic and amine groups,
(b) including the OH groups
attached to the ring, and
(c) including the OH group
of the carbon chain.

We might also question whether the OH group in the carbon chain is needed.
After all, both adrenaline and ephedrine contain the group, but amphetamine
doesn't.

■    How might you try to determine if this OH group is necessary for
     binding?

■    By making and testing a molecule such as **6.24**, in which the OH has
     been replaced by a hydrogen atom.

**6.24**

Actually, we already know that an OH in this position is *not essential* for
biological activity because compounds such as amphetamine are active. It
does contribute to the *selectivity* of the compound though. When compounds
similar to adrenaline – but with the H and OH groups interchanged – are
tested, they are found to be more than 50 times *less* active than the adrenaline
compounds themselves:

arrangement of groups in adrenaline  H and OH groups interchanged compared with those in adrenaline

You might remember that this is the same kind of result that is seen with ephedrine and pseudoephedrine. Ephedrine has the H and OH groups arranged as in adrenaline and it has anti-asthmatic activity; pseudoephedrine has the H and OH groups arranged as shown above and it has activity on the heart but no anti-asthmatic activity.

Clearly, the spatial position of this particular OH group is important too. So our picture of the receptor should be modified still further to accommodate binding to the alcohol OH group (Figure 6.8c). This cartoon-like picture of the receptor is a very crude two-dimensional representation of the interactions that are involved in three-dimensions when a molecule binds to it, but we can begin to see that the more binding sites there are the more specific are the structures of the molecules that bind.

## Activity 5  Binding sites and drug selectivity

How many binding sites do we need to get selective binding? To answer that question, try the following activity. Suppose a model of a receptor has two binding sites, 6.5 cm apart (Figure 6.9).

Now make two models of mirror image molecules as shown in Figure 6.10.

Now, let's assume the blue site binds to a blue centre and the red site binds to a red centre. Use your models to see if you can arrange for the blue and red centres of each of the molecules to bind to their appropriate sites in the receptor.

You should find that both can be easily arranged so that the blue group can bind to the blue site and the red group to the red site.

So our finding is that a two-site receptor is not sufficient to distinguish between these different molecules.

What happens if we add another binding site, so the receptor now has three sites? Let's assume the third site recognizes green groups (Figure 6.11).

Now try to arrange your models so that they bind to the receptor *at all three sites*. What do you find?

You should find that only one of the models will fit all three sites at the same time; the other can fit only two of the sites.

Two conclusions that we can draw from this simple activity are: (i) a receptor requires at least three binding sites in order to differentiate between molecules that are mirror images and (ii) the more binding sites there are the more selective the binding can be.

**Figure 6.9**
Model of a two-site receptor.

**Figure 6.10**
Models of mirror image molecules.

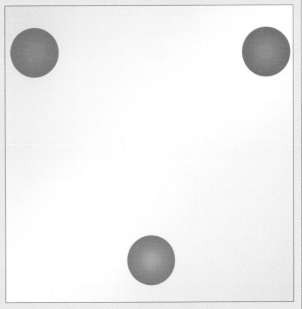

**Figure 6.11**
A model of a three-site receptor.

**Figure 6.13**
A representation of the adrenaline receptor.

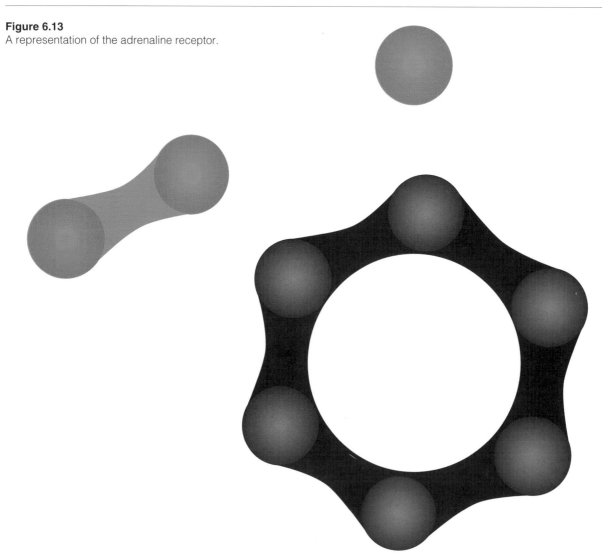

Our cartoon of the receptor (Figure 6.8c) shows how, even though the receptor has several binding sites, compounds such as the amphetamines can bring about a biological effect. The amphetamines contain aromatic and amine groups, which can bind to two of the sites. So, even with several binding sites, a receptor is not guaranteed to have a specific response to only one or even a limited range of compounds. To obtain selective drug action, what is needed is a receptor with several binding sites (at least three, preferably more), and a drug with several groups (at least three, preferably more) that will bind to these receptor sites. Now it's clear why developing a drug without side-effects is so very difficult to achieve!

### Activity 6  Adrenaline and its receptor site

Use your model kit to build a model of adrenaline, as shown in Figure 6.12. A two-dimensional representation of the lung adrenaline receptor is reproduced to the size of the molecular model kit in Figure 6.13. See if you can get your model to fit to the binding sites of the 'receptor'. The red sites bind to oxygen atoms, the blue sites to nitrogen atoms. You may need to rotate various parts of the model around single bonds, and you will need to fold part of the 'receptor' out of the flat plane of the book (this will give you a basic impression of the three-dimensional nature of receptor binding sites).

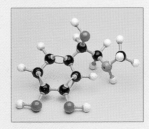

**Figure 6.12**
A ball-and-stick model of adrenaline.

**Question 19** Build molecular models of the compounds **6.25**, **6.26** and **6.27**. Use Table 6.1 to identify the difference in structure between them. Which of them will bind to both the aromatic binding site and the amine binding site of the adrenaline receptor?

NH₂ — **6.25**   CH₂—NH₂ — **6.26**   CH₂—CH₂—NH₂ — **6.27**

**Question 20** A receptor has been identified that is capable of binding an NH$_2$ group and an SH group. On the scale of the molecular model kit these binding sites are 12.5 cm apart (Figure 6.14).

**Figure 6.14**
A two-site receptor for SH and NH$_2$ groups.

Use the kit to design a molecule that would be capable of binding to the receptor. (Hint: think what other groups might be needed to separate the two groups by the correct distance.) Would either of the compounds **6.28** and **6.29** bind to this receptor?

**6.28**                                  **6.29**

**Question 21** You suspect that the oxygen atom of compound **6.30** is important for it to bind to a receptor. Use Table 6.1 to suggest two compounds that you would use to test whether or not your suspicions were correct.

**6.30**

It is possible to combine the information obtained from these studies with the observation that isoprenaline is more selective than adrenaline to design compound **6.31**. This compound contains all the features we've discovered except that it has a tertiary butyl group attached to the nitrogen atom rather than an isopropyl group.

**6.31** salbutamol                    isopropyl group        tertiary butyl group

These hydrocarbon groups are similar, but for this set of compounds the tertiary butyl group gives the compound a longer duration of biological activity. Those of you with asthma will have an intimate knowledge of this compound, for it is salbutamol – the compound prescribed as Ventolin. Salbutamol has superseded isoprenaline as the compound of choice in the treatment of asthma, largely because of its selectivity of action. Isoprenaline has roughly equal activity as a bronchial dilator and as a heart stimulant. In contrast, salbutamol – which is just as good a bronchial dilator as isoprenaline – is about 200 times better as a bronchial dilator than as a heart stimulant. So, the side-effects of taking salbutamol have been reduced drastically compared with the first lead compound ephedrine, which is both addictive and a heart stimulant, and adrenaline, which is a heart stimulant. Even so, research to find a more effective drug continues on at least two fronts; first there is the need for a more selective drug still, and second there is the more pressing need to discover a drug that will be able to afford protection against an asthma attack for periods longer than the 4 hours that salbutamol provides.

Our story of the discovery of salbutamol has developed a long way from the original lead provided by ma huang. It is worth reviewing the process involved:

*First*, a naturally occurring material, in this case a plant, is observed to have desirable biological activity.

*Second*, the constituent responsible for the biological activity is isolated from the material and its chemical structure identified.

*Third*, the structure of the active constituent is used as a starting point for the development of molecules with similar structures in an attempt to improve on the biological activity of the naturally occurring compound.

*Fourth*, an understanding of the molecular features required for the interactions with biomolecules that give rise to biological activity is built up.

*Fifth*, the important molecular interactions are used to design further compounds that are expected to be both potent and selective.

Having seen how this sequence of activities has been used to develop drugs that interact with *receptor* proteins, we shall now turn our attention to a different type of biological target molecule, enzymes.

## 6.1 Summary of Chapter 6

In this Chapter you have found out that:

Ephedrine can be isolated from the Chinese herbal remedy ma huang.

Ephedrine has anti-asthmatic properties as well as heart stimulant properties.

Using the molecular structure of ephedrine as a lead the amphetamines were developed; these have undesirable side-effects – they increase blood pressure and are addictive.

Ephedrine and amphetamine exert their anti-asthmatic and heart-stimulating activities by binding to the adrenaline receptor.

Compounds based on the structure of adrenaline are non-addictive because the presence of two OH groups on the benzene ring means that these compounds are unable to cross the blood–brain barrier.

By modifying the structure of adrenaline, first isoprenaline and subsequently salbutamol were developed as anti-asthmatic drugs; salbutamol is much more selective for the lung adrenaline receptors than the heart receptors.

You have also seen:

That to test whether a group within a molecule is important to biological activity it is possible to design (and subsequently test) a similar molecule in which either the group has been replaced by a hydrogen atom or has been interchanged with a similar group, for example OH for $NH_2$.

That to test whether the distance between particular groups is important to biological activity, new compounds can be designed in which spacer $CH_2$ groups are inserted between the groups under study.

How to use molecular models to determine whether or not a particular compound will fit to a representation of a receptor, as well as to design molecules that can fit to particular binding sites in a receptor.

That a carbon atom with four different groups surrounding it is said to be chiral; molecules that contain chiral carbon atoms can exist as different isomers.

# Chapter 7
# Drugs targeted at enzymes

In Chapter 7, we explore how it is possible to explain the interaction of a drug with its molecular target (in this case an enzyme) through an understanding of its molecular structure. When this kind of information is combined with a reasonable understanding of the important molecular features of the enzyme, the result is a powerful approach to the design of new drugs. Two compounds are looked at in detail; sulfonamides, which are effective against bacterial infections, and captopril, which is used to treat high blood pressure.

In Part 1, you discovered that enzymes are nature's catalysts. Their role is to provide the right conditions for the molecules in the cells to react rapidly and efficiently. The reactions take place in a controlled way because each enzyme usually catalyses only one specific reaction. More often than not, the transformation of one compound into another takes place in a series of steps, each step being catalysed by a single specific enzyme. For example, in the human body the synthesis of adrenaline occurs from phenylalanine in a series of five steps, each controlled by a different enzyme. This is shown in Figure 7.1, where we've left out the chemical structures for simplicity. You don't need to remember this scheme! The enzymes are shown over the arrows for each step. If any one of these enzymes doesn't function properly, then it's possible that the body won't produce the required amount of adrenaline. Depending on just how incorrectly these enzymes function, the result could be obvious ill-health.

For example, when babies are newly born, one of the first things that happens to them is that a blood sample is taken from their heel (Figure 7.2).

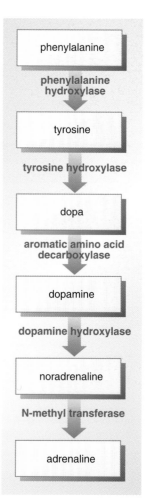

**Figure 7.1**
The pathway for the conversion of phenylalanine into adrenaline.

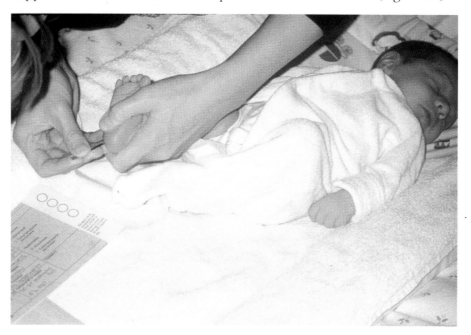

**Figure 7.2**
A blood sample being taken from a new-born baby.

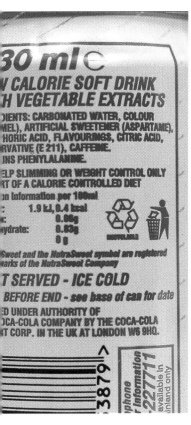

**Figure 7.3**
Diet Coca-Cola, a product
that contains phenylalanine.

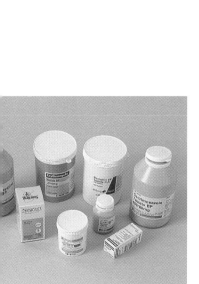

**Figure 7.4**
A selection of medicines
containing antibiotics.

Why is this done? Well, about 1 in 1500 people in the population suffer from phenylketonuria. As you discovered in Part 1, these people lack the enzyme phenylalanine hydroxylase, which converts phenylalanine into tyrosine. This turns out not to affect adrenaline production too much because tyrosine can be made by other means, but unchecked it causes very severe brain damage. Phenylalanine accumulates because it's not being converted into tyrosine. In an attempt to remove the build-up of phenylalanine the body uses another enzyme, which is able to convert phenylalanine into a different compound, phenylpyruvate, which can be excreted in the urine. Unfortunately, phenylpyruvate can also accumulate in the brain, where it can interfere with the processes normally carried out by pyruvate, a compound of similar molecular structure. This interference causes brain damage, so it is absolutely essential that the lack of the enzyme is detected early in life because that is when the brain develops rapidly and brain damage cannot be reversed. The blood sample is tested for abnormal levels of phenylalanine. The disease is treated by making sure that phenylalanine in the diet is reduced to an absolute minimum. That's why manufacturers of foodstuffs such as the sweetener Nutrasweet must state that they contain phenylalanine (Figure 7.3).

Of course, ill health doesn't arise just because our own bodies start to malfunction. We are often ill because of infection either by bacteria or viruses. Both types of micro-organism use enzymes to control the biochemistry that enables them to survive. Often, the biochemistry of bacteria and viruses is sufficiently different from human biochemistry that it becomes possible to target drugs specifically to disrupt just the biochemistry of the infecting organism so that our cells are unaffected.

In this Chapter we're going to study two different drugs, both of which interact with enzymes. The first, sulfonamides, are compounds that are used to ward off infection by bacteria. The second, captopril, is used to reduce high blood pressure and has been designed to interfere with an enzyme that is involved in blood pressure regulation. The sulfonamides work against the enzymes of invading organisms, whereas captopril has to target a specific human enzyme and leave others alone.

## 7.1 Sulfonamide antibacterials

It is almost impossible for us to imagine life today without the antibiotic compounds that combat bacterial infections. When we visit the doctor with an infectious illness we almost expect to be prescribed some kind of antibiotic, even if we don't know anything about the infection or the antibiotic. Most of us don't realise that antibiotics are effective only against bacteria and not viruses, for instance. These days, there is a range of different antibiotics available, classified broadly into groups according to a common feature in their molecular structure. You will probably be familiar with several of these types. For example, the most common and well-known are the penicillins, such as Amoxil, and cephalosporins, such as Keflex.

Some of the other types of antibacterial compound are the aminoglycosides (streptomycin and kanamycin – used to treat TB), chloramphenicol (used to treat conjunctivitis), the macrolides (erythromycin), the quinolones (nalixidic acid), the tetracyclines (oxytetracycline) and the sulfonamides (sulphamethoxazole). No doubt you've come across some of these other compounds, too. Yet we haven't always had such a powerful armoury of antibacterial medicines. All of the classes of compounds mentioned above have been developed since 1930. Before then there were few effective means of treating infection: antiseptics and disinfectants for cleaning surface wounds; inoculation of antitoxins for combating illnesses such as diphtheria, typhoid or dysentery; and extracts of certain plants, such as myrrh, poplar, arnica, echinacea, and chamomile, which have some antimicrobial activity. Two classes of compounds rapidly filled this gap: the sulfonamides and the penicillins. Some penicillins are naturally occurring compounds formed by certain moulds, but most are semi-synthetic, because the compounds formed by the moulds are modified chemically to produce more effective antibiotics. Sulfonamides, however, are purely synthetic materials and are not found in nature. How could such purely synthetic compounds be developed as very important antibacterials – Sir Winston Churchill was treated successfully for pneumonia with one of the earliest, sulfapyridine (Figure 7.5), in 1943 – when no lead compound existed? The answer can be traced back to the genius of Paul Ehrlich (Box 7.1) who, more than anyone else, established the discipline of chemotherapy.

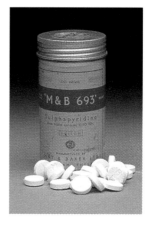

**Figure 7.5**
M&B 693, probably the most famous of the sulfonamide antibacterial drugs, sulfapyridine.

---

**Box 7.1  Paul Ehrlich**

Paul Ehrlich (Figure 7.6) – 'a very good stainer but won't pass his exams' – studied medicine, researching into the way that certain dyes stained cells for study under the microscope (Figure 7.7).

**Figure 7.6**
Paul Ehrlich, 1854–1915.

This interest took a novel direction when, instead of removing tissue from animals and then staining it, he injected the dyes into living

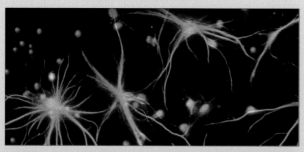

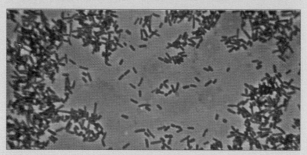

**Figure 7.7**
Cells stained with various dyes.

animals and allowed them to diffuse to the tissues before these were removed for examination. This apparently simple idea had a profound effect on the understanding of how chemicals dispose themselves throughout the body.

He discovered, for example, that the dye methylene blue selectively stained nerve fibres. This led him to propose that it might have analgesic (pain-relieving) activity. It does, but it also causes kidney damage. Later, after a period in Egypt to recuperate from tuberculosis, he demonstrated that methylene blue also had antimalarial activity, but it was not as effective as quinine for which adequate supplies were available following successful transplanting of cinchona from South

America to Dutch East Indies (modern Indonesia). This work eventually led to him proposing the concept of a receptor for a molecule.

Ehrlich received the Nobel Prize for Medicine in 1908, for work he carried out with Robert Koch and Emil von Behring. His contribution was to transform successfully diphtheria antitoxin into a preparation that was clinically effective on a reliable basis. His perceptively simple insight, that the potency of a medicine is a property of the medicine and not of the system used to test it, made a profound contribution to medical science. Through it, standardization of batches against a standard of known activity became routine.

Ehrlich's fame as the 'founder' of *chemotherapy* – a word he coined to describe his work – came from his pioneering work on arsenic-containing compounds. Ehrlich found that one of these compounds, called atoxyl, despite being inactive in test-tube experiments, was active in animals against the trypanosome parasite that causes sleeping sickness. He realized this must be due to some metabolic conversion within the animal into an active agent. Ehrlich and his collaborators synthesized hundreds of compounds related to atoxyl, some of which were used with limited success. When it was pointed out that the organism responsible for syphilis is similar to trypanosomes, Ehrlich had all the arsenic-containing compounds re-tested. One, numbered '606' was found to eradicate the syphilis-causing organism, *Treponema pallidum*. The compound, renamed *salvarsan*, was able to cure syphilis in one 900 mg dose. What had previously been an incurable disease was now brought under control.

Ehrlich spent the remainder of his life improving the effectiveness of the arsenical drugs. These remained the only effective means of treating syphilis till the advent of penicillin. He is remembered for his pioneering work in the understanding of how molecules interact with biological tissues and in the use of 'magic bullet' chemicals to aim at specific biological targets.

Ehrlich spent the early part of his career studying the way cells could be stained for microscopic examination. Gradually, this led him to propose the idea that therapeutic compounds acted upon the cells to which they were bound, or in the case of dyes, stained. This idea proved to be the beginnings of theories about the interactions between drugs and receptors that we discussed earlier when finding out about cocaine and Ventolin.

So, when the German pharmacologist Gerhard Domagk together with chemists Fritz Mietzsch and Joseph Klarer set out to discover a drug that would be effective against bacterial infection, among the compounds they tested were the azo dyes (Box 7.2).

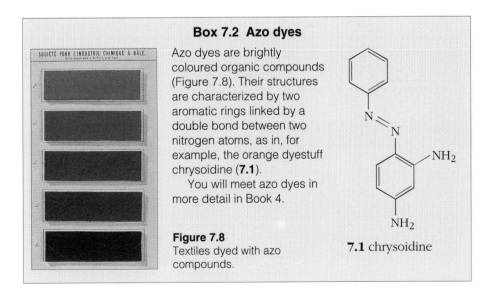

### Box 7.2  Azo dyes

Azo dyes are brightly coloured organic compounds (Figure 7.8). Their structures are characterized by two aromatic rings linked by a double bond between two nitrogen atoms, as in, for example, the orange dyestuff chrysoidine (**7.1**).

You will meet azo dyes in more detail in Book 4.

**Figure 7.8**
Textiles dyed with azo compounds.

**7.1** chrysoidine

Among the many thousands of azo compounds tested were those that contained the sulfonamide group:

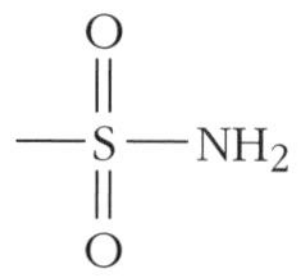

Work concentrated on these because it was known that the sulfonamide group enabled the dyes to bind to wool (which, chemically, is a protein) much more strongly. It's not unreasonable to suppose that if the group enables the dyes to have a high affinity for wool, then it might also confer high affinity on the proteins of microbes too.

When such compounds were injected into mice that had been inoculated with a virulent strain of bacteria – *Streptococcus pyrogenes*, the bacterium responsible for the deaths from pneumonia during the worldwide influenza epidemic of 1918–19 – they were found to be particularly effective in protecting the infected mice. In one group of fourteen infected mice left untreated, thirteen died within three or four days; in contrast all twelve of the treated group survived for at least a week. One compound, Prontosil (**7.2**), was found to be active in clinical trials in humans, and Domagk even used it successfully to treat his own daughter, who had developed life-threatening septicaemia after pricking her finger on a needle.

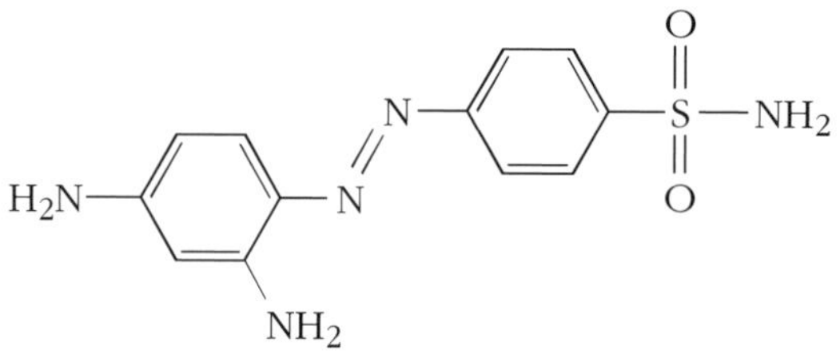

**7.2** Prontosil

So here was a lead compound. But how does it work? What molecular features should be varied? One puzzle that required solving was the observation that Prontosil is active in animals but not against bacteria in test-tubes. Why? Perhaps Prontosil is transformed in animals (termed *in vivo*) but not by the bacteria *in vitro* (which literally means 'in glass'). This idea led other workers to suggest that one such breakdown product might be sulfanilamide (**7.3**), which can be formed from Prontosil by breaking the azo —N=N— linkage and adding two hydrogen atoms. Indeed, a derivative of sulfanilamide can be found in the urine of patients treated with Prontosil, and when sulfanilamide is tested in its own right it is found to be as active as Prontosil itself.

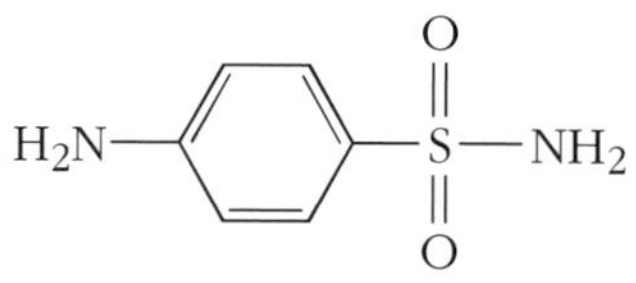

**7.3** sulfanilamide

Sulfanilamide now becomes the lead compound, but how does that work? Which molecular features of this compound can be varied? We'll explore first how answers to the question about its mode of action were unravelled.

Unlike Prontosil, which is brick red, sulfanilamide is a colourless substance, so clearly the concept of needing a *dye* to interact with cellular proteins is incorrect. Even so, perhaps sulfanilamide still binds in some way to these proteins, but how? Several important observations can be made. Although sulfanilamide is a powerful anti-bacterial, sometimes it is ineffective, particularly if the infection is surrounded by pus. Similarly, in laboratory experiments, the antibacterial activity of sulfanilamide is diminished if pus is added. Yeast extracts can have the same effect.

▨    What might you infer from these observations?

▨    A couple of possibilities come to mind; either sulfanilamide has a greater affinity for pus than for the bacteria, or the pus (or yeast) contains a substance that inhibits the action of the drug.

By focusing attention on yeast extracts, two relatively simple reactions were able to provide important clues as to how the effects of sulfanilamide can be inhibited. First, the inhibitory effect of yeast resides in a base-soluble extract.

▨    Think back to the purification of phenol from coal tar (Section 3.1). What types of material are extractable into basic solutions?

▨    Organic acids. With base, these form ionic carboxylate compounds, which are soluble in water.

So it would appear that the material that inhibits sulfanilamide behaves like an acid. Second, treatment of the yeast extract with nitrous acid destroys all its inhibitory activity. The reaction with nitrous acid is typical of amine groups, particularly those in which the amine group is directly attached to a benzene ring as in aniline, the simplest compound of this type:

aniline

The reaction removes the amine group, so the loss of activity demonstrates the amine group to be important biologically.

Combining these two observations led to the suggestion that the substance present in yeast extracts is *para*-aminobenzoic acid (PABA) (**7.4**). Indeed, PABA can be isolated from yeast and is essential for the growth of bacteria – a kind of bacterial vitamin. Co-administration of PABA and sulfanilamide protects bacteria against the action of the drug; the more sulfanilamide present, the more PABA is required. Obviously the two compounds compete for some process essential to the growth of bacteria. This seems reasonable if we compare the structures of the two substances.

**7.4** PABA

---

### Activity 7  Models of PABA and sulfanilamide

Use the molecular model kit to make models of both PABA and sulfanilamide. For the sulfonamide group of sulfanilamide, you will need to use a yellow sulfur centre that has four holes in it, rather than two. You will find that you can't represent the two S=O bonds with a flexible double bond because there aren't enough holes in the sulfur centre to do so. You'll have to make do with using only one short stiff bond to represent each of the S=O bonds. Compare these models to identify similarities and differences between the molecular structures of the two compounds. (Keep the models that you have made because you will need them to answer Question 23.)

---

If the two compounds really do compete with each other at some active site, then the differences in molecular structure identified in Activity 7 seem not too important.

To be able to explain how sulfanilamide works we need to know the role that PABA plays in the growth of bacteria. PABA is one of three essential constituents that are used to make folic acid (Figure 7.9). Don't worry about the complex structure of folic acid, you won't need to remember it and we are only interested in noticing the role of PABA in its structure.

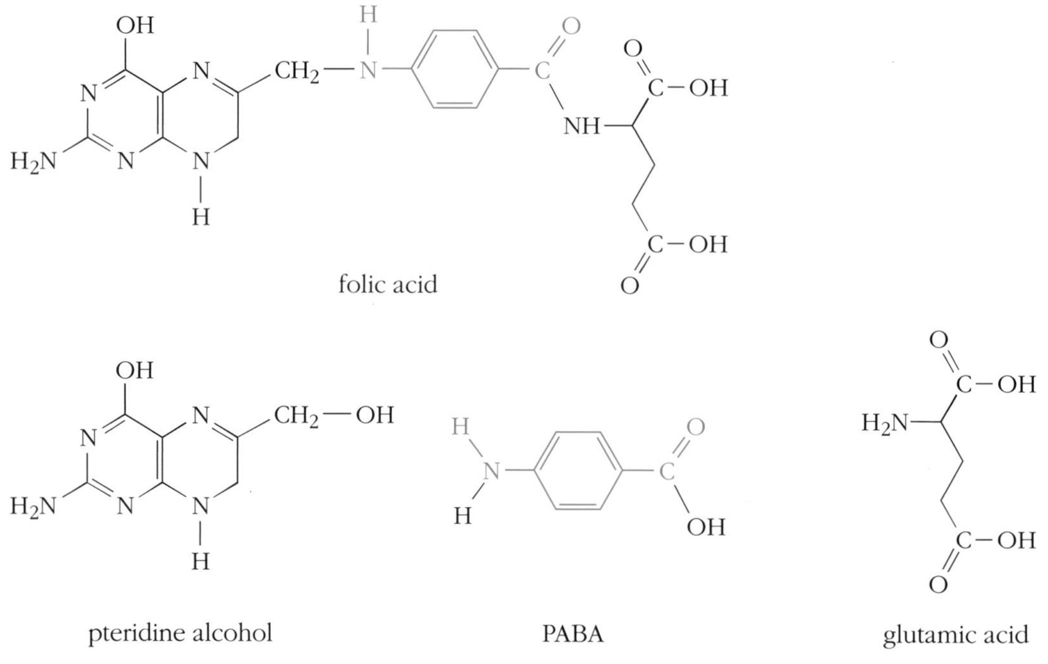

folic acid

pteridine alcohol                              PABA                              glutamic acid

Folic acid is absolutely essential to the growth of bacteria because it enables them to synthesize DNA, which they must do if they are going to replicate. Bacteria contain several enzymes that enable them to make folic acid from the three constituents, PABA, pteridine (ter-id-een) alcohol and glutamic acid. One enzyme is needed to link PABA and glutamic acid together, to form an intermediate – PABA-Glu. Another enzyme takes the PABA-Glu and links it to the activated pteridine alcohol to form folic acid (Figure 7.10). Again you

**Figure 7.9**
The relationship between PABA and folic acid.

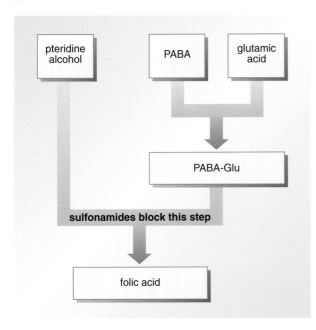

**Figure 7.10**
Steps in the formation of folic acid.

don't need to remember this, but it does help you to appreciate how sulfonamides work. It is this second enzyme with which sulfonamide drugs interfere.

It would appear that sulfanilamide and the other sulfonamide drugs sufficiently resemble PABA-Glu for the enzyme to accept them in competition with PABA-Glu. As there is only one site to occupy per enzyme molecule, if sulfanilamide occupies it then PABA-Glu can't. This means that the formation of folic acid is blocked, because sulfanilamide can't form folic acid.

But the sulfonamides don't just inhibit folic acid synthesis by blocking an enzyme site needed by PABA-Glu. It seems that the enzyme is capable of taking the sulfonamide and the activated pteridine alcohol and linking them together as it would when synthesizing folic acid. The product is not folic acid though, it is the useless end-product **7.5**, which is unable to aid the synthesis of DNA. Unable to synthesize any more DNA, the bacteria cease dividing. Though each bacterial cell is still viable, the progress of the infection stops. This gives the natural defence mechanisms of the body – antibodies and phagocytes – a chance to destroy the remaining bacteria, and the patient can recover.

**7.5** product formed from pteridine alcohol and sulphanilamide

■ So, are sulfonamides bacteriocidal or bacteriostatic?

■ Since they do not destroy bacteria, but only arrest their growth, they must be bacteriostatic.

It may have crossed your mind that humans also need to synthesize DNA, so why aren't sulfonamides toxic to us? The reason lies in the different ways humans and bacteria get their folic acid. Humans, like bacteria, need folic acid for DNA synthesis. Indeed, for humans folic acid is a vitamin. But unlike bacteria, which have to synthesize folic acid, we get ours already made from our diet. You may recall from Part 1 that some of the dietary sources of folic acid are green vegetables, potatoes, offal, Marmite (yeast extracts) and cornflakes (Figure 7.11).

**Figure 7.11**
Some dietary sources of folic acid.

We take in folic acid from our diet because we lack the enzymes needed to make it. This means that only bacteria have the enzyme that sulfonamides inhibit. So bacteria are sensitive to sulfonamides while we aren't. But why don't the invading bacteria use the folic acid that we ingest from our food? Well, because bacteria have to make folic acid, they haven't developed a mechanism for absorbing folic acid into their cells. So we can eat all the folic acid we want, but the bacteria can't use it. Sulfonamides are really very selective drugs indeed.

Now that we have addressed the question of how sulfonamides work, we can turn our attention to the question of which molecular features of sulfanilamide can be varied to provide more effective drugs. As sulfonamides interfere with the use of PABA-Glu by the enzyme that synthesizes folic acid, it might prove instructive to compare the two structures (Figure 7.12).

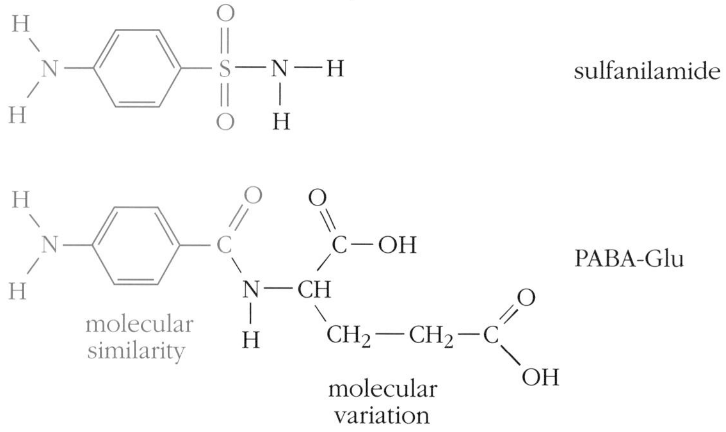

**Figure 7.12**
Comparison of the structures of sulfanilamide and PABA-Glu.

Clearly sulfanilamide resembles one half, the PABA half, of PABA-Glu, and this is the half the enzyme recognizes – so this must remain the same. The glutamyl half of PABA-Glu is very different from the H atom of sulfanilamide, so it seems reasonable to assume that we can vary this H atom for other groups. Among the thousands of compounds synthesized and tested are those in which the group on the sulfonamide nitrogen atom has a ring structure containing nitrogen, oxygen, or sulfur atoms. A representative sample of compounds currently in use is contained in Table 7.1. These compounds have been developed both for their antibacterial ability and for the differing times they can remain in the body. A measure of how long a compound remains in the body is the half-life, which is the time taken for 50% of a dose to be excreted. Sulfapyridine was the first such sulfonamide into clinical practice, reducing mortality rates in patients with lobar pneumonia from 1 in 4 to 1 in 25. The benefit of the longer acting compounds is that they require less frequent administration; sulfamethoxine, for example, need be administered only once a week!

The development of an understanding of how sulfonamides work is a landmark in medicinal chemistry because it was the first explanation of drug action at the molecular level. For his work on the development of sulfonamides, Domagk was awarded the Nobel Prize for Medicine.

**Question 22** Based on the success of the sulfonamide antibiotics, a pharmaceutical company has proposed to set up a research programme to develop an analogous series of antibiotics based on the phosphanilamide structure **7.6**. Use the data in Table 7.1 to propose a compound derived from phosphanilamide that you might expect to have highest biological activity.

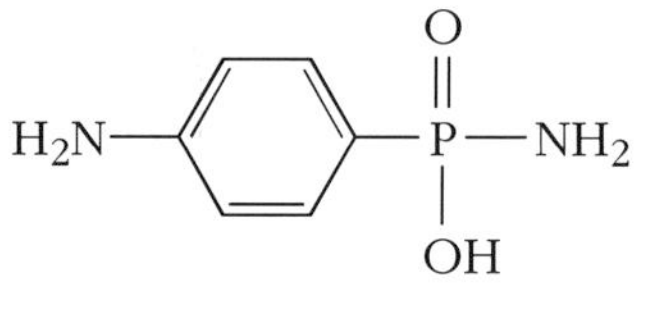

**7.6**

**Table 7.1** Some sulfonamide drugs.

| Compound name | Structure | Half-life (hours) | Biological activity compared with sulfanilamide |
|---|---|---|---|
| sulfanilamide | | 9 | 1 |
| sulfapyridine | | 8 | – |
| sulfathiazole | | 4 | 80 |
| sulfisoxazole | | 6 | 61 |
| sulfamerazine | | 24 | 142 |
| sulfamethoxine | | 150 | 160 |

**Question 23**  Using the model of sulfanilamide you built earlier, make a model of phosphanilamide by replacing the yellow sulfur centre with a purple phosphorus centre. You should notice that only one of the oxygen atoms is double bonded to the phosphorus atom, but there won't be enough holes in the phosphorus centre to make a double bond. You will  have to make do with a single bond for your model. Notice too that the other oxygen atom forms a single bond to phosphorus and is also singly bonded to a hydrogen atom.

Now, compare the model of phosphanilamide with that of PABA. Why might the biological activity of the compounds based on phosphanilamide be little affected by varying the groups attached to the nitrogen atom?

## 7.2  Captopril

So far, we've found that the development of new drugs relies heavily on having a lead compound. More often than not the lead compound is naturally occurring, often one, like cocaine, that has been isolated from a plant. Alternatively, synthetic compounds like sulfonamides are found to have unexpected biological activity, providing novel types of compound to study. Once the structure of the lead compound is known, similar compounds (analogues) can be made and tested so that the molecular features that give rise to the biological activity can be optimized. You might reasonably guess that that was how captopril, a drug used to treat high blood pressure, was discovered. Actually, a somewhat different approach was followed. Not that there is a lack of traditional remedies for high blood pressure. A quick look in a modern herbal reveals that there are several that can reduce blood pressure.

> *If you suffer from high blood pressure, you would be wise to adopt a meat-free diet, consisting largely of fresh vegetables, whole cereals and fruit. In particular, try eating half a clove of fresh garlic a day. Celery also helps to reduce blood pressure. Avoid caffeine, which contributes to stress and tension. Instead of tea or coffee, drink water, grape juice and an infusion of equal parts of hawthorn berries, yarrow and limeflower. Rutin tablets taken regularly can also bring the pressure down. Buckwheat is rich in rutin so that this may be eaten, or a tea can be made from it and taken regularly.*

> *It is important to get rid of excess fluid from your body. To do this, during spring and summer, eat plenty of fresh dandelion leaves in salads. These are a good diuretic and have the added advantage of being rich in potassium. An infusion of cornsilk is also an effective diuretic, with a reputation for lowering blood pressure.*

(The Complete New Herbal, *Penguin, 1988*)

[Cornsilk is the 'beard' that comes with corn-on-the-cob, and limeflowers are the flowers of the linden tree *Tilia europea*.]

Many of these were known to the 17th century herbalist Nicholas Culpeper, who wrote

> **lime tree**… *the flowers are excellent for apoplexy and palpitation of the heart.*

> **hawthorn**… *the seeds in the berries beaten to a powder being drunk in wine, are good against the stone and dropsy [dropsy is a heart condition that involves excess fluid retention].*

> **dandelion**… *it openeth the passages of the urine both in young and old…it helpeth also to procure rest and sleep.*

**Figure 7.13**
Lime trees, hawthorn and dandelions – plants that have the ability to relieve high blood pressure.

Modern research has shown that both limeflowers and hawthorn berries contain a group of chemical compounds called flavonoids, and it is these that reduce blood pressure. However, captopril is not a flavonoid, nor was it developed from them.

Instead, captopril was designed through using what has become known as the **rational approach** to drug design. For this, there has to be a fairly good, though not necessarily complete, understanding of the biological system that gives rise to a particular effect. If one is known, then it is potentially possible to design a compound that can interfere with the system in a desirable way. We're now going to see how this was achieved for captopril, where only a reasonable understanding was known. Later in the Course (Book 4) you'll see how a new anti-influenza drug has been developed with a precise picture of the biological target.

One mechanism by which human blood pressure is controlled is the renin–angiotensin system. In this system, a protein angiotensinogen (anything

'...ogen' means it forms whatever is before the '...ogen'; so hydrogen is 'former of water', and angiotensinogen 'former of angiotensin') is cleaved by the enzyme renin to form angiotensin I, which in turn is cleaved to form angiotensin II by an enzyme found in the lungs and blood vessels called angiotensin-converting enzyme, or ACE for short:

$$\text{angiotensinogen} \xrightarrow{\text{renin}} \text{angiotensin I} \xrightarrow{\text{ACE}} \text{angiotensin II}$$

Angiotensin II is the chemical in this system that has all the biological activity. First, it constricts blood vessels, which causes blood pressure to increase – it takes more pressure to pump a fluid through narrow tubes than wide ones. Second, it controls the release of a steroid hormone, aldosterone, which regulates the excretion of potassium ions, $K^+$, and the retention of sodium ions, $Na^+$, and water. Retention of sodium ions and water also increases blood pressure.

Unlike angiotensin II, angiotensin I has no biological activity of its own, making ACE a key enzyme in blood pressure regulation. In fact, more so than the above picture might indicate, since ACE converts another biological compound, bradykinin, which reduces blood pressure by dilating blood vessels, into biologically inactive compounds. So, as well as increasing blood pressure in its own right, it stops another compound from lowering blood pressure.

This understanding gives us a molecular approach to treating high blood pressure: if we can reduce the amount of angiotensin II being produced then blood pressure should fall. How is it possible to achieve this? Well, ACE accepts angiotensin I and converts it into the product, angiotensin II. So, if it is possible to block angiotensin I from being accepted by the enzyme, then no angiotensin II can be produced. This ought to be possible if a drug is administered that the enzyme accepts in preference. In essence, the drug and angiotensin I compete for the enzyme. So the problem boils down to one of designing a molecule that has the right molecular features that allow it to bind to the enzyme in preference to angiotensin I. The starting point here is not the molecular structure of a known drug, but the nature of the enzyme-catalysed process. Let's take a look at it.

Angiotensin I is a peptide formed by ten amino acids linked together in a linear chain. Using the three-letter abbreviations for the amino acids that were introduced in Part 1, angiotensin I can be written as shown in Figure 7.14a; the amino acid aspartic acid (Asp) is linked to arginine (Arg), which is linked to valine (Val) and so on till leucine (Leu). ACE takes angiotensin I and specifically chops off the final two amino acids from the carboxylic acid end to form angiotensin II, which is made up from eight amino acids (Figure 7.14b).

**Figure 7.14**
(a) The sequence of aminoacid residues in angiotensin I.
(b) The formation of angiotensin II from angiotensin I.

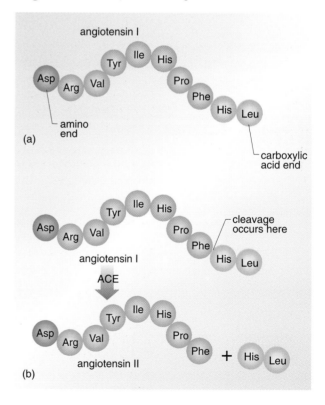

What's needed, then, is a molecule that mimics the carboxylic acid end of angiotensin I, but before we can explore what such a molecule looks like we need first to gain a better understanding of what the enzyme does.

When any peptide or protein is cleaved by an enzyme, an amide bond linking two amino acid groups together is broken:

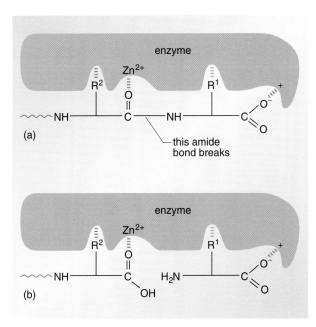

Now, we know that ACE cleaves *two* amino acids from the carboxylic acid end of the peptide. At the outset of research in the mid-1960s, it was known that each ACE molecule contains one zinc ion, $Zn^{2+}$. This makes ACE highly reminiscent of a well-known and well-studied enzyme, carboxypeptidase A, which you met in Part 1. This enzyme also contains one $Zn^{2+}$ ion, but it cleaves only *one* amino acid from the carboxylic acid end of a peptide. For carboxypeptidase A, the carboxylic acid at the end of the peptide is crucial to binding to the enzyme. In the body, the carboxylic acid exists as its ion $RCO_2^-$ and interacts with a positively charged ammonium group on the enzyme. Moreover, the oxygen atom of the amide bond that is cleaved interacts with the $Zn^{2+}$ ion. The role of the $Zn^{2+}$ ion is to activate the amide bond to cleavage. Two other interactions are also important (Figure 7.15a); the groups $R^1$ and $R^2$ occupy sites on the enzyme with which they can interact through London forces. These interactions are preserved in the products too (Figure 7.15b). So, the new carboxylic acid group formed as the amide bond is broken also binds to the $Zn^{2+}$ ion.

**Figure 7.15**
Schematic representation of the interactions between carboxypeptidase A and (a) its substrate and (b) its products.

Now let's try to translate what can be learnt from carboxypeptidase to ACE to build up a simple model of what interactions might be involved in enzyme–substrate binding.

A first, and reasonable, supposition is that the carboxylic acid end is essential, as it is for carboxypeptidase.

▨     Why is this a reasonable supposition?

▮     Because it is from the carboxylic acid end of angiotensin I that the two amino acids are cleaved.

A second, and also reasonable, supposition is that the $Zn^{2+}$ ion activates the amide bond to be broken. With ACE, however, it is not just one amino acid that is chopped off but *two*. So, in ACE the $Zn^{2+}$ binding site must lie farther from the binding site for the carboxylic acid group than it does in carboxypeptidase. If these assumptions are correct then we can begin to

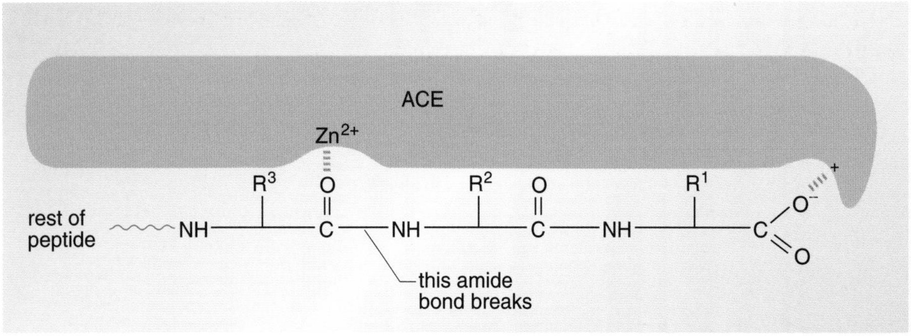

**Figure 7.16**
The beginnings of a schematic model for ACE.

build up a schematic model, shown in Figure 7.16, of how the natural peptide interacts with ACE. We ought not to forget that in reality these interactions take place in three dimensions.

So, we might predict that a first requirement for any drug will be that it contains a carboxylic acid functional group separated from another group capable of binding to a $Zn^{2+}$ ion. The distance between these two groups ought to be similar to that in the peptide, that is separated by about six bonds:

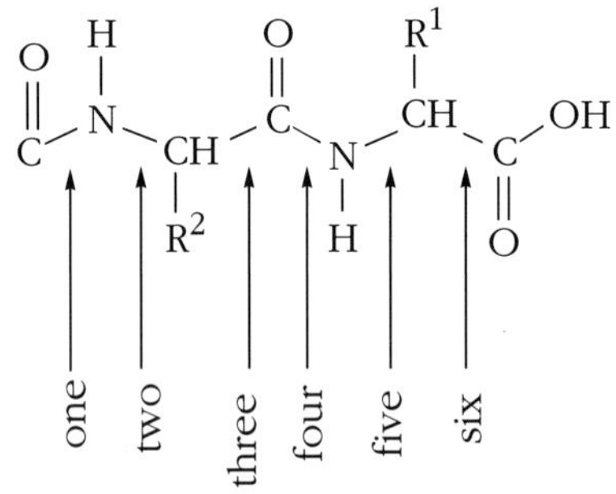

Of course, the drug itself ought not to be a substrate for ACE, otherwise it too would be broken down and therefore unavailable to carry out its function.

▫    Remembering the chemistry that ACE carries out, what type of bond must a drug molecule not contain?

◼    It must not contain an amide at the site of binding to $Zn^{2+}$, otherwise it will be cleaved and the drug destroyed.

The model for ACE that we've arrived at so far doesn't take any account of the types of interaction that occur with the groups $R^1$ and $R^2$. From Figure 7.16 these could be any groups, but this would be unlikely. Most enzymes will bind to a preferred type of group at each position. The problem facing us is the same as that facing the original researchers, 'Which groups to choose?'. Without any further information we would have to try a 'suck-it-and-see' approach; try one group, then another, and another and so on till the best one was found. This would be very time-consuming. Fortunately, a further piece of information was available. A series of peptides isolated from the venom of various species of viper was found to block the formation of angiotensin II by ACE. All of the peptides in this series contained the amino acid proline (**7.7**) as the terminal amino acid.

**7.7**

Significantly, these compounds are able to reduce blood pressure, as we would predict if they compete with angiotensin I for ACE. The compounds therefore provide us with the confidence that the original hypothesis was correct and also a pointer to the kinds of structure that are needed for a potential drug molecule. They also suggest that the schematic model of the receptor needs refining to incorporate the binding of a terminal proline (Figure 7.17).

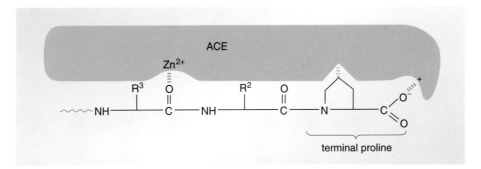

**Figure 7.17**
A modified schematic model for ACE.

■ Jot down all the requirements that we've identified so far that ought to be incorporated into the structure of an ACE drug.

■ The drug should have:

● a carboxylic acid at one end, preferably as part of a proline group;

● a C=O group that can bind to a $Zn^{2+}$ ion;

● the two groups should be separated by about six bonds;

● the C=O group that binds to the $Zn^{2+}$ ion should not be part of an amide group.

If we start putting these requirements together we get a partial molecular structure that looks something like

carboxylic acid group

group for binding
to $Zn^{2+}$ ion

proline residue

We now have to fill in the missing fragments of the structure.

■   How many extra bonds are needed to meet the requirement that there should be six between the carboxylic acid group and the $Zn^{2+}$ binding group?

■   The proline group contains two of the bonds and six are required, so another four bonds are needed to get the correct spacing.

■   Which group can we use to act as a molecular spacer? How many will be needed to get the correct spacing for our ACE drug?

■   The $CH_2$ group is often used as a spacer. We will need three such groups to get the correct spacing.

Our design for an ACE drug is now beginning to look as follows:

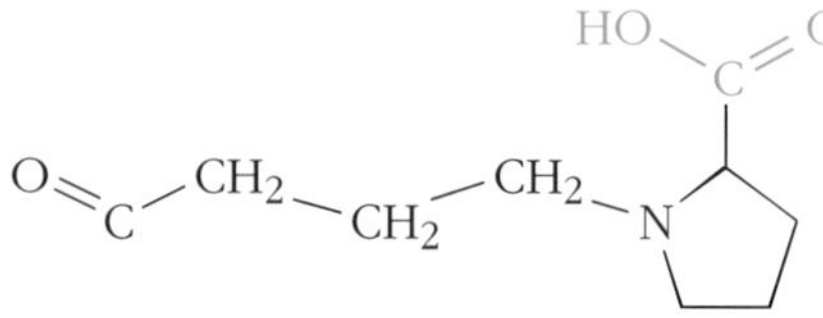

Notice how inserting three $CH_2$ spacer groups involves four additional bonds. Using $CH_2$ groups in this way has allowed us to ensure that there is a C—C bond rather than a C—N bond at the end that binds to $Zn^{2+}$. This is just what is needed, because C—C bonds are resistant to cleavage.

■   In what way is the structure of the molecule still incomplete?

■   The carbon atom at the $Zn^{2+}$-binding end is only involved in three bonds, whereas it requires four.

If you look back to Figure 7.15, which relates to the action of carboxypeptidase, you should notice that in the substrate it is an amide that binds to $Zn^{2+}$ whereas in the product it is a carboxylic acid that binds to $Zn^{2+}$. This information should prompt us to suggest that the $Zn^{2+}$-binding group in our proposed drug should be a carboxylic acid. So our drug design is as follows:

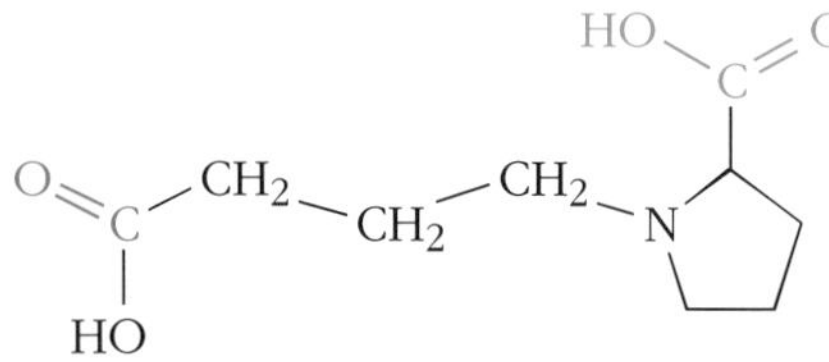

This is a perfectly reasonable molecule to try to make and test, but in practice, succinylproline (**7.8**) is the compound of choice. The only difference between the two is that in succinylproline the carbon atom of the spacer group directly bonded to the nitrogen atom is part of a C=O system rather than $CH_2$. There are two reasons for this. The first is that in the normal substrates for the enzyme this carbon atom is part of a C=O group.

So succinylproline resembles the normal substrates better than does the compound we designed. The second is to do with the way the compounds are made in the laboratory. It turns out that it is easier to make the compound with a C=O rather than a $CH_2$ system.

**7.8** succinylproline

Succinylproline does compete with angiotensin I for ACE, but as the data in Table 7.2 reveal, compared with one of the peptides isolated from snake venom – teprotide – it is one thousand times less active. So we need to modify the structure of succinylproline in some way to increase activity. One possibility is to assume that there is a site on the enzyme that interacts with the group $R^2$ of the substrate (Figure 7.18).

**Table 7.2** Relative activities of some compounds that bind to ACE.

| Compound | Relative activity |
| --- | --- |
| teprotide | 1 |
| **7.8** | 0.001 |
| | 0.01 |
| | 0.0004 |
| | 25 |

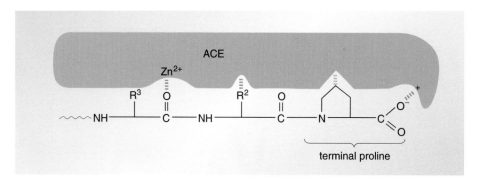

**Figure 7.18**
A further modified model for ACE.

We would then need to position a similar group in succinylproline. The most simple group to add is methyl, $CH_3$, because it is small and isn't a functional group. If we make this change then the compound we obtain has the structure **7.9**.

**7.9** methyl-substituted succinylproline

▨ What do you notice about the groups around the carbon atom that carries the methyl group in **7.9**? What is special about this carbon atom?

◼ The groups are all different so the carbon atom is chiral.

This means there are two compounds with this structure; Table 7.2 shows that one of these is ten times more active than succinylproline – but still one hundred times less active than teprotide – whereas the other is about half as active as succinylproline. These results tell us that there must indeed be a site on the enzyme that interacts with the methyl group but that it is specifically oriented in space – don't forget, our model is a two-dimensional representation of what occurs in three dimensions.

The results so far are promising, but clearly we need to build something extra into the molecules that will make them interact with the enzyme more strongly. One approach might be to substitute other groups for the methyl group in methyl-substituted succinylproline till we have optimized that interaction with the enzyme. Another is to optimize the interaction with the zinc ion. In the natural substrate, this interaction involves an amide group, in our model drug compounds it involves a carboxylic acid. But we might question whether these are the groups that form the strongest interactions with $Zn^{2+}$ ions.

▨ Take a look at the Table 7.3, which contains the relative binding abilities of four simple organic compounds for $Zn^{2+}$ ions. From these values which group do you think binds best to $Zn^{2+}$?

**Table 7.3** Relative ability of some simple compounds to bind $Zn^{2+}$ ions.

| Compound | Relative binding ability |
|---|---|
| $H_2N-CH_2-CH_2-NH_2$ | 800 |
| $H_2N-CH_2-CH_2-OH$ | 1 |
| $H_2N-CH_2-CH_2-SH$ | $4 \times 10^7$ |
| $H_2N-CH_2-COOH$ | 200 |

■ From the relative sizes of the binding abilities it is quite clear that the sulfur-containing compound binds much more strongly to $Zn^{2+}$ than compounds containing the other groups, by a factor of almost a million.

**7.10** captopril

The data in Table 7.3 strongly suggest that, if binding to $Zn^{2+}$ is important, we should modify our drug molecule. We should remove the carboxylic acid group, COOH, and replace it with SH, which is called the thiol (thigh-ol) group. If we do that, combined with all our deductions so far, the compound we get is **7.10**. When this compound is tested for its ability to compete with angiotensin I for ACE it is found to be twenty five times more active than teprotide and about two and a half thousand times more active than the corresponding succinylproline compound (Table 7.2). Binding to the $Zn^{2+}$ site of the enzyme is quite clearly important. Compound **7.10** is known as captopril (Figure 7.19) and it is an effective treatment for both high blood pressure and congestive heart failure. In 1980 captopril was the first compound designed to compete with angiotensin I for ACE to come on to the drug market. Since then others, such as enalapril and cilazapril, have appeared, each developed by continuing the arguments used to design captopril. On its own, captopril is able to normalize the blood pressure in around 50% of those suffering high blood pressure. In combination with a diuretic – that is, a drug that aids the flow of urine and therefore diminishes water retention – this figure rises to 90%. This is very reminiscent of the treatment of high blood pressure using herbal medicines with which we started this section.

**Figure 7.19**
Captopril, enalapril and cilazapril, drugs used to treat high blood pressure by interfering with the mode of action of angiotensin-converting enzyme.

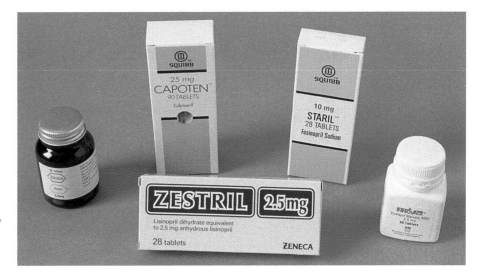

In its own way, the development of captopril has proved to be a landmark in the chemistry of drug design. Whereas in earlier times drugs were developed from lead compounds discovered to have biological activity, captopril was developed from the known function of the target enzyme and designed to interact with the important features of the enzyme. By building up a simple model of the important enzyme sites, it has been possible to design a drug that is able to compete with angiontensin I for those sites, and by so doing to stop angiotensin I being converted into angiotensin II.

## 7.3  Summary of Chapter 7

In this Chapter you have found out that:

Drugs can be developed that will interfere with enzyme-catalysed processes.

Sulfonamide antibacterials were developed from observations on azo dyes.

Sulfonamide drugs work by interfering with the enzyme-catalysed reactions that bacteria use to make folic acid.

The molecular structure of sulfonamides resembles that of *para*-aminobenzoic acid (PABA), and they inhibit the formation of folic acid by taking the place of PABA. The compounds so formed have no biological activity.

Captopril is a drug that is used to reduce high blood pressure; it works by interfering with angiotensin-converting enzyme.

Captopril was developed by building up a model of the molecular requirements that are needed for it to bind to the enzyme active site, rather than simply modifying the molecular structure of a lead compound.

# Chapter 8
# Drugs of the future

Our developing story of how chemistry plays a role in maintaining our health has revolved around the way in which new materials or compounds that have beneficial effects are first of all discovered and then developed into more powerful and useful agents.

■ Try to recall two ways in which lead compounds have been identified.

■ In general, the most common way is to isolate a compound from a plant or similar naturally occurring material. A similar process is to test novel synthetic compounds for biological activity and to use those with promising activity as lead compounds. A more recent method is to identify the biological target and to design compounds that contain molecular features that allow them to interfere with the target and interrupt the processes that depend on its functioning.

Given that there is a vast range of medicines currently available to treat a whole gamut of diseases, it seems appropriate to ask 'Why is so much effort still put into drug discovery?', and 'How is the role of chemistry in health going to develop in the future?'.

The first question can be answered in several ways. One reason for the need to continue to develop new drugs against infectious diseases, for example, is that the bacteria or viruses can become resistant to drugs in current use. This is the particularly worrying present-day situation with regard to antibiotics. We are beginning to see bacteria that are resistant to all the known types of antibiotic. This happens because a strain of bacteria is not homogeneous, in the same way that not all humans are identical. So when an infection is treated only the susceptible cells are killed off, leaving the resistant cells to replicate. Continued use of one type of antibiotic, or repeated use of different antibiotics, can eventually lead to super-resistant strains. This is why there is concern about the overuse of antibiotics and why general practitioners of medicine are often reluctant to prescribe antibiotics for low-grade infections. There is concern too about the excessive use of antibiotics in animals that are part of the food chain.

There are several ways in which bacteria may develop resistance to drugs targeted at enzymes. Two examples will serve to illustrate the problem. Resistance to the sulfonamide drugs, for example, arises because the bacteria can step up their production of PABA, the natural enzyme substrate with which sulfonamides compete. This enables the bacteria to produce sufficient folic acid so that they can start multiplying again. In contrast, resistance to penicillins has arisen because the resistant bacteria possess a drug-destroying enzyme.

Another reason for continued drug development is that some of the drugs available provide successful treatments, yet they are not perfect. Salbutamol is a good example. This drug is an effective treatment for asthma, but it needs to be taken three or four times daily. It would seem inconceivable that salbutamol should not be made available while a drug that needs less frequent administration is developed. So salbutamol is in current use, while more suitable drugs are developed. For other illnesses it is better understanding of the molecular events involved that drives continued drug development. For instance, gastric ulcers occur when the underlying layers of the gut wall are exposed to the acidic secretions of the stomach following localized erosion of the mucous membrane.

▨   Given this information, what kind of substances do you think might alleviate gastric ulcers?

▨   Since it is the acidic secretions that are partly responsible, neutralizing the acid by basic materials ought to alleviate the condition.

Indeed, for many years the main treatment of gastric ulcers relied on the use of antacids to neutralize the acid in the stomach. Even today, antacids are used to 'settle an upset stomach'. Basic materials such as magnesium oxide (milk of magnesia), magnesium trisilicate, aluminium hydroxide (Aludrox) and sodium bicarbonate are familiar ingredients of antacid preparations. Unfortunately, for neutralization to occur throughout the day unrealistically large quantities of these materials are required. Once it was known that the naturally occurring compound histamine was partly responsible for the secretion of acid in the stomach, then a different approach became possible. Histamine acts by binding to receptors on the cells that produce hydrochloric acid. Drugs that block this action of histamine will suppress acid production, giving the body an opportunity to repair the mucous membrane lining of the stomach and heal the ulcer. By 1976 SmithKline Beecham's anti-ulcer drug Tagamet had been launched, followed in 1981 by Glaxo's Zantac. Not only are these two drugs very effective treatments for gastric ulcers, they are also the two most profitable drugs worldwide. In 1992, they together grossed 4 billion US dollars.

Of course, there are diseases that are still without a cure. Many forms of cancer fall within this category. Because cancer cells and normal cells differ very little, any drug that is able to destroy cancer cells will usually destroy normal cells. Drugs used to treat cancer are often very toxic, and need to be administered with care. Patients often suffer nausea, hairloss, debilitating weakness, and so on. So the need to develop improved, more selective, drugs goes on. As it does for those new diseases to which we are exposed, such as AIDS.

Drug development is not just a philanthropic exercise however. Although many of the scientists attracted to work in this field do so out of a genuine desire to create new compounds of benefit to the general well-being of humankind, there can be no doubting that there is big money to be made in discovering a novel medicine that can capture a niche in the market. Pharmaceutical companies are enormous wealth-generators, making a significant contribution to the gross national product. A brief glance at Figure 8.1 reveals the size of the pharmaceutical activities of the top ten companies.

Somewhat more revealing is the size of the market that can be captured by particularly successful drugs that are able to meet a widespread need (Figure 8.2).

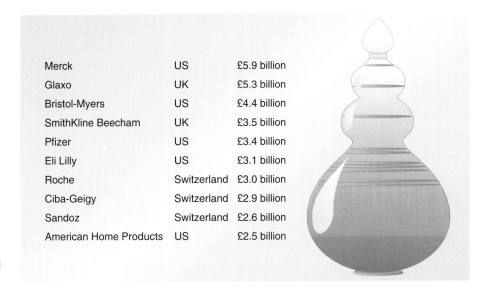

**Figure 8.1**
The top ten pharmaceutical companies for 1993.

| Merck | US | £5.9 billion |
| Glaxo | UK | £5.3 billion |
| Bristol-Myers | US | £4.4 billion |
| SmithKline Beecham | UK | £3.5 billion |
| Pfizer | US | £3.4 billion |
| Eli Lilly | US | £3.1 billion |
| Roche | Switzerland | £3.0 billion |
| Ciba-Geigy | Switzerland | £2.9 billion |
| Sandoz | Switzerland | £2.6 billion |
| American Home Products | US | £2.5 billion |

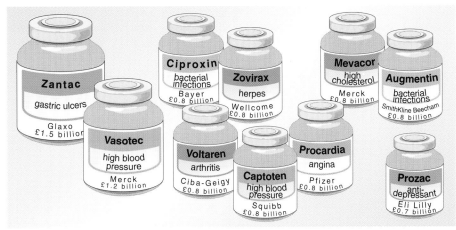

**Figure 8.2**
The worldwide top ten pharmaceutical products (1993).Ventolin, Glaxo's anti-asthma drug, appears as 22nd on this list, grossing sales of £0.5 billion.

The answer to the question about the direction of drug development is that it seems to lie partly along conventional lines, and partly along lines that will develop as we obtain more detailed knowledge about the molecular structures of the biological targets. The conventional method will continue to make use of the compounds that can be isolated from naturally occurring materials, either from plants or from micro-organisms such as yeast or bacteria. It is not unknown for employees of pharmaceutical companies to collect soil samples from their travels around the world so that the microorganisms contained in them can be grown and examined for any interesting biological properties! Most pharmaceutical companies also continue to have an interest in herbal remedies and in testing tropical plants, hoping to identify important new leads. For example, two compounds that have become mainstays of treating childhood leukaemia and Hodgkin's disease are vincristine and vinblastine. Both are isolated from the Madagascar periwinkle *Catharanthus roseus* (Figure 8.3a). A current 'hot' remedy is *Qinghaosu*. This is a Chinese remedy, which uses *Artemisia annua* to treat malaria (Figure 8.3b). The plant contains a compound, artemisinin, that has very important antimalarial activity, especially as it is active against parasites that are resistant to the drugs currently in use.

(a)

(b)

Needless to say, there is much concern within the pharmaceutical community at the widespread loss of tropical rainforest and other environments which contain many species that have never been tested. But it isn't just the pharmaceutical companies who see this important resource as crucial to the potential development of health care, as this extract from an advertisement from the WorldWide Fund for Nature testifies:

**Figure 8.3**
(a) *Catharanthus roseus* and (b) *Artemisia annua*, two plants that contain compounds of pharmaceutical value.

> *THEY DIE, YOU DIE*
>
> *Imagine your fate is entwined with that of a South American vine, or a fragile pink flower in far-off Madagascar.*
> *If these plants were threatened with extinction, you would spring to their defence.*
> *What if we told you that many patients facing major surgery rely on a muscle relaxant extracted from an Amazonian vine, Chondrodendron tomentosum?*
> *Or that four out of five children with leukaemia survive, thanks to the chemicals vincristine and vinblastine donated by the rosy periwinkle?*
> *Would the fate of these plants still rouse your concern? If so, read on.*
> *It is essential that you be aroused beyond mere concern, to action.*
> *Millions of people with heart ailments depend on foxgloves. These flowers provide the digitoxin which regulates their heartbeat.*
> *Many sufferers of hypertension and high blood pressure owe a debt to the Indian Snakeroot shrub for its reserpine.*
> *Extracts from an Amazonian oak tree coagulate proteins, immensely helping scientists in their search for an AIDS vaccine.*
> *People sleep deeply and breathe easily during operations thanks to scopolamine derived from mandrake, henbane and thorn apples.*
> *Cancer of the lung, kidney and testis responds to Etoposide, a drug synthesized from may apples.*

*Women who take the contraceptive pill for granted would not be taking it at all were it not for the yam.*

*Peptic ulcers heal faster thanks to the pale blue petals and flat brown pods of the liquorice flower, origin of carbenoxalone.*

*Even the healthiest amongst us take compounds first discovered in fragrant meadowsweet and willow bark and now known as aspirin.*

*Though these thirteen plants have healed and soothed millions of people, they're but the merest sample from nature's medicine chest. Over a quarter of all prescribed medicines are based on plants.*

*Yet, of the estimated 250 000 flowering plants believed to be in existence, tens of thousands remain undiscovered and only some 5 000 have been tested exhaustively for their pharmaceutical attributes. Now this vast store of known and potential medicines is under threat and we are all of us obliged to protect it.*

*You see, half of the Earth's species thrive in the warmth and wetness of tropical rainforests. Just ten square kilometres of Amazonian jungle contain some 2 200 species of plant (numbers of lower plants like lichen and fungi are incalculable, as is their value: cyclosporin, a product of two kinds of fungus, has helped revolutionize transplant surgery in the last decade).*

*Man is destroying these rainforests. 40 hectares a minute. An area the size of Austria every year.*

The more 'high-tech' route for drug development lies in establishing the precise three-dimensional molecular structures of potential biological targets. These structures can be fed into a computer and visualized on screen. Using the computer, drug molecules can then be precisely designed, and moved around on-screen to see how well they will fit into the active parts of these biological targets. Without going to the effort of synthesizing hundreds of compounds and testing each one, this computer method makes it possible to modify molecular structures on screen until the fit of the drug to its target is optimal. Then drug synthesis can begin. Another possibility is to build into the computer program a way of representing the intermolecular interactions of attraction and repulsion that the molecules experience as they approach each other. This is a bit like the forces that you can feel when you bring two magnets near to each other. Then, as molecules are moved toward the target structure, the interactions between the two will indicate which parts will be repelled and which attracted. This, too, will help in the design of molecules by optimizing interactions *before* any compound is made in the laboratory.

An extension of this development, one that seems very exciting, is the use of virtual reality in which it will be possible for the drug designer to visualize the molecular world of the biological target. It will be possible to walk around and inside the three-dimensional structure in order to identify potential binding sites as well as to get a better picture of how the drug molecules will fit. You will come across the use of these techniques in Book 4.

# Epilogue

There can be no doubting that chemistry has a major contribution to make to issues of health and disease. Yet in your study of Part 2 you may have begun to feel a little uneasy that underlying drug development is a rather reductionist view of how our bodies work. In the same way that a garage mechanic mends a car – by replacing worn or broken parts, greasing the joints, fine-tuning the electrical circuitry – drug development seems to be based on being able to understand illness as due to specific molecular causes – an enzyme that isn't working, a process that is not controlled properly. Given what we know about drug side-effects, and that drugs are not a panacea for all ills, this approach seems hopelessly optimistic. That is a fair, though not entirely justified, criticism. The benefit derived from the development of antibiotics is one example of the success of the approach. Here, specific molecular events in the life-cycle of the invading bacteria are the targets. The antihypertensives – such as captopril – and antiulcer drugs – such as Zantac – have also been developed from a molecular understanding of the illness for which they are prescribed. Yet we might legitimately ask 'What causes the high blood pressure and stomach ulcers in the first place?', and we are unlikely to receive an answer couched in molecular terms. In fact, I'd go so far as to say physical and mental stress are likely to figure large in any response, as, no doubt, would diet. So the drugs are relieving the symptoms rather than treating the causes. A more obvious illness for which this is true is depression. Though there are drugs that can be used to alleviate the illness with greater or lesser success, it is quite clear that drugs alone are unlikely to be of lasting benefit. Our environment, our way of life and the things we consume all contribute to our mental and physical state of health. As a society we have become much more aware of this of late, and there is a desire to embrace a holistic approach to health care. This approach necessitates treating illness through an assessment of each person's individual environment and way of life. This, of course, means that drugs can play only one part in the overall treatment. The others depend on the kind of environment and society that we choose, or are forced, as individuals and groups, to adopt. Nevertheless, we should not lose sight that drugs will have a large part to play, though we should never allow it to be the only one.

# Objectives for Book 3 Part 2

After you have studied Book 3 Part 2 you should be able to do the following:

1    Understand the meaning of the words emboldened in the text.

2    Use a molecular model kit to build and represent structures of molecules and to compare structures of different molecules.

3    Discuss the processes that are involved in the design of new molecules for a particular function or use.

4    Abstract and use relevant data, e.g. solubility or biological activity, to choose molecular characteristics that could be incorporated into the design of a compound to give it a particular property.

5    Identify the types of interaction that molecules use to exert their biological effects.

6    Describe the molecular features of anionic, cationic and neutral detergents and describe how they behave as detergents.

7    Describe what is meant by a reversible reaction.

8    Describe how soaps work at the molecular level and discuss some limitations of their use.

9    Discuss the development of detergents from soaps.

10    Know how to incorporate biodegradability into detergent design.

11    Design a detergent, given data about the solubility of ionic compounds.

12    Describe what is meant by a semi-synthetic detergent.

13    Design a non-ionic detergent.

14    Outline the differences between ethanolamide and polyethylene glycol surfactants.

15    Describe why cationic surfactants are (i) good fabric conditioners and (ii) useful antibacterial agents.

16    Choose an appropriate cleaning agent, given a molecular description of the material to be cleaned.

17    Recognize the structure of a phenol.

18    Explain how phenols can be extracted from coal tar.

19    Describe how phenols exert antiseptic properties.

20    Explain how chlorine-based disinfectants work.

21    Explain what is meant by an active chlorine compound.

22    Assess critically those aspects of homoeopathy that relate to the structure of liquids and to the concentration of active ingredients.

23    Appreciate the structures of complex organic molecules in terms of their molecular framework and functional groups.

24    Give an outline of the major biological targets of drug action.

25    Describe how a picture of a receptor can be built up from a knowledge of the molecular structures of those compounds that are active and those that aren't.

26    Using molecular models, design molecules with specific structures that will interact with enzymes or receptors.

27    Propose modifications to make to molecular structures to test whether or not particular fragments contribute to biological activity.

28    Compare the infrared spectra of similar compounds to identify the characteristic absorption of the functional group they contain.

# Comments on Activities

### Activity 1

Your list may look something like the one in Table A1.

**Table A1**  The active ingredients in various types of household cleaning agent.

| | | |
|---|---|---|
| soap | anionic surfactant<br>sodium laureth sulfate<br>cocamide DEA<br>glycol distearate<br>PEG 75 lanolin | } usually in liquid soaps |
| washing-up liquids | anionic surfactants<br>non-ionic surfactants<br>amphoteric surfactants | } 'environmentally friendly' products will say these are derived from coconut oil (or vegetable oil) |
| cream cleaners | anionic surfactants<br>non-ionic surfactants | |
| bleach | sodium hypochlorite | |
| washing powders/<br>liquids | anionic surfactants<br>non-ionic surfactants<br>soap | |
| disinfectants | chloroxylenol<br>dichloroxylenol<br>chlorinated phenols<br>cationic detergent<br>(or surfactant) | |
| | non-ionic detergent<br>(or surfactant)<br>benzalkonium chloride<br>dialkyldimethylammonium<br>chloride<br>cetrimide | |
| toilet cleaner | anionic surfactant<br>non-ionic surfactant<br>soap<br>sodium hypochlorite | |
| shampoo | sodium laureth sulfate<br>cocamide DEA | |

You will probably have noticed that most of these contain 'anionic surfactants'. We'll have more to say shortly about what these are.

## Activity 6

The aromatic ring and OH groups fit easily into their respective binding sites, but to fit the blue nitrogen centre to its binding site, the page has to be folded upwards.

## Activity 7

When the two compounds are aligned with the amine groups and benzene rings next to each other the following comparisons can be made:

### *Similarities*

- Both contain an amine group and a benzene ring.

- Both have a rather flat, planar structure, except that the sulfonamide group of sulfanilamide gives this part of the molecule a three-dimensional appearance.

- The overall dimensions of the two molecules are practically the same; from the amino group at one end to the carboxylic acid or sulfonamide group at the other, the lengths are the same, and the width across the aromatic ring is also the same. Actually, PABA is 670 pm long whereas sulfanilamide is 690 pm long.

### *Differences*

- The sulfonamide group contains an extra oxygen atom compared with the carboxylic acid group in PABA.

- The sulfonamide group contains two N—H bonds whereas the acid group contains one O—H bond.

- The atoms of the carboxylic acid group in PABA all lie in the same plane whereas the atoms of the sulfonamide group are placed tetrahedrally around the central sulfur atom. This means that the H—O—C=O atoms of PABA and H—N—S=O atoms of sulfanilamide can't be made to take up identical positions in space: if the H—N—S and H—O—C atoms are placed in identical positions, then the oxygen atoms can't be so placed; or, if the S=O and C=O atoms are made to occupy identical positions the N—H and O—H groups occupy different spatial positions (use your models to see that this is so).

  The difference between an OH group and an $NH_2$ group is not so great as it may seem; you've already discovered from the study of salbutamol that these two groups can often be interchanged.

# Answers to Questions

**Question 1** Because olive oil contains 80% oleic acid groups this should form the 'purest' soap. The soaps made from olive oil are called Castille soaps.

**Question 2** The structure of the phosphate anion is

$$^-O-\overset{\overset{\displaystyle O}{\|}}{\underset{\underset{\displaystyle O^-}{|}}{P}}-O^-$$

So, if we replace one of the $O^-$ groups by the hydrocarbon chain R we get the following anionic detergent

$$R-\overset{\overset{\displaystyle O}{\|}}{\underset{\underset{\displaystyle O^-}{|}}{P}}-O^-$$

and if we replace a second $O^-$ group by another hydrocarbon chain we get the following

$$R-\overset{\overset{\displaystyle O}{\|}}{\underset{\underset{\displaystyle R}{|}}{P}}-O^-$$

Comparing the data in Table 1.2, it is clear that the ionic compounds of phosphate and carbonate have much the same solubility, perhaps with the exception of sodium compounds. So we might predict that the phosphate-based detergents would have similar properties to the soaps; that is, the sodium and potassium compounds would be soluble whereas the magnesium and calcium compounds would precipitate out of solution.

**Question 3** Ions that are the starting points for the design of potential detergents require two negative charges so that the proposed detergent ion has one negative charge. This requirement rules out the hypochlorite, nitrite and methanesulfonate anions because they only carry one negative charge; the structures derived from these anions on replacing $O^-$ by a long-chain hydrocarbon group (denoted by R) are

$$^-O-Cl \quad\Longrightarrow\quad R-Cl$$

$$^-O-N{=}O \quad\Longrightarrow\quad R-N{=}O$$

$$^-O-\overset{\overset{\displaystyle O}{\|}}{\underset{\underset{\displaystyle O}{\|}}{S}}-CH_3 \quad\Longrightarrow\quad R-\overset{\overset{\displaystyle O}{\|}}{\underset{\underset{\displaystyle O}{\|}}{S}}-CH_3$$

The two anions hyponitrite and oxalate are possible starting points because they carry two $O^-$ groups. Replacing one of these in each by a hydrocarbon tail gives two new molecules that would have the anionic heads and hydrocarbon tails required of a detergent.

$$^-O-N{=}N-O^- \implies R-N{=}N-O^-$$

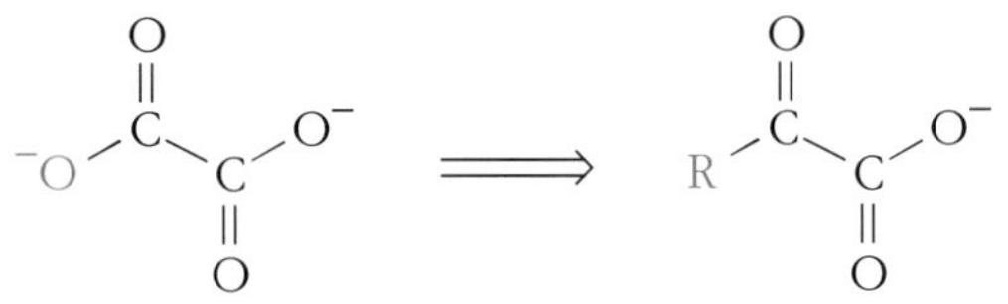

For reasons that we won't go into here, the ion derived from hyponitrite is unsuitable because it is too unstable. Nevertheless, the approach you've taken here is quite reasonable and appropriate.

**Question 4** The data in Table 1.3 show that the magnesium and calcium compounds of pyrophosphate and orthosilicate are very insoluble, whereas the selenate compounds of these two cations are reasonably soluble, as are the selenate compounds of sodium and potassium ions. So selenate seems to be a reasonable starting point, and the potential detergent designed from this would have the following structure:

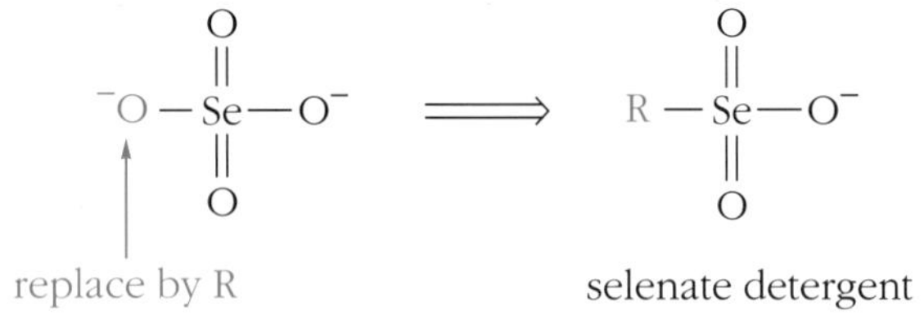

replace by R                                        selenate detergent

Selenium-based detergents are unlikely to be commercially viable; first, because selenium compounds are between 10 and 200 times more expensive than the corresponding sulfur compounds – and second, because, despite being an essential element, selenium is toxic to humans in doses larger than 450 micrograms per day.

**Question 5** The information contained in Figure 1.13 indicates that after 7 days only soaps and alkyl sulfates are completely degraded, whereas the linear and branched alkyl sulfonates are only about 30% and 5% degraded, respectively. This makes the soaps and the sulfates the only viable options. Soaps appear to degrade about twice as fast as the sulfates, but if this is not an issue then the sulfates are the superior option because of their higher solubility.

**Question 6** Your flow diagram should look something like the one shown in Figure A1.

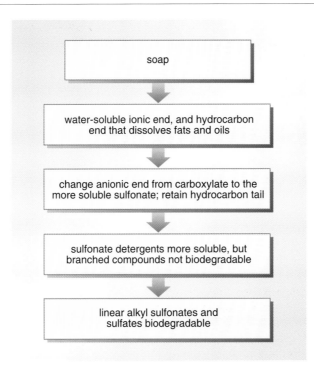

**Figure A1**
Answer to Question 6.

**Question 7** The name would suggest that there are 75 repeat units, and that the source of the fatty alcohol is lanolin (which is otherwise known as wool fat).

**Question 8** Coconut ethanolamide can form a PEG surfactant from reaction between the alcohol group and ethylene oxide:

**Question 9** The sulfonium chloride would be expected to be a cationic surfactant. A surfactant molecule should have a long-chain hydrocarbon tail attached to a head group capable of interacting with water. Here the positively charged sulfur group (called a sulfonium cation) is a positively charged ionic group capable of interacting with water, just as ammonium cations can. It also contains the hydrophobic long-chain hydrocarbon group capable of forming a non-polar environment at the centre of a micelle.

**Question 10** The best cleaning agents are those that are able to dissolve grease but won't stick to the surface of the material to be cleaned.

### Glass

Because glass has a negatively charged surface, the most appropriate agents are the anionic and neutral surfactants. Both will solubilize grease, but the negative charge of the anionic surfactant will be repelled by the surface (because like charges repel), and the neutral surfactant will form few binding interactions with the surface. A cationic surfactant would form strong ionic binding interactions with the surface, a greasy layer would form on top of the glass.

### Plastic

The positively charged surface of plastics is best cleaned by a cationic surfactant. The positively charged surfactant will solubilize any oily deposit but be repelled by the plastic surface. A neutral surfactant would be satisfactory also because the surfactant molecules would form few binding interactions with the surface. An anionic surfactant, however, would adhere to the surface because of the binding ionic interactions between the positive charge on the surface and the negative charge of the surfactant.

**Question 11**  Two changes are needed: first, the benzene ring on the stamp doesn't contain any double bonds; second, the OH group is not shown to be attached to a ring carbon atom.

**Question 12**  Phenol itself has antiseptic properties, and phenols that contain hydrocarbon chains attached to the benzene ring are better antiseptics. Eugenol contains a benzene ring attached to an OH group so it is a phenol, and it is a phenol with a hydrocarbon chain attached to the ring. This would make it an ideal candidate as an antiseptic.

**Question 13**  Iodine exists as $I_2$ molecules, I—I (Book 1, Figure 8.2). This should be an active iodine compound because it contains an iodine atom bonded to an electron-attracting atom, in this case also iodine. This is analogous to the chlorine atoms in $Cl_2$ molecules. The amide groups of enzymes and proteins will be susceptible to attack by an active iodine compound and will form structures such as

This will disrupt the hydrogen bonding that the amide group normally gets involved in. It will also alter the chemical reactivity of the amide and make it more reactive. The enzyme or protein structure will therefore be destroyed. Iodine therefore acts as a general antiseptic by destroying all such materials in the region of the cut.

**Question 14**  Of the three spectra, only the middle one contains a strong absorption at $1\,740\,cm^{-1}$, which is characteristic of an ester. This must be due to methyl butanoate.

**Question 15**  We said earlier that the absorption near to $3\,000\,cm^{-1}$ is due to C—H bonds. The three spectra have only one other absorption in the spectrum that is characteristically similar. This is the broad, U-shaped absorption that is centred at about $3\,350\,cm^{-1}$. So this must be the characteristic absorption of the alcohol (OH) group.

**Question 16** The two absorptions in the vicinity of $1\,740$ cm$^{-1}$ clearly demonstrate the presence of ester functional groups. For cocaine, the two ester groups absorb in slightly different regions of the spectrum, but in general it is *not* the case that one can identify the number of ester groups present in a compound from the number of absorptions.

**Question 17** The models clearly show that the blue nitrogen and red oxygen atom centres representing compound **4.24** can be overlapped with those of cocaine, whereas those in the model representing compound **4.23** can't. The distance between the nitrogen and oxygen centres is shorter in **4.23** than in cocaine. So, we'd expect **4.24** to be better local anaesthetic.

**Figure A2**
Answer for Question 18.

**Question 18** Following Figure 4.31, a flow chart for the development of anaesthetics from cocaine might look as shown in Figure A2.

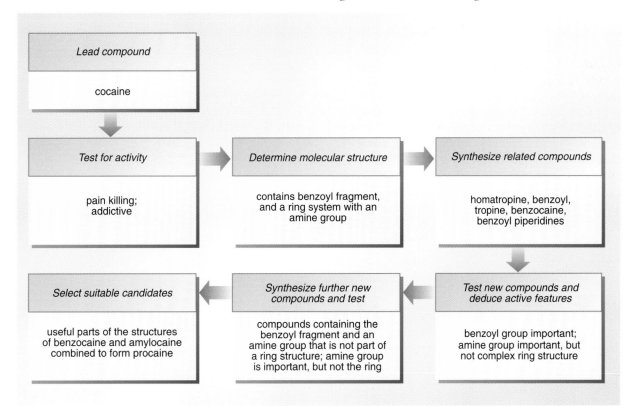

You may have placed certain events in different places, but don't worry if your flow chart is not exactly the same as the one here provided that you identified the majority of the steps involved.

**Question 19** The difference between them is the $-CH_2-$ spacer groups. Compound **6.25** can only fit one of the sites; compound **6.26** will fit one of the sites exactly, and will almost fit the second site; compound **6.27** fits both sites.

**Question 20** The following is probably the molecule with the simplest structure that can bind to both sites of the receptor:

The molecule containing only two carbons in the chain, $HS-CH_2-CH_2-NH_2$, is unable to span the distance between the binding sites. Compound **6.28** can be arranged to fit the two sites but **6.29** can't. The shortest carbon chain between the SH and NH$_2$ groups contains *four* carbon atoms in both cases. However, the carbon chain of **6.28** is flexible and can twist so that the groups take up the correct positions in space, but the benzene ring of **6.29** has no flexibility so the NH$_2$ and SH groups can't take up a proper orientation.

**Question 21** Two possible compounds are

In the former, the oxygen-containing OCH$_3$ group has been removed and replaced by an H atom; in the latter a smaller modification is made in that the CH$_3$ group remains but the O atom has been replaced by CH$_2$.

**Question 22** The data on biological activity in Table 7.1 reveal that the compound with highest biological activity has the following group attached to the sulfonamide nitrogen atom in place of one of the H atoms in the sulfonamide group of sulfanilamide:

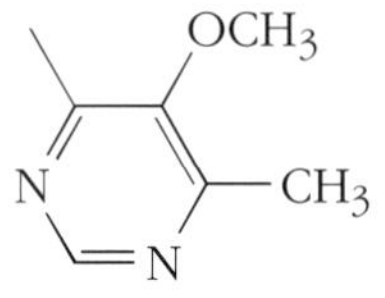

It would make sense to incorporate this group into the phosphanilamide structure by using it to replace one of the H atoms in the NH$_2$ group of phosphanilamide. This makes the target compound:

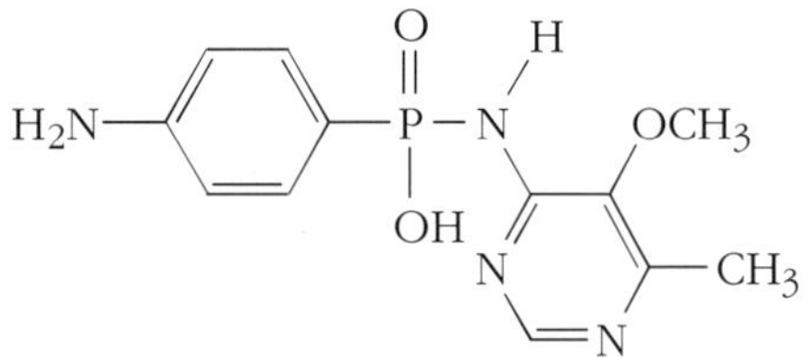

**Question 23** Phosphanilamides would be expected to exert their biological activity by resembling PABA. Phosphanilamide has two systems that might resemble the $H-O-C=O$ arrangement in PABA. The first is the $H-N-P=O$ system, involving the nitrogen atom as in sulfonamides. If this were the group to resemble PABA then varying the groups on nitrogen ought to affect biological activity. Alternatively, phosphanilamide contains the $H-O-P=O$ system, which can adopt an almost identical spatial arrangement of atoms as

the H—O—C=O system in PABA. If the H—O—P=O system were the group to resemble PABA, then groups on the nitrogen atom (which would have no involvement in enzyme inhibition) might have little effect on biological activity.

As far as I'm aware, antibiotics based on phosphanilamide have not been investigated, so neither of the ideas in Questions 22 and 23 has been tested. Nevertheless, you have been able to apply ideas learnt from the Course so far to think about the structure of molecules in a creative and productive way. This is what lies at the heart of chemistry.

# Acknowledgements

Grateful acknowledgement is made to the following sources for permission to reproduce material in this part of Book 3:

*Figure 1.1* British Museum; *Figure 1.12* US Dept. of Agriculture; *Figure 3.1* by courtesy of the Wellcome Trustees, London; *Figure 3.7* Imperial War Museum; *Figure 4.2* The Wellcome Institute Library, London; *Figure 4.3* Black Country Museum; *Figures 4.8, 4.11, 4.21 and 8.3a* courtesy of Kew Gardens; *Figure 4.15* Ardea London; *Figures 4.22 and 4.24* Advertising Archives; *Figures 4.23 and 8.3b* Peter Arnold Inc., New York; *Figures 4.30, 7.2 and 7.7* Science Photo Library; *Figure 5.3* Heather Clarke; *Figure 7.6* Hoechst Ltd; *Figure 7.8* Ciba-Geigy Ltd; *Figure 7.13* courtesy of Cambridge Botanical Gardens (lime tree).

# Index